Thermodynamics of Solids

WILEY SERIES ON THE SCIENCE AND TECHNOLOGY OF MATERIALS

Advisory Editors: J. H. Hollomon, J. E. Burke, B. Chalmers, R. L. Sproull, A. V. Tobolsky

Thermodynamics of Solids

by
Richard A. Swalin

PROFESSOR OF METALLURGY
INSTITUTE OF TECHNOLOGY
UNIVERSITY OF MINNESOTA

John Wiley & Sons, Inc., New York · London

Preface

The material and method of presentation used in this book have evolved over a period of years from lectures presented to undergraduate and graduate students in the area of material science. It has become increasingly clear to me that thermodynamics, although powerful because of the simplicity and plausibility of its basic postulates, is more readily grasped by the student (and researcher as well) if the thermodynamic quantities are interpreted in terms of an atomistic picture. As a result I have attempted to weave the atomistic and the classical thermodynamic approaches together throughout the framework of the book. I believe that it is artificial to attempt to separate these approaches from each other since, in attempting to understand the nature of solids, one uses these approaches simultaneously. Pedagogically, I believe, this method is warranted because the reader is assisted in understanding the abstract thermodynamic quantities if he can visualize the quantities in terms of atomic models. I hope that this method will assist in bridging the hiatus between the approach of the physicist to thermodynamics and the approach of the chemist to thermodynamics. The physicist, for example, has never been able to feel close to the concepts of activity and activity coefficient in the sense that the chemist uses them. By giving the activity coefficient an atomistic interpretation, for example, it is hoped that such language barriers may be overcome. Such barriers are luxuries that can no longer be afforded since traditional boundaries between disciplines no longer have much meaning and the understanding of a given phenomenon will generally involve the participation of scientists of many types of background.

The first part of the book presents the basic thermodynamic concepts which will form the working tools throughout the book. Some emphasis is placed on the thermodynamic interpretation of certain types of phase diagrams. The reason for this is that thermodynamic information for solid state systems is scarce but phase diagrams are plentiful. By rather

v

simple processes, much thermodynamic information may be gleaned from these diagrams. The emphasis here is not upon the use of thermodynamics to assist phase diagram construction but upon the use of phase diagrams to obtain thermodynamic quantities. The last part of the book is concerned with the thermodynamics of defects and defect interactions in metals, elemental semiconductors, and compounds. The reason for this emphasis hardly needs explanation since it is well known that a great many of the important properties of crystals are dependent upon these defects. Considerable emphasis is placed upon the electrical properties of oxide semiconductors. Two reasons exist for this. In the first place, oxide semiconductors are becoming of great importance in technological applications such as the maser and optical maser, to cite only two. In the second place there is a dearth of information concerning the relation of defect structure to other properties in these materials. There is no question that such effects will be found, however, by investigators in the future.

RICHARD A. SWALIN

Minneapolis, Minnesota
December, 1961

Contents

chapter 1

Introduction

The application of thermodynamics to the study of crystals offers a powerful quantitative tool for the investigation of important properties. With the aid of thermodynamics, for example, one is able to control the structure of a material without knowing atomic details of the crystals. One of the principal reasons for this power is that one does not need to postulate any specific model of the crystal. Rather, by applying the three laws of thermodynamics in conjunction with standard mathematical techniques many macroscopic or phenomenological properties can be obtained unambiguously. Thermodynamics, by itself, is rather unsatisfying, however, since because of its generality and simplicity, virtually nothing is learned about the detailed relationship among atoms and defects in crystals. In order to obtain insight concerning these quantities appeal must be made to statistical mechanics. With the aid of statistical mechanics, the investigator is able to obtain atomistic interpretations of properties of atoms and defects in crystals. Knowledge of both classical thermodynamics and statistical mechanics represents, therefore, a powerful combination in the study of crystals.

Properties of crystals on two levels are of interest to us thermodynamically. First, there are the gross properties such as chemical reactivity of one species with another and consideration of the extent to which a given reaction will proceed. Secondly, there are the fine scale properties such as the concentration of various types of defects and defect interactions. By defect is meant lattice vacancies, electrons in the conduction band of semiconductors, dislocations, impurity atoms, etc. These two levels are not completely unrelated, however, since the concentration of various types of defects in a compound may be markedly influenced by exposure of the gross crystal to various environments. By appropriate exposure, for example, the electrical conductivity of a compound semiconductor may be changed by several orders of magnitude. The subject of defect interactions in compounds has received much wider attention in Europe than in the United States in the past. In fact, discussion of the subject is found in very few American textbooks. Interest in this particular topic has been accelerating, however, because of the increasing technological interest in compound semiconductors.

Before approaching the study of crystals, however, it will be desirable to review in some detail the laws of classical and statistical thermodynamics.

chapter 2

The First Law of Thermodynamics

2.1 STATEMENT OF THE FIRST LAW

From a physical point of view this is the law most easily understood. The three laws of thermodynamics are all derived from experiment, the first being simply a statement of the conservation of energy. It says that the increase in *internal energy*, ΔE, of a *system* is equal to the difference between the heat put into the system from the surrounding Q and the work done by the system on the surrounding W. Thus

$$\Delta E = Q - W \tag{2.1}$$

It is important to note the sign convention. Q is a positive quantity when the flux of heat is from the surroundings to the system of interest, whereas W is positive for the reverse path (see Fig. 2.1). For calculations it is often desirable to write equation 2.1 in the form of infinitesimals. Thus, let us

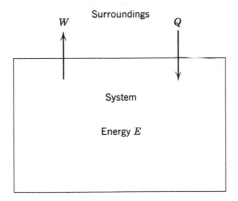

Fig. 2.1 Illustration of the first law of thermodynamics.

3

put an infinitesimal amount of heat DQ into the system and remove an infinitesimal amount of work DW. The difference in internal-energy dE is

$$dE = DQ - DW \qquad (2.2)$$

It will be recalled that Q and W are not state properties whereas E is, i.e., the former two quantities depend on the path of the process whereas the internal energy is a function only of the initial and final states. As a result Q and W cannot be expressed in the forms of exact differentials except in certain cases.

2.2 CALCULATIONS OF WORK

Mechanical Work

The term DW is very general, and could refer to electrical work, gravitational work, mechanical work, work against a magnetic field, etc. In most of our applications the term DW will refer to mechanical work

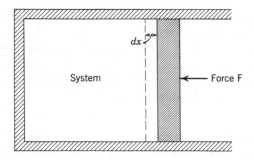

Fig. 2.2 Illustration of mechanical work.

only, i.e., work against pressure. In order to obtain an expression for DW, visualize our system put into a piston arrangement as shown in Fig. 2.2. Let the system have a cross-sectional area A and apply a force F to the system through the piston. Upon application of the force, the system will change its dimension in the x direction by an amount equal to dx. From elementary mechanics, the work done by the system is defined as the product of a force and a displacement so

$$DW = \text{F}\, dx \qquad (2.3)$$

Since force is equal to pressure P times cross-sectional area A,

$$DW = PA\, dx \qquad (2.4)$$

or

$$DW = P\, dV \qquad (2.5)$$

In this example, dV for the system is negative and hence DW is negative.

Equation 2.5 is only applicable if the process is carried out *reversibly*. By reversible it is meant that the force shown in Fig. 2.2 is applied infinitesimally fast. Because of this restriction, it would take an infinite time to achieve a reversible process. Experimentally, however, this problem presents little difficulty, since a given process can usually be carried out arbitrarily slowly in order to approach reversibility within the accuracy of experimental techniques. Substitution of equation 2.5 into equation 2.2 yields

$$dE = DQ - P\,dV \tag{2.6}$$

Other Types of Work

Let us now consider the work done in increasing the area of a surface, taking the system shown in Fig. 2.3. This system has an area of A and a surface tension of σ (units of force/unit distance). In order to expand the

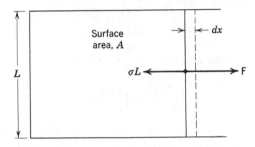

Fig. 2.3   Illustration of surface work.

x dimension by an amount dx, an external force F infinitesimally larger than the opposing surface tension must be applied. The total force acting in this surface must be slightly larger than $(-\sigma L)$. Since $DW = $ (force) $\times$ (distance), in this case

$$DW = -\sigma L\,dx = -\sigma\,dA \tag{2.7}$$

Let us now consider the electrical form of work. If electrical work is being performed reversibly, i.e., if the electric potential of the system, $\mathscr{E}$, is only infinitesimally larger than that of the surroundings,

$$DW = \text{(electric potential)} \times \text{(charge)}$$

Thus
$$DW = \mathscr{E}\,dZ \tag{2.8}$$

where Z represents a unit of charge. It is convenient to express the charge unit in faradays: thus $Z = \mathscr{F}n$ where $\mathscr{F}$ is the number of charges in a faraday and n is the number of faradays. Hence

$$DW = \mathscr{E}\mathscr{F}\,dn \tag{2.9}$$

2.3 THE ENTHALPY FUNCTION AND HEAT CAPACITY

At this point, it is convenient to define a thermodynamic function called the *enthalpy*. The enthalpy H of a system is defined as

$$H = E + PV \qquad (2.10)$$

For most of the processes of interest here, it will be convenient to work with the enthalpy instead of the internal energy for reasons shown below. We define *heat capacity*, C, as

$$C \equiv \frac{DQ}{dT} \qquad (2.11)$$

The heat capacity then refers to the amount of heat DQ absorbed by a system which undergoes a temperature change dT. Dividing the terms in equation 2.6 by dT yields

$$\frac{dE}{dT} = \frac{DQ}{dT} - P\frac{dV}{dT} \qquad (2.12)$$

If we hold the volume constant, $\left(\dfrac{dV}{dT}\right) = 0$ and

$$\left(\frac{DQ}{dT}\right)_V = \left(\frac{\partial E}{\partial T}\right)_V = C_V \qquad (2.13)$$

Thus the heat capacity for a system whose volume is maintained constant, C_V, is equal to the ratio of the change in internal energy to temperature change.

Differentiating equation 2.10, we find

$$dH = dE + P\,dV + V\,dP \qquad (2.14)$$

and, if equation 2.6 is substituted into 2.14,

$$dH = DQ + V\,dP$$

Dividing by dT,

$$\frac{dH}{dT} = \frac{DQ}{dT} + V\frac{dP}{dT}$$

If the pressure is held constant, we find

$$\left(\frac{\partial H}{\partial T}\right)_P = \left(\frac{DQ}{dT}\right)_P \qquad (2.15)$$

The term on the right hand side of equation 2.15 is the heat capacity defined by 2.11, with the restriction of constant pressure. It is referred to as C_P, the heat capacity of a substance at constant pressure. Thus

$$C_P = \left(\frac{\partial H}{\partial T}\right)_P \qquad (2.16)$$

Examination of equation 2.6 shows that if the volume of the system is held constant

$$dE = DQ \text{ (constant volume)} \tag{2.17}$$

and thus the internal energy change dE is identical to the heat input DQ. Similarly from equation 2.10

$$dH = DQ \text{ (constant pressure)} \tag{2.18}$$

It is seen that, for a system under constant pressure, the heat input is equal to the enthalpy change dH. In dealing experimentally with solids, one generally works with systems at constant pressure, and hence enthalpy changes are easier to measure than energy changes.

The heat capacity of a substance is generally a strong function of temperature. As we shall see in a later section, $C_P = C_V = 0$ at $T = 0$. For many solid elements C_P approaches a value of about 6 cal/mole degree or $3R$ at high temperatures. For the investigator interested in the detailed nature of substances, knowledge of the heat capacity is important since, from the temperature dependence of the heat capacity, information about the mechanism of the manner in which energy is absorbed in the substance can be gained. For purposes of computation, it is convenient to express the heat capacity as an empirical function of temperature. It is cumbersome, generally, to attempt to express the temperature dependence of the heat capacity by a single equation over a very broad temperature range. At very low temperatures, C_V is approximately given by an expression of the type

$$C_V = K \left(\frac{T}{\theta}\right)^3 \tag{2.19}$$

where K is a constant equal to 464.5 cal/mole degree and θ is known as the Debye temperature. Equation 2.19 was derived theoretically by Debye and is approximately valid at $T < 0.1\theta$. The Debye temperature is of the order of $300°K$ for many substances. More will be said about the fundamental nature of heat capacities in a later chapter. At elevated temperatures (above room temperature, generally), the heat capacities of most substances are expressed adequately by an empirical equation of the type

$$C_P = a + bT + cT^{-2} \text{ cal/mole degree} \tag{2.20}$$

where a, b, and c are empirical constants. Experimental values for a variety of materials are listed in Table 2.1.

In Table 2.1, the symbols s, l, and m.p. refer to solid, liquid, and melting point respectively. Extensive tabulations of heat capacity data are given in several sources. Those sources of particular interest to us are *Metallurgical Thermochemistry*, Third Edition, by O. Kubaschewski and E. Evans,

TABLE 2.1

Heat Capacity Constants for Number of Substances[a]

Substance	a	$b \times 10^3$	$c \times 10^{-5}$	Temperature range (°K)
Ag(s)	5.09	2.04	0.36	298–m.p.
Ag(l)	7.30	—	—	m.p.–1600
AgBr(s)	7.93	15.40	—	298–m.p.
AgCl(s)	14.88	1.00	−2.70	298–m.p.
BCl(l)	16.86	2.86	−2.44	298–1000
CaTiSiO$_5$(s)	42.39	5.54	−9.63	298–1670
CaTiSiO$_5$(l)	66.8	—	—	1670–1811
SiO$_2$(quartz)	11.22	8.20	−2.70	298–848
MnSiO$_3$(s)	26.42	3.88	−6.16	298–1500

[a] From O. Kubaschewski and E. Evans, *Metallurgical Thermochemistry*, Third Edition, Pergamon, London, 1958.

and Bureau of Mines *Bulletin* 584, by K. K. Kelley, entitled "Contributions to The Data on Theoretical Metallurgy XIII. High Temperature Heat-Content, Heat Capacity and Entropy Data for the Elements and Inorganic Compounds."

2.4 HEATS OF FORMATION

One of the limitations of thermodynamics is that absolute values of thermodynamics quantities cannot be obtained. As a result a reference state is needed so that quantities can be given in terms of the difference between the state of interest and the reference or *standard state*. The

TABLE 2.2

Standard States

Usual standard states for heats of reaction

Solid	The most stable form of the element at one atmosphere pressure and the temperature specified
Liquid	The most stable form at one atmosphere at the temperature specified
Gas	One atmosphere pressure and the temperature specified

particular choice of a standard state is therefore arbitrary. The most generally used standard states for solids, liquids, and gases from the point of view of convenience are listed in Table 2.2.

It is clear from Table 2.2 that the standard state depends upon temperature. For example, tin has two allotropes. Gray tin is stable below 13°C, and white tin is stable between 13°C and the melting point. Thus, the standard state for tin would change from the gray tin form to white tin as the temperature becomes greater than 13°C. In some tabulations, however, diamond is used as the standard state for carbon even though graphite is the stable allotrope. One must be careful, when using data from various sources, to see that the standard states are the same.

It is convenient to list values of the heat of formation (or enthalpy of formation) of species at a standard temperature. The common practice is to use 298°K as the reference temperature. Some typical values of heats of formation are listed in Table 2.3. The symbol $\Delta H_f°$ refers to the enthalpy

TABLE 2.3
Heats of Formation at 298°K[a]

Substance	$\Delta H_f°$ (kcal/mole)	Substance	$\Delta H_f°$ (kcal/mole)
Sn (gray)	−0.50	H(g)	52.1
Sn (white)	0	MgO(s)	−143.7
AgCl(s)	−30.3	MoO$_2$(s)	−139.5
Al$_2$O$_3$(s)	−400.0	SiO$_2$ (quartz)	−210.2
Graphite	0	MnSiO$_3$(s)	−5.9
Diamond	0.454	MnO(s)	−92.0

[a] From O. Kubaschewski and E. Evans, *Metallurgical Thermochemistry*, Third Edition, Pergamon, London, 1958.

or heat of formation of the phase from elements in their standard states at 298°K. The superscript (°) refers to standard state.

The values listed in Table 2.3 are relative to the standard states listed in Table 2.2. Writing the chemical reaction equation, for the formation of MnSiO$_3$, we would obtain

$$Mn(s, 298°K, 1\ atm) + Si(s, 298°K, 1\ atm) + \tfrac{3}{2}O_2(g, 298°K, 1\ atm)$$

$$= MnSiO_3(s, 298°K, 1\ atm)$$

In the future, the notation (1 atm) in parentheses, will be disregarded when solids and liquids are involved. It will be understood that this restriction exists, however. The superscript ° for $\Delta H_f°$ denotes that the value refers to one atmosphere pressure for all quantities involved in the reactions. The heat of formation of an element which is thermodynamically stable at 298°K will, of course, be equal to zero, as shown in Table 2.3 for both white tin and graphite. A negative value for ΔH_f° refers to an *exothermic* process whereas a positive value of ΔH_f° refers to an *endothermic* process.

2.5 HEATS OF REACTION

Since thermodynamic functions are state properties, the path through which we achieve a given reaction is unimportant. Only the initial and final states are important. As a result, the enthalpy for a particular reaction may be obtained from the algebraic sum of the appropriate reactions involved in heat of formation reactions.

Illustration 1

Problem. Find the enthalpy of the following reaction at 298°K and one atmosphere pressure.

$$MnSiO_3(s, 298) = MnO(s, 298) + SiO_2(\text{quartz}, 298)$$

Solution. To find ΔH° for the reaction, the standard enthalpies of formation of MnO and SiO_2 are added together and that for $MnSiO_3$ subtracted, using data from Table 2.3:

(1) $Mn(s, 298) + \frac{1}{2}O_2(g, 298, 1 \text{ atm}) = MnO(s, 298)$

$$(\Delta H_f^\circ)_1 = -92.0 \text{ kcal}$$

(2) $Si(s, 298) + O_2(g, 298, 1 \text{ atm}) = SiO_2(\text{quartz}, 298)$

$$(\Delta H_f^\circ)_2 = -210.2 \text{ kcal}$$

(3) $MnSiO_3(s, 298) = Mn(s, 298) + Si(s, 298) + \frac{3}{2}O_2(g, 298, 1 \text{ atm})$

$$(\Delta H_f^\circ)_3 = 5.9 \text{ kcal}$$

Adding these together yields the desired reaction

$$\Delta H^\circ = -92.0 - 210.2 + 5.9 + -296.3 \text{ kcal}$$

The values of ΔH_f° listed in Table 2.3 represent enthalpies of reactions involving reactions between elements at 298°K. Generally, however, it is of interest to know the enthalpy of reaction, ΔH°, at a temperature different from 298°K.

For a substance of a given composition, its enthalpy is a function of the state variable of T, P, and V. These variables are not independent, however, since an equation of state is assumed to exist which relates the volume to the external pressure and temperature. For a crystal, we must add the additional restriction that the crystal is in its lowest energy state, i.e., no defects such as grain boundaries, excess vacancies, dislocations, exist. If this restriction is not placed (at least in principle) the volume will be influenced by history and will not be a state property. Since there is a relation between V, P, and T, only two can be considered as independent variables and thus according to general mathematical principles, the thermodynamic variables themselves can also be expressed as functions of any two of the variables. Thus $\Delta H° = f(T, P), f(T, V)$, or $f(V, P)$. The choice of which functional relation to use depends upon the particular situation being considered. Using $H = f(T, P)$ we obtain, using the basic theorem of partial differentiation,

$$dH° = \left(\frac{\partial H°}{\partial T}\right)_P dT + \left(\frac{\partial H°}{\partial T}\right)_T dP$$

Since $C_P = (\partial H°/\partial T)_P$ and the pressure is constant, we obtain

$$dH° = C_P\, dT$$

To find the change in enthalpy of the substance between 298°K and T, we integrate between 298°K and T. Thus

$$H°_T - H°_{298} = \int_{298}^{T} dH° = \int_{298}^{T} C_P\, dT$$

Illustration 2

Problem. Find the following enthalpy of reaction at 1000°K.

$$MnSiO_3(s, 1000) = MnO(s, 1000) + SiO_2(\text{quartz}, 1000)$$

Solution. To solve this problem, find the enthalpy of reaction at 298°K from the heats of formation as in Illustration 1.

(1) $MnSiO_3(s, 298) = MnO(s, 298) + SiO_2(\text{quartz}, 298)$ $\Delta H°_{298}$

Now bring both products and reactants to 1000°K algebraically.

(2) $MnO(s, 298) = MnO(s, 1000)$

$$H°_{1000} - H°_{298} = \int_{298}^{1000} (C_P)_2\, dT$$

(3) $SiO_2(s, 298) = SiO_2(s, 1000)$

$$H°_{1000} - H°_{298} = \int_{298}^{1000} (C_P)_3\, dT$$

(4) $MnSiO_3(s, 1000) = MnSiO_3(s, 298)$

$$-(H°_{1000} - H°_{298}) = -\int_{298}^{1000} (C_P)_4\, dT$$

Adding reactions 1 through 4 yields the enthalpy of the desired reaction and is given by

$$\Delta H_T^\circ = (\Delta H^\circ)_{298} + \int_{298}^{1000} [(C_P)_2 + (C_P)_3 - (C_P)_4]\, dT$$

Since C_P is given by equations of the form of equation 2.20,

$$\Delta H_T^\circ = \Delta H_{298}^\circ + \Delta a \int_{298}^{1000} dT + \Delta b \int_{298}^{1000} T\, dT + \Delta c \int_{298}^{1000} T^{-2}\, dT$$

and

$$\Delta H_T^\circ = \Delta H_{298}^\circ + \Delta a(1000 - 298) + \frac{\Delta b}{2}\,[(1000)^2 - (298)^2]$$

$$- \Delta c\left[\frac{1}{1000} - \frac{1}{298}\right]$$

From Table 2.1

$$\Delta a = 11.11 + 11.22 - 26.42 = -4.09$$

$$\Delta b = 1.94 \times 10^{-3} + 8.20 \times 10^{-3} - 3.88 \times 10^{-3} = 6.26 \times 10^{-3}$$

$$\Delta c = -0.88 \times 10^5 - 2.70 \times 10^5 + 6.16 \times 10^5 = 2.58 \times 10^5$$

and

$$\Delta H_T^\circ = \Delta H_{298}^\circ + 560 \text{ cal/mole} = 295{,}740 \text{ cal/mole}$$

In many cases, one or more of the components of a reaction undergoes a phase change between 298°K and the temperature of interest. If this were the case in the previous illustration the heat capacity of the low temperature form of the substance would be used between 298°K and the transformation temperature and the heat capacity of the high temperature modification would be used between the transition temperature and the temperature of interest. Another term would also be needed for the enthalpy change of the phase change at the transition temperature.

Illustration 3

Problem. Calculate the enthalpy change of the following reaction at 1200°K.

$$Ag(l, 1200) + \tfrac{1}{2}Cl_2(g, 1200, 1 \text{ atm}) = AgCl(l, 1200)$$

Solution. From Table 2.3, we find the heat formation at 298°K

(1) $Ag(s, 298) + \tfrac{1}{2}Cl_2(g, 298, 1 \text{ atm}) = AgCl(s, 298)$ ΔH_f°

Using the algebraic approach, we obtain

(2) $\quad$ AgCl(s, 298) = AgCl(s, $T_{m.p.}$) $\qquad H^\circ_{m.p.} - H^\circ_{298} = \int_{298}^{T_{m.p.}} (C_P)_s \, dT$

(3) $\qquad\qquad$ AgCl(s, $T_{m.p.}$) = AgCl(l, $T_{m.p.}$) $\qquad \Delta H_3 = \Delta H_f$

(4) $\quad$ AgCl(l, $T_{m.p.}$) = AgCl(l, 1200) $\qquad H^\circ_{120} - H^\circ_{m.p.} = \int_{T_{m.p.}}^{1200} (C_P)_l \, dT$

(5) $\quad \frac{1}{2}Cl_2(g, 1200, 1\ atm) = \frac{1}{2}Cl_2(g, 298, 1\ atm)$

$$- (H^\circ_{1200} - H^\circ_{298}) = \frac{1}{2} \int_{1200}^{298} C_P \, dT$$

(6) $\quad$ Ag(s, $T_{m.p.}$) = Ag(s, 298) $\qquad -(H^\circ_{m.p.} - H^\circ_{298}) = \int_{T_{m.p.}}^{298} (C_P)_s \, dT$

(7) $\qquad\qquad$ Ag(l, $T_{m.p.}$) = Ag(s, $T_{m.p.}$) $\qquad \Delta H_7 = -\Delta H_f$

(8) $\quad$ Ag(l, 1200) = Ag(l, $T_{m.p.}$) $\qquad -(H^\circ_{1200} - H_{m.p.}) = \int_{1200}^{T_{m.p.}} (C_P) \, dT$

Addition of reactions 1 through 8 gives us the desired reaction and, upon substitution of the appropriate heat capacities and heats of fusion, ΔH° the desired heat of reaction is obtained at 1200°K.

chapter **3**

The Second Law of Thermodynamics and the Free Energy Function

3.1 DEFINITION OF ENTROPY

The second law of thermodynamics is extremely important from the standpoint of predicting whether a given reaction will proceed. The criterion of the sign of the enthalpy change of a reaction is not sufficient as one might intuitively think. For example, consider the enthalpies of formation of white and gray tin listed in Table 2.3. If we consider the transformation

$$Sn(\text{white}, 298) = Sn(\text{gray}, 298)$$

we find that 0.50 kcal/mole are evolved in the reaction as written, implying that gray tin is in a lower energy state. At 298°K, however, white tin is found to exist as the stable form. It is clear, therefore, that some other criterion is necessary for predicting stability. The criterion that has been found to be satisfactory is defined as the *entropy*. Consider a reversible process in which the system absorbs in a reversible manner an infinitesimal quantity of heat DQ. The entropy is then defined as

$$dS = \frac{DQ}{T} \text{ (reversible)} \tag{3.1}$$

In spite of the fact the DQ is not a state property, it can be readily shown that the ratio DQ/T is a state property. To illustrate this, consider the first law as applied to a reversible process involving a perfect gas. For a mole of such gas

$$PV = RT \tag{3.2}$$

14

and, writing the first law in differential form,

$$dE = DQ - P\,dV \tag{3.3}$$

Expressing $E = f(T, V)$ yields

$$dE = \left(\frac{\partial E}{\partial T}\right)_V dT + \left(\frac{\partial E}{\partial V}\right)_T dV \tag{3.4}$$

For a perfect gas, the term $(\partial E/\partial V)_T = 0$ and thus

$$dE = C_V\,dT \tag{3.5}$$

Substitution of equation 3.5 and 3.2 into equation 3.3 yields

$$DQ = C_V\,dT + \frac{RT}{V}\,dV \tag{3.6}$$

The right hand side of equation 3.6 is an inexact differential. By dividing through by T, we obtain

$$\frac{DQ}{T} = C_V\,\frac{dT}{T} + R\,\frac{dV}{V} \tag{3.7}$$

Thus the right hand side is converted into an exact differential and therefore the quantity DQ/T or dS must be an exact differential. As a result the quantity dS depends only upon the state of the system and is independent of the path. Rearranging equation 3.1 and substituting 3.3 gives a useful form of the first law for a reversible process:

$$dE = T\,dS - P\,dV \tag{3.8}$$

Since consideration of the entropy function will be of use in the future let us examine in further detail methods of calculation of the quantity for reversible processes.

3.2 ENTROPY OF ISOTHERMAL PHASE TRANSITIONS

Consider a reversible phase transition such as the conversion of gray tin to white tin. The transformation temperature is 13°C and hence this process only occurs reversibly at 13°C or 286°K. At any other temperatures at constant pressure, it is impossible to carry out the process reversibly. Consider further that the process occurs at constant pressure. Since

$$H = E + PV$$

and since the process is occurring reversibly, this function may be differentiated:

$$dH = dE + P\,dV + V\,dP \tag{3.9}$$

Substitution of equation 3.3 into 3.9 with the restriction of constant pressure yields

$$DQ = dH$$

Thus from (3.1) we find that

$$dS = \frac{dH}{T} \tag{3.10}$$

and integrating at constant temperature

$$\int_{\text{gray}}^{\text{white}} dS = \frac{1}{T} \int_{\text{gray}}^{\text{white}} dH$$

we obtain

$$\Delta S_t = \frac{\Delta H_t}{T}$$

where ΔH_t represents the enthalpy change of the transformation. For the reaction

$$Sn(\text{gray, 286}) = Sn(\text{white, 286})$$

ΔH_t has been measured as 0.50 kcal/mole and hence $\Delta S_t = 500/286 = 1.75$ cal/mole degree. The unit (cal/mole degree) is usually called an entropy unit or simply e.u.

The entropy of 1.75 e.u. is gained by the system consisting of tin. It is of interest to consider what happens to the surroundings. Since 500 cal entered the system on transformation of a mole of tin, 500 cal had to leave the surroundings. Since the process is isothermal, the surroundings must be at the same temperature and therefore

$$(\Delta S)_{\text{surr}} = -\frac{\Delta H_t}{T} = -1.75 \text{ e.u.}$$

The total entropy change of the universe consisting of our system plus its surroundings is the sum of the two entropies:

$$\Delta S_t + \Delta S_{\text{surr}} = 1.75 - 1.75 = 0$$

3.3 ENTROPY CALCULATION WHEN TEMPERATURE CHANGES

As in the last section, the restrictions of reversibility and constant pressure will be placed on the process. Thus

$$dS = \frac{dH}{T} \tag{3.10}$$

As shown in Chapter 2 for this type of process

$$dH = C_P \, dT \tag{3.11}$$

Substituting equation 3.11 into 3.10, we find for the entropy change of the system

$$dS = \frac{C_P}{T} dT = C_P \, d \ln T \tag{3.12}$$

Since, as discussed in Chapter 2, C_P is generally expressed as an analytic function of temperature, ΔS can be readily obtained by integration of equation 3.12.

Since the enthalpy is being transferred by the surroundings to the system, it is clear that DQ (system) $= - DQ$ (surroundings) and hence

$$dS(\text{system}) + dS(\text{surroundings}) = 0$$

as derived for an isothermal process.

As a generalization the following statement can be made: *the sum of the entropy change of a system plus the entropy change of the surrounding during a reversible process is zero.*

3.4 ENTROPY CHANGES FOR IRREVERSIBLE PROCESSES

The relation

$$dS = \frac{DQ}{T}$$

is only valid for a reversible process. To illustrate the calculation of an entropy change for an irreversible process, consider the freezing of a supercooled liquid. We have the following reaction at temperature $T_1 < T_{m.p.}$.

$$A(l, T_1) = A(s, T_1) \qquad -\Delta H_f$$

For a process such as this it is impossible to freeze the liquid reversibly, since the criterion of reversibility implies that at any instant during freezing, the process may be reversed by an infinitesimal opposing stress. Once a supercooled liquid begins to freeze, it is, of course, impossible to reverse the process by an infinitesimal stress (i.e., infinitesimal change of temperature). To reverse the process would require bringing the temperature above the melting point. If the supercooling is substantial, corresponding to the quantity $(T_{m.p.} - T_1)$ being substantial, this change in temperature is certainly not infinitesimal. On the other hand, the situation is considerably different for the surrounding (i.e., heat reservoir). During the irreversible process described here the system evolves an amount of heat ΔH_f. If the reservoir is sufficiently large, the quantity of heat ΔH_f is transferred to the reservoir with only an infinitesimal change in temperature. Thus it may be considered that the surroundings have a constant temperature T_1. Furthermore the heat, even though being evolved spontaneously from the system, may be transferred in a reversible fashion to the reservoir. It will be recalled that the criterion of reversibility means that the process may be reversed by an infinitesimal stress. If the reservoir is large compared with the system the heat content of the reservoir is large compared with the system. Let us now apply an infinitesimal stress to the reservoir (increase the temperature by an amount dT). Because of the difference in size of the reservoir and system, heat will now flow out of reservoir and thus may readily stop the former process. As a result, the entropy change of the surroundings can be calculated directly as done previously, but that for the system may not since the criterion of reversibility is not met in this case. Since entropy is a state property, we may, however, carry the system through several reversible steps and finally reach the end result. Each step, however, must be capable of being carried out, physically, in a manner approaching reversibility.

For the reaction under consideration the following steps are the obvious ones: (a) Liquid A is transferred reversibly from T_1 to $T_{m.p.}$; (b) At $T_{m.p.}$ the liquid is allowed to freeze reversibly; and (c) Solid A is brought from $T_{m.p.}$ to T_1. Thus

$$
\begin{array}{lll}
(1) & A(l, T_1) = A(l, T_{m.p.}) & \Delta S_1 \\
(2) & A(l, T_{m.p.}) = A(s, T_{m.p.}) & \Delta S_2 \\
(3) & A(s, T_{m.p.}) = A(s, T_1) & \Delta S_3 \\
\hline
\text{(sum)} & A(l, T_1) = A(s, T_1) & \Delta S_{\text{syst}}
\end{array}
$$

The entropy of the reaction of interest equals $(\Delta S_1 + \Delta S_2 + \Delta S_3)$. Using the equations of the last section, it is seen that

$$\Delta S_1 = \int_{T_1}^{T_{m.p.}} \frac{(C_P)_l}{T_1} dT$$

$$\Delta S_2 = \frac{-\Delta H_f}{T_{m.p.}}$$

$$\Delta S_3 = \int_{T_{m.p.}}^{T_1} \frac{(C_P)_s}{T} dT$$

Thus

$$\Delta S_{\text{syst}} = \int_{T_1}^{T_{m.p.}} \left(\frac{(C_P)_l - (C_P)_s}{T} \right) dT - \frac{\Delta H_f}{T_{m.p.}}$$

Consider now the surroundings. As was pointed out, the irreversible process is able to transfer heat reversibly to the isothermal reservoir. The entropy change of the reservoir is simply equal to

$$\Delta S_{\text{surr}} = \frac{\Delta H_f}{T_1}$$

If we know ΔH_f, therefore, we shall be able to calculate ΔS_{surr}. Generally, however, ΔH_f is not known experimentally at T_1 since it is generally only measured experimentally at the transformation temperature, $T_{\text{m.p.}}$. We may find ΔH_f at T_1 readily, however, by use of heat capacities. Consider the three steps discussed above to have enthalpy changes ΔH_1, ΔH_2, and ΔH_3 associated with them. By summation it is found that

$$-\Delta H_f = (\Delta H_1 + \Delta H_2 + \Delta H_3)$$

and by using principles already discussed

$$\Delta H_1 = \int_T^{T_{\text{m.p.}}} (C_P)_l \, dT$$

$$\Delta H_2 = -(\Delta H_f)_{T_{\text{m.p.}}}$$

$$\Delta H_3 = \int_{T_{\text{m.p.}}}^{T_1} (C_P)_s \, dT$$

and

$$-\Delta H_f = \int_{T_1}^{T_{\text{m.p.}}} [(C_P)_l - (C_P)_s] \, dT - \Delta H_{f,T_{\text{m.p.}}}$$

Illustration

Calculate the entropy changes of system and surroundings for the case of the freezing of supercooled liquid silver at 800°C. The melting point of silver is 961°C and the heat of fusion is 2.69 kcal/mole.

From Table 2.1 the constants for the heat capacities of liquid and solid silver are obtained. Examination of the data shows that C_P for liquid silver is indicated to be valid from the melting point to 1600°K whereas we are interested in C_P for supercooled liquid. The best approach in this case is to extrapolate the C_P data for the liquid determined at high temperature to the lower temperature. From the above equations we may write for the reaction

$$\text{Ag}(l, 1073) = \text{Ag}(s, 1073) \qquad \Delta S$$

$$\Delta S = \int_{1073}^{1234} \frac{\Delta a}{T} \, dT + \int_{1073}^{1234} \Delta b \, dT + \int_{1073}^{1234} \frac{\Delta c}{T^3} \, dT - \frac{2690}{1234}$$

$$\Delta S = \Delta a \ln T \Big|_{1073}^{1234} + \Delta b T \Big|_{1073}^{1234} - \tfrac{1}{2}\Delta c \frac{1}{T^2}\Big|_{1073}^{1234} - 2.18$$

$$\Delta a = 2.21, \qquad \Delta b = -2.04 \times 10^{-3}, \qquad \Delta c = -0.36 \times 10^5$$

Substitution yields

$$\Delta S_{\text{Ag}} = -2.20 \text{ e.u.}$$

To evaluate ΔS_{surr}, evaluate ΔH_f by the method discussed. Thus

$$-\Delta H_f = \int_{1073}^{1234} \Delta a \, dT + \int_{1073}^{1234} \Delta b T \, dT + \int_{1073}^{1234} \frac{\Delta c}{T^2} \, dT - 2690$$

Substitution of Δa, Δb, and Δc yields

$$\Delta H_f = 2715 \text{ cal/mole}$$

As a result

$$\Delta S_{\text{surr}} = \frac{\Delta H_f}{T_1} = + \frac{2715}{1073} = +2.53 \text{ e.u.}$$

and the entropy change of the universe is equal to

$$\Delta S_{\text{Ag}} + \Delta S_{\text{surr}} = 0.33 \text{ e.u.}$$

From the illustration, we see that the sum of the entropy change of system and surrounding is greater than zero. It will be recalled from the earlier section that the similar sum for a reversible process is equal to zero. It may be shown, in fact, that these examples can be generalized as follows:

(a)   For a reversible process, $\Delta S_{\text{syst}} + \Delta S_{\text{surr}} = 0$.
(b)   For a spontaneous process, $\Delta S_{\text{syst}} + \Delta S_{\text{surr}} > 0$.
(c)   For a process which will not proceed (the reverse process will of course be spontaneous in this case), $\Delta S_{\text{syst}} + \Delta S_{\text{surr}} < 0$.

From (b) it follows that

$$dS_{\text{syst}} > \frac{DQ}{T} \text{ (for an irreversible process)} \qquad (3.13)$$

These statements are, in effect, a statement of the second law of thermodynamics.

As a result of (a), (b), and (c) we now have a method for determining whether or not a given process will proceed spontaneously under the set of conditions imposed upon it.

3.5 RELATIONS OBTAINED USING THE SECOND LAW

Relation between C_P and C_V

It will be recalled that $C_P = (\partial H/\partial T)_P$ and $C_V = (\partial E/\partial T)_V$, so it will be necessary to obtain a relation between $(\partial H/\partial T)_P$ and $(\partial E/\partial T)_V$. It seems reasonable to start with the definition of enthalpy:

$$H = E + PV$$

and on differentiation

$$dH = dE + P \, dV + V \, dP$$

If we divide the above equation by dT,

$$\frac{dH}{dT} = \frac{dE}{dT} + P\frac{dV}{dT} + V\frac{dP}{dT}$$

Placing the restriction of constant pressure we have

$$\left(\frac{\partial H}{\partial T}\right)_P = \left(\frac{\partial E}{\partial T}\right)_P + P\left(\frac{\partial V}{\partial T}\right)_P \tag{3.14}$$

We are interested in $(\partial E/\partial T)_V$, so it will be necessary to eliminate $(\partial E/\partial T)_P$ in favor of $(\partial E/\partial T)_V$. To do this let us express $E = f(V, T)$, thus

$$dE = \left(\frac{\partial E}{\partial V}\right)_T dV + \left(\frac{\partial E}{\partial T}\right)_V dT \tag{3.15}$$

Dividing through by dT and keeping P constant, we find

$$\left(\frac{\partial E}{\partial T}\right)_P = \left(\frac{\partial E}{\partial V}\right)_T \left(\frac{\partial V}{\partial T}\right)_P + \left(\frac{\partial E}{\partial T}\right)_V \tag{3.16}$$

Substitution of equation 3.16 into 3.14 yields

$$\left(\frac{\partial H}{\partial T}\right)_P = \left(\frac{\partial E}{\partial T}\right)_V + \left[\left(\frac{\partial E}{\partial V}\right)_T + P\right]\left(\frac{\partial V}{\partial T}\right)_P$$

or

$$C_P = C_V + \left[\left(\frac{\partial E}{\partial V}\right)_T + P\right]\left(\frac{\partial V}{\partial T}\right)_P \tag{3.17}$$

Experimentally, one can measure P and $(\partial V/\partial T)_P$ quite easily, but it is generally more difficult to obtain the change of internal energy with volume at constant T, $(\partial E/\partial V)_T$. Therefore, let us attempt to express this quantity in terms of more readily available quantities. By expressing $E = f(T, V)$ we find

$$dE = \left(\frac{\partial E}{\partial T}\right)_V dT + \left(\frac{\partial E}{\partial V}\right)_T dV \tag{3.18}$$

For a reversible process

$$dE = T\,dS - P\,dV \tag{3.19}$$

and subtracting equation 3.19 from 3.18 we find

$$dS = \frac{1}{T}\left(\frac{\partial E}{\partial T}\right)_V dT + \frac{1}{T}\left[\left(\frac{\partial E}{\partial V}\right)_T + P\right] dV \tag{3.20}$$

Equation 3.20 is expressed in terms of dT and dV. Let us now expand $S = f(T, V)$.

$$dS = \left(\frac{\partial S}{\partial T}\right)_V dT + \left(\frac{\partial S}{\partial V}\right)_T dV \tag{3.21}$$

By comparison of coefficients in equations 3.20 and 3.21 we see that

$$\left(\frac{\partial S}{\partial T}\right)_V = \frac{1}{T}\left(\frac{\partial E}{\partial T}\right)_V \tag{3.22}$$

and

$$\left(\frac{\partial S}{\partial V}\right)_T = \frac{1}{T}\left[\left(\frac{\partial E}{\partial V}\right)_T + P\right] \tag{3.23}$$

The second derivative of (3.22) with respect to volume at constant temperature and the second derivative of (3.23) with respect to temperature at constant volume are equal since

$$\frac{\partial^2 S}{\partial T\,\partial V} = \frac{\partial^2 S}{\partial V\,\partial T} \tag{3.24}$$

and therefore

$$\frac{\partial}{\partial V}\left(\frac{\partial S}{\partial T}\right)_V = \frac{1}{T}\frac{\partial}{\partial V}\left(\frac{\partial E}{\partial T}\right)_V$$

and

$$\frac{\partial}{\partial T}\left(\frac{\partial S}{\partial V}\right)_T = \frac{\partial}{\partial T}\left\{\frac{1}{T}\left[\left(\frac{\partial E}{\partial V}\right)_T + P\right]\right\}$$

In view of equation 3.24 we find

$$\frac{1}{T}\frac{\partial}{\partial V}\left(\frac{\partial E}{\partial T}\right)_V = \frac{\partial}{\partial T}\left\{\frac{1}{T}\left[\left(\frac{\partial E}{\partial V}\right)_T + P\right]\right\}$$

and

$$\frac{1}{T}\frac{\partial^2 E}{\partial V\,\partial T} = \frac{1}{T}\left[\frac{\partial^2 E}{\partial T\,\partial V} + \left(\frac{\partial P}{\partial T}\right)_V\right] - \frac{1}{T^2}\left(\frac{\partial E}{\partial V}\right)_T + P$$

Thus

$$\left[\left(\frac{\partial E}{\partial V}\right)_T + P\right] = T\left(\frac{\partial P}{\partial T}\right)_V \tag{3.25}$$

In this way, we have eliminated $(\partial E/\partial V)_T$ in favor of $(\partial P/\partial T)_V$, which by experience we know can readily be expressed in terms of easily measurable quantities. Thus $V = f(P, T)$ and

$$dV = \left(\frac{\partial V}{\partial P}\right)_T dP + \left(\frac{\partial V}{\partial T}\right)_P dT$$

Dividing this expression by dT and holding V constant yields

$$0 = \left(\frac{\partial V}{\partial P}\right)_T\left(\frac{\partial P}{\partial T}\right)_V + \left(\frac{\partial V}{\partial T}\right)_P$$

or

$$\left(\frac{\partial P}{\partial T}\right)_V = -\left(\frac{\partial V}{\partial T}\right)_P \bigg/ \left(\frac{\partial V}{\partial P}\right)_T$$

Since the volume thermal expansion coefficient, α, of a substance is defined as

$$\alpha \equiv \frac{1}{V}\left(\frac{\partial V}{\partial T}\right)_P$$

and the compressibility β is defined as

$$\beta \equiv -\frac{1}{V}\left(\frac{\partial V}{\partial P}\right)_T$$

we have

$$\left(\frac{\partial P}{\partial T}\right)_V = \frac{\alpha}{\beta} \tag{3.26}$$

Substituting 3.26 into 3.25 and thence into 3.17, we have

$$C_P = C_V + \frac{\alpha^2 V T}{\beta} \tag{3.27}$$

Equation 3.27 shows that C_V may be obtained from C_P if the molar volume, compressibility, and thermal expansion coefficient are available for a substance. For a solid, the heat capacity at constant volume, C_V, is generally more difficult to obtain experimentally than these particular physical parameters which are obtained from standard laboratory experiments.

Thermoelastic Effect

As the term thermoelastic implies, this phenomenon relates a temperature change of a system to mechanical stress. Consider a system well insulated from its surroundings. This is called an *adiabatic* system. Let us now apply a hydrostatic pressure P to the system. Since reversibility is the basic restriction we must place in order to treat the system thermodynamically, the pressure P must be applied in such a manner that the system is strained elastically and not plastically. A change in temperature dT will now result from a change in pressure dP. Since the process is performed adiabatically, there is no heat exchange with the surroundings. Thus DQ is zero and Q is constant. Thus we need an expression for $(\partial T/\partial P)_Q$. It seems reasonable to begin with a statement of the first law:

$$dE = DQ - P\,dV$$

Since Q is constant, DQ is zero and

$$dE = -P\,dV$$

Expressing $E = f(T, V)$,

$$dE = -P\,dV = \left(\frac{\partial E}{\partial T}\right)_V dT + \left(\frac{\partial E}{\partial V}\right)_T dV \tag{3.28}$$

Dividing through equation 3.28 by dP, holding Q constant, and rearranging terms we have

$$C_V\left(\frac{\partial T}{\partial P}\right)_Q = -\left[\left(\frac{\partial E}{\partial V}\right)_T + P\right]\left(\frac{\partial V}{\partial P}\right)_Q \qquad (3.29)$$

The term $[(\partial E/\partial V)_T + P]$ is equal to $(\partial P/\partial T)_V T$ as shown by equation 3.25, and $(\partial P/\partial T)_V$ is equal to α/β as expressed by 3.26. Substituting, we have

$$\left(\frac{\partial T}{\partial P}\right)_Q = -\frac{T\alpha}{C_V\beta}\left(\frac{\partial V}{\partial P}\right)_Q \qquad (3.30)$$

The term $(\partial V/\partial P)_Q$ is not readily obtainable experimentally so it is worthwhile to investigate whether or not it can be eliminated in favor of more easily obtainable quantities, such as α and β. To obtain this term as $f(\alpha, \beta)$ let us express $V = f(T, P)$. Thus

$$dV = \left(\frac{\partial V}{\partial T}\right)_P dT + \left(\frac{\partial V}{\partial P}\right)_T dP$$

or

$$dV = V\alpha\, dT - V\beta\, dP \qquad (3.31)$$

Dividing through by dP, and holding Q constant,

$$\left(\frac{\partial V}{\partial P}\right)_Q = V\alpha\left(\frac{\partial T}{\partial P}\right)_Q - V\beta \qquad (3.32)$$

Substituting equation 3.32 into 3.30 and collecting terms, we find

$$\left(\frac{\partial T}{\partial P}\right)_Q = \frac{VT\alpha}{[C_V + VT\alpha^2/\beta]} \qquad (3.33)$$

The term in brackets in equation 3.33 is equal to C_P, as found in the last section, and thus

$$\left(\frac{\partial T}{\partial P}\right)_Q = \frac{VT\alpha}{C_P} \qquad (3.34)$$

From equation 3.34, since all quantities on the right hand side are positive, we find that application of external pressure to a system results in a temperature rise.

Illustration

Problem. Suppose that a particular materials application calls for a specific tensile stress to be applied to a well insulated crystal at 300°K. This system is subjected to tensile stress fluctuations $\Delta\sigma$. It is suggested that continuous temperature measurement might provide a method of measuring these stress fluctuations. The recording equipment available is capable of detecting temperature variations of ±0.001°C. Calculate the minimum stress variations which can be detected by this equipment. The crystal has a density ρ of 10 gm/cm³, a molecular weight of 100, a value of α equal to $4.00 \times 10^{-5}/°C$, and a heat capacity of 6.50 cal/mole degree.

Solution. Since the system is well insulated, equation 3.34 may be used to solve this problem. Equation 3.34 expresses the change in temperature with respect to hydrostatic pressure applied to the system. Our case here, however, deals first with a stress of opposite sign and second with a uniaxial instead of hydrostatic stress. It will be left to the reader to show that for an isotropic substance

$$\left(\frac{\partial T}{\partial \sigma}\right)_Q = - \frac{VT\alpha}{3C_P}$$

Bearing in mind the restriction of constant Q we may write

$$\frac{dT}{T} = - \frac{V\alpha}{3C_P} \, d\sigma$$

If it is assumed that α and C_P are little affected by the strain, then upon integration

$$\ln\left(\frac{T + \Delta T}{T}\right) = - \frac{V\alpha \, \Delta\sigma}{3C_P}$$

If $\Delta T \ll T$, $\ln[(T + \Delta T)/T]$ may be expanded in an infinite series and high order terms neglected. Doing this and using the relation

$$V = \frac{M}{\rho}$$

where M is the molecular weight and ρ is the density, we find

$$\Delta\sigma = - \frac{3C_P \, \Delta T \rho}{MT\alpha} \tag{3.35}$$

Substituting the appropriate physical quantities, we find $\Delta\sigma = \pm 1.63 \times 10^{-1}$ cal/cm³. To put in the practical form of gm/cm², convert calories to dyne-cm and divide by gravitational acceleration. Doing this we find $\Delta\sigma = \pm 6.94 \times 10^3$ gm/cm² or ± 985 lb/cm². From 3.35 it is seen that a tensile stress causes a temperature decrease whereas the opposite occurs for a compressive stress.

3.6 THE FREE ENERGY FUNCTION

As discussed in an earlier section, evaluation of the quantity ($\Delta S_{syst} + \Delta S_{surr}$) for a given reaction is sufficient for establishing whether a given reaction (chemical or mechanical) will proceed spontaneously under the conditions imposed. It is not always convenient to calculate ΔS_{surr}, however: it would be better to find some other function. Let us consider a spontaneous reaction under isothermal and isobaric conditions. From the second law

$$dS_{syst} + dS_{surr} > 0$$

Even though the reaction is proceeding irreversibly, heat may be transformed to the surroundings in a reversible fashion however, so that according to the second law

$$dS_{surr} = \frac{DQ}{T} \text{ (to surr)} = -\frac{DQ}{T} \text{ (from surr to syst)}$$

As shown previously, under isobaric conditions $DQ = dH$ and

$$dS_{surr} = -\frac{dH}{T} \text{ (to syst)}$$

and thus

$$dS_{syst} > \frac{dH}{T} \text{ (to syst)}$$

or

$$dH < T \, dS_{syst}$$

or

$$dH - T \, dS_{syst} < 0 \qquad (3.36)$$

Equation 3.36 shows that, for a spontaneous reaction, the enthalpy change of the system minus the absolute temperature times the entropy change of the system is less than zero. Similarly for a reaction at equilibrium, it follows that

$$dH - T \, dS_{syst} = 0 \qquad (3.37)$$

and for an impossible reaction

$$dH - T \, dS_{syst} > 0 \qquad (3.38)$$

As a result the quantity $(dH - T \, dS_{syst})$ can be used as an index as to whether or not a reaction is spontaneous thus obviating the necessity of considering the entropy change of the surrounding. In the future, therefore, we shall be concerned only with the entropy of the system and the use of the subscripts (surr) and (syst) will be discontinued. The relation $(dH - T \, dS)$ is known as the Gibbs free energy, dG. Thus

$$dG = dH - T \, dS \qquad (3.39)$$

and integrating yields

$$G = H - TS \qquad (3.40)$$

If a reaction were considered at constant volume instead of constant pressure, the relation would be $(dE - T \, dS)$ and it is convenient to define this as the Helmholtz free energy dF. Thus

$$F = E - TS \qquad (3.41)$$

There is some confusion about symbols in the literature. F and A are often used in place of G and F respectively so caution must be exerted.

Some Useful Relations

We now have enough equations to develop some useful general thermo-dynamic relations. As a first step let us differentiate equation 3.40. We find

$$dG = dH - T\,dS - S\,dT$$

Since $dH = dE + P\,dV + V\,dP$, we obtain upon substitution

$$dG = dV + P\,dV + V\,dP - T\,dS - S\,dT$$

From the first law, $dE = DQ - P\,dV$, if only mechanical work is being considered, and on substitution

$$dG = DQ + V\,dP - T\,dS - S\,dT$$

If we are considering a reversible process, we have from the second law, $dS = DQ/T$, and on substitution for DQ in the equation above we find

$$dG = V\,dP - S\,dT \tag{3.42}$$

Similar steps for the Helmholz free energy yield

$$dF = -P\,dV - S\,dT \tag{3.43}$$

It must be emphasized that equations 3.42 and 3.43 are valid only for reversible processes.

Dividing equation 3.42 by dP and holding T constant gives

$$\left(\frac{\partial G}{\partial P}\right)_T = V \tag{3.44}$$

Thus we see that if the Gibbs free energy is measured as a function of pressure, the slope of the resultant line is equal to the volume of the system at the particular pressure chosen. Similarly for a reaction in which ΔG is evaluated it may be shown that

$$\left(\frac{\partial \Delta G}{\partial P}\right)_T = \Delta V \tag{3.45}$$

Since ΔG refers to the difference in free energy of products and reactions, ΔV refers to the difference in volume between products and reactants. Another useful relation is obtained if equation 3.42 is divided by dT and the pressure is held constant:

$$\left(\frac{\partial G}{\partial T}\right)_P = -S \tag{3.46}$$

or

$$\left(\frac{\partial \Delta G}{\partial T}\right)_P = -\Delta S \tag{3.47}$$

It will be left to the reader to show that under reversible conditions

$$\left(\frac{\partial F}{\partial V}\right)_T = -P \tag{3.48}$$

and

$$\left(\frac{\partial F}{\partial T}\right)_V = -S \tag{3.49}$$

Since external pressure is easier to control in the case of solids than the volume of the system, the Gibbs function is much more useful. By studying the variation of the Gibbs free energy of a system with pressure under isothermal conditions and the variation with temperature under isobaric conditions, the volume and entropy may be obtained. These relations are useful in thermodynamic computations and are indispensible in the investigation of kinetics of reactions.

There is a very useful relation between G and H which will be derived below. Let us start with equation 3.40,

$$G = H - TS \tag{3.40}$$

By dividing through by T, we obtain

$$G/T = H/T - S \tag{3.50}$$

Differentiating with respect to temperature at constant pressure we have

$$\left[\frac{\partial(G/T)}{\partial T}\right]_P = \left[\frac{\partial(H/T)}{\partial T}\right]_P - \left(\frac{\partial S}{\partial T}\right)_P \tag{3.51}$$

The first term on the right hand side can be expanded as follows:

$$\left[\frac{\partial(H/T)}{\partial T}\right]_P = \frac{1}{T}\left(\frac{\partial H}{\partial T}\right)_P + H\left[\frac{\partial(1/T)}{\partial T}\right]_P$$

Substituting this into equation 3.51, we have

$$\left[\frac{\partial(G/T)}{\partial T}\right]_P = \frac{1}{T}\left(\frac{\partial H}{\partial T}\right)_P + H\left[\frac{\partial(1/T)}{\partial T}\right]_P - \left(\frac{\partial S}{\partial T}\right)_P \tag{3.52}$$

By definition

$$\frac{1}{T}\left(\frac{\partial H}{\partial T}\right)_P \equiv \frac{C_P}{T} \tag{3.53}$$

Also

$$\left[\frac{(1/T)}{T}\right]_P = -\frac{1}{T^2} \tag{3.54}$$

and from the second law

$$dS = \frac{DQ}{T} = \frac{dH_P}{T} \tag{3.55}$$

Thus $C_P\, dT = T\, dS$ and upon rearrangement

$$\left(\frac{\partial S}{\partial T}\right)_P = \frac{C_P}{T} \tag{3.56}$$

Substitution of 3.53, 3.54, and 3.56 into 3.52 yields

$$\left[\frac{\partial(G/T)}{\partial T}\right]_P = -\frac{H}{T^2}$$

Multiplying both sides by T^2 gives

$$\frac{1}{1/T^2}\left[\frac{\partial(G/T)}{\partial T}\right]_P = H \tag{3.57}$$

Inclusion of the T^2 term in brackets yields

$$\left[\frac{\partial(G/T)}{\partial(1/T)}\right]_P = H \tag{3.58}$$

or for a reaction having a free energy change

$$\left[\frac{\partial(\Delta G/T)}{\partial(1/T)}\right]_P = \Delta H \tag{3.59}$$

Thus if $(\Delta G/T)$ is plotted versus the reciprocal of absolute temperature, the slope is equal to ΔH. Equation 3.59 is important both in thermodynamics and kinetics. Some idea of the general usefulness of the free energy function should already be apparent to the reader. By measuring the variation of ΔG with respect to temperature at constant pressure, the entropy change of the reaction ΔS may be obtained at any temperature from the slope. Similarly if $\Delta G/T$ is plotted versus the reciprocal of the absolute temperature at constant pressure, the slope is equal to the enthalpy change for the reaction, and if ΔG is plotted versus pressure, the slope is equal to the volume change between products and reactants. The most useful application of the free energy concept, namely that pertaining to the equilibrium constant, will be discussed in a later chapter.

Maxwell's Equations

Consider the following four equations derived previously, which are applicable only under reversible conditions.

$$dE = T\, dS - P\, dV$$
$$dH = T\, dS + V\, dP$$
$$dF = -P\, dV - S\, dT$$
$$dG = V\, dP - S\, dT$$

Taking the first equation, dividing through by dS, and holding V constant we have

$$\left(\frac{\partial E}{\partial S}\right)_V = T \tag{3.60}$$

Similarly, dividing through by dV and holding S constant, we find

$$\left(\frac{\partial E}{\partial V}\right)_S = -P \tag{3.61}$$

Since

$$\frac{\partial}{\partial V}\left(\frac{\partial E}{\partial S}\right)_V = \frac{\partial}{\partial S}\left(\frac{\partial E}{\partial V}\right)_S = \frac{\partial^2 E}{\partial S\,\partial V}$$

if we differentiate equation 3.60 with respect to V, and equation 3.61 with with respect to S, they may then be equated

$$\frac{\partial}{\partial V}\left(\frac{\partial E}{\partial S}\right)_V = \left(\frac{\partial T}{\partial V}\right)_S$$

and

$$\frac{\partial}{\partial S}\left(\frac{\partial E}{\partial V}\right)_S = -\left(\frac{\partial P}{\partial S}\right)_V$$

Thus

$$-\left(\frac{\partial P}{\partial S}\right)_V = \left(\frac{\partial T}{\partial V}\right)_S \tag{3.62}$$

This is the first of Maxwell's equations.

Taking the second equation and dividing through by dS, holding P constant, we have

$$\left(\frac{\partial H}{\partial S}\right)_P = T \tag{3.63}$$

and similarly dividing by dP, holding S constant

$$\left(\frac{\partial H}{\partial P}\right)_S = V \tag{3.64}$$

Taking the second partial derivative of 3.63 with respect to P, holding S constant, and the second derivative of 3.64 with respect to S holding P constant, yields

$$\frac{\partial}{\partial P}\left(\frac{\partial H}{\partial S}\right)_P = \left(\frac{\partial T}{\partial P}\right)_S \tag{3.65}$$

and

$$\frac{\partial}{\partial S}\left(\frac{\partial H}{\partial P}\right)_S = \left(\frac{\partial V}{\partial S}\right)_P \tag{3.66}$$

Equating 3.65 to 3.66 gives the second Maxwell equation

$$\left(\frac{\partial T}{\partial P}\right)_S = \left(\frac{\partial V}{\partial S}\right)_P \tag{3.67}$$

Taking the third equation and dividing through by dV, holding T constant, gives

$$\left(\frac{\partial F}{\partial V}\right)_T = -P \tag{3.68}$$

and similarly, dividing by dT and holding V constant gives

$$\left(\frac{\partial F}{\partial T}\right)_V = -S \tag{3.69}$$

Taking the second derivative of 3.68 with respect to T and holding V constant we have

$$\frac{\partial}{\partial T}\left(\frac{\partial F}{\partial V}\right)_T = -\left(\frac{\partial P}{\partial T}\right)_V \tag{3.70}$$

and similarly taking the second derivative of 3.69 with respect to V, holding T constant,

$$\frac{\partial}{\partial V}\left(\frac{\partial F}{\partial T}\right)_V = -\left(\frac{\partial S}{\partial V}\right)_T \tag{3.71}$$

Equating 3.70 to 3.71, we find the third Maxwell relation

$$\left(\frac{\partial S}{\partial V}\right)_T = \left(\frac{\partial P}{\partial T}\right)_V \tag{3.72}$$

Taking the fourth equation, dividing through by dP, holding T constant

$$\left(\frac{\partial G}{\partial P}\right)_T = V \tag{3.73}$$

and similarly dividing by dT holding P constant

$$\left(\frac{\partial G}{\partial T}\right)_P = -S \tag{3.74}$$

Taking the second derivatives as in the former three cases, we have the fourth Maxwell relation

$$\left(\frac{\partial V}{\partial T}\right)_P = -\left(\frac{\partial S}{\partial P}\right)_T \tag{3.75}$$

These four relations (particularly the last two) are very useful in thermodynamic derivations, since they often allow the substitution of a more desirable quantity in an equation.

3.7 SUMMARY OF THERMODYNAMIC RELATIONS

So far many important thermodynamic relations have been derived. There are many more relations which can prove useful in particular circumstances. It would be desirable to be able to present the numerous

TABLE 3.1

Summary of Thermodynamic Relations[a]

X	Y	Z	$\left(\dfrac{\partial Y}{\partial X}\right)_Z$	X	Y	Z	$\left(\dfrac{\partial Y}{\partial X}\right)_Z$
T	V	P	αV	T	P	V	α/β
T	S	P	C_P/T	T	S	V	$C_P/T - \alpha^2 V/\beta$
T	V	P	$C_P - \alpha PV$	T	E	V	$C_P - \alpha^2 VT/\beta$
T	H	P	C_P	T	H	V	$C_P - \alpha^2 VT/\beta + \alpha V/\beta$
T	F	P	$-\alpha PV - S$	T	F	V	$-S$
T	G	P	$-S$	T	G	V	$\alpha V/\beta - S$
P	V	T	$-\beta V$	T	P	S	$C_P/\alpha VT$
P	S	T	$-\alpha V$	T	V	S	$-\beta C_P/\alpha T + \alpha V$
P	E	T	$\beta PV - \alpha VT$	T	E	S	$\beta PC_P/\alpha T - \alpha PV$
P	H	T	$V - \alpha VT$	T	H	S	$C_P/\alpha T$
P	F	T	βPV	T	F	S	$\beta PC_P/\alpha T - \alpha PV - S$
P	G	T	V	T	G	S	$C_P/\alpha T - S$

[a] From J. Lumsden, *Thermodynamics of Alloys*, Institute of Metals, London, 1952.

relations in a convenient form. To this end a wide variety of techniques have been used for summarizing relationships. In Table 3.1 are shown many convenient relations in a simple form after Lumsden.[1] All symbols used have been previously defined.

[1] J. Lumsden, *Thermodynamics of Alloys*, Institute of Metals, London, 1952.

chapter 4

The Statistical
Interpretation of Entropy

4.1 BOLTZMANN'S DEFINITION

Entropy is one of the most important quantities of thermodynamics, and one of the least understood. As a result, students often memorize the definitions and, because of the lack of physical interpretation, forget it. In later chapters we shall often need the entropy concept as a working tool in the study of crystal properties, so it should be properly understood.

The most important and far reaching laws of science are often the simplest mathematically. The definition of entropy is no exception. According to Boltzmann, there is a relationship between the entropy of a system in a given state and the probability of existence of the state. He suggested that it might be possible to calculate the probability of different states of a system from the various distributions possible. Planck[1] wrote Boltzmann's statement mathematically as

$$S = k \ln \mathcal{W} + \text{const} \tag{4.1}$$

where $\mathcal{W}$ represents the probability of a given state, k is Boltzmann's constant, and S is the entropy contribution to the system due to the given state. In order to obtain $\mathcal{W}$, something has to be known about the distribution of atoms and molecules in the system of interest; alternatively, experimental values of entropy may be interpreted in terms of the properties of the atoms and molecules which make up the system. Until now we have been concerned with *classical thermodynamics*. This chapter introduces *statistical thermodynamics*.

[1] M. Planck, *Vorlesungen uber die Theorie der Warmestrahlung*, First Edition, Springer, Berlin, 1906.

In principle, the properties of a system can be calculated by the summation of the properties of each individual molecule in the system at a given time. Obviously, this is a rather hopeless challenge since a normal system contains of the order of 10^{22} atoms or molecules. By application of statistics this problem can be surmounted, however. For example, the instantaneous pressure of a gas upon the walls of a vessel could be obtained from a consideration of the velocity vectors of each gas molecule in box at a given time. It is simpler, however, to calculate time average quantities.

4.2 ELEMENTARY STATISTICAL CONCEPTS

In order to obtain expressions for the entropy in terms of the probability of a state, some simple statistical consideration will be desirable.

Let us consider first a case where we have, say eight objects numbered 1 through 8, and four boxes. Let us attempt to answer the following question: In how many different ways can these objects be placed in these boxes assuming that each box is large enough to hold all of the objects? We may put the object labeled 1 in any one of the four boxes. Similarly, since each event is considered to be independent we may do likewise for object 2, etc. The total number of ways of putting object 1 in the boxes is four. The total number of possibilities for object 2 is four, etc., up through object 8. The total number of ways or *complexions* of arranging all the balls is therefore $\prod_{n=1}^{8} 4 = 4^8$. If the objects are put into the boxes in a random fashion, each complexion of the total of 4^8 has the same probability of occurring. That is to say, there will be an equal probability of finding all 8 objects in box 1 as in box 2, etc. Similarly, the probability of any one of these complexions occurring will be equal to the probability of finding balls 1 and 2 in box 1 with box 2 being empty and boxes 3 through 8 containing balls 3 through 8 respectively, etc.

In the situations which we will be dealing with (atoms in crystals) we can differentiate types of atoms. For example, we can distinguish a gold atom from a copper atom. We cannot, however, distinguish, within a given type, one atom from another. The situation discussed above is not therefore completely applicable to our case: we shall not be interested in which object is in a given box, but in how many of the same type of objects are in each box. To illustrate, let us calculate the number of complexions for which there are 2 balls in each box. Such a total is called a *statistical state*. Thus, we need to calculate how many ways we have of arranging 2 objects in box 1, 2 of the remaining 8 in box 2, 2 of the remaining 6 in box 3, etc. The first step is to calculate the number of ways of picking 2 objects out of 8 for box 1. This can be readily calculated by using a theorem which states that the number of combinations of N things taken n at a time is given by

$$\mathscr{W} = {}_NC_n = \frac{N!}{n!\,(N-n)!} \qquad (4.2)$$

As a result, the number of ways of putting 2 objects in the box out of a total of 8 is

$${}_8C_2 = \frac{8!}{2!\,6!} = \frac{8 \times 7}{2} = 28$$

We have 6 objects left. Therefore the number of combinations of taking 2 objects out of the remaining 6 for box 2 is

$${}_6C_2 = \frac{6!}{2!\,4!} = \frac{6 \times 5}{2} = 15$$

Similarly for box 3, we have 4 objects left and

$${}_4C_2 = \frac{4!}{2!\,2!} = \frac{4 \times 3}{2} = 6$$

For box 4, since 2 objects are left

$${}_2C_2 = \frac{2!}{2!\,0!} = 1$$

Now we are ready to answer the question: How many ways are there of putting 2 objects in box 1, 2 objects in box 2, etc? To obtain this answer we need to multiply the above combinations. The number of ways is equal to

$$\mathscr{W} = {}_8C_2 \times {}_6C_2 \times {}_4C_2 \times {}_2C_2 = \frac{N!}{n_1!\,n_2!\,n_3!\,n_4!} = \frac{8!}{(2!)^4} = 2520$$

Now let us answer the question: If the objects are being put into the boxes in a random fashion, so that any complexion is equally probable, what is the *probability* of achieving the statistical state in which we have 2 objects in each box? As we have just calculated, there are 2520 complexions associated with this state. Earlier we found that there is a total of 4^8 complexions. Therefore the probability p of our statistical state is

$$p = \frac{2520}{4^8}$$

Interestingly enough, it will be found that the probability of the statistical state just described, where we have an equal distribution of objects, is larger than the probability of any other statistical state. As a generalization we will find that the number of ways of arranging N objects so that we have n_1 objects in the first cell (or box), n_2 in the second, etc., is

$$\mathscr{W} = \frac{N!}{n_1! \, n_2! \, n_3! \cdots} \qquad (4.3)$$

As just discussed the statistical state with the highest probability or largest value of $\mathscr{W}$ is one in which the objects are distributed uniformly. This state then is the one which will occur most often and hence represents the *most probable state*. From equation 4.1 we find further that since the most probable state has the largest value of $\mathscr{W}$, it also has the highest value of entropy of any state. As a result, if a system goes from a given statistical state to a more probable statistical state, $\mathscr{W}$ increases and hence, from applying equation 4.1, the entropy increases. Since such a process would be expected to be spontaneous, the entropy of the process should increase in agreement with the Second Law.

In dealing with entropy calculations, we shall be interested in values of $\ln \mathscr{W}$ and hence be concerned with the logarithm of factorials. There is a convenient approximation, useful for this situation, known as Stirling's formula which is applicable only when N is very large. In most of the cases of interest to us, $N \sim 10^{22}$ atoms and thus this criterion is met. In this case Stirling's approximation is given by

$$\ln N! \cong N \ln N - N \qquad (4.4)$$

Let us now consider the case of a molar volume of crystal containing N_0 lattice sites.

Let us calculate the entropy change ΔS_m associated with the random mixing of n atoms of type B and $(N - n)$ atoms of type A on these N_0 sites (see Fig. 4.1). The entropy to be calculated will be the entropy of the following reactions.

$$(N_0 - n) \, \text{A} + n\text{B} = \text{Solution} \, [(N_0 - n) \, \text{A}, \, n\text{B}]$$

and is known as the mixing entropy ΔS_m. Thus

$$\Delta S_m = S_{\text{A,B}} - S_{\text{A}} - S_{\text{B}}$$

According to the Boltzmann equation

$$\Delta S_m = k(\ln \mathscr{W}_{\text{A,B}} - \ln \mathscr{W}_{\text{A}} - \ln \mathscr{W}_{\text{B}})$$

Let us now consider $\mathscr{W}_{\text{A,B}}$, the number of ways of arranging $(N_0 - n)$ A atoms and n B atoms on N_0 sites. According to our previous derivations, let us consider that the crystal consists of N_0 cells which will hold one atom. If we are able to distinguish one atom from another

$$\mathcal{W} = \frac{N_0!}{n_1!\, n_2!\, n_3 \,\cdots\, n_N!}$$

Since each of the N sites can hold only one atom, n_1, n_2, etc., equals one and therefore

$$\mathcal{W} = N_0!$$

This situation is not really applicable to our case since we cannot distinguish one A atom from another, but we can distinguish an A atom from

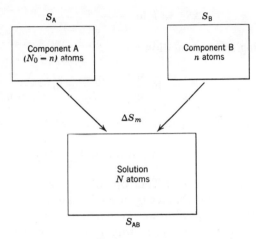

Fig. 4.1 Illustration of a mixing process.

a B atom. The appropriate value of $\mathcal{W}$ will therefore be less than $N_0!$, since this includes the number of ways of arranging distinguishable A atoms among $(N_0 - n)$ sites and distinguishable B atoms among n sites. The number of ways of arranging $(N_0 - n)$ atoms on $(N_0 - n)$ sites and n B atoms on B sites will be $(N_0 - n)!$ and $n!$ respectively. Therefore the number of ways of mixing indistinguishable A atoms with indistinguishable B atoms will be reduced by the factor

$$\frac{1}{(N_0 - n)!\, n!}$$

and thus

$$\mathcal{W} = \frac{N_0!}{n!\, (N_0 - n)!} \tag{4.5}$$

For a system consisting of n_A atoms of component A, n_B atoms of component B, etc.,

$$\mathscr{W} = \frac{N_0!}{n_A! \, n_B! \, n_C! \cdots} \tag{4.6}$$

The mixing entropies of the pure crystals A and B are obtained in the same way. $\mathscr{W}_A$ and $\mathscr{W}_B$ would be equal to $(N - n)!$ and $n!$ for distinguishable atoms, but since they are indistinguishable, these values are divided by $(N - n)!$ and $n!$ respectively to give

$$\mathscr{W}_A = \mathscr{W}_B = 1$$

Thus

$$\Delta S_m = k \ln \frac{N_0!}{n! \, (N_0 - n)!}$$

Applying Stirling's approximation

$$\Delta S_m = N_0 k \left[\frac{n}{N_0} \ln \frac{N_0}{n} + \frac{N_0 - n}{N_0} \ln \frac{N_0}{N_0 - n} \right]$$

Defining atom fractions X_A and X_B as $[(N_0 - n)/N_0]$ and (n/N_0) respectively,

$$\Delta S_m = -R[X_A \ln X_A + X_B \ln X_B] \tag{4.7}$$

Equation 4.7 is the well known "entropy of mixing" equation, which will also be derived in a later chapter by use of classical thermodynamics.

From the previous discussion we can see that entropy is associated with the concept of *randomness*. The more random we make a system, in general, the higher the entropy will be. Also our discussion, thus far, has been concerned with *mixing randomness*. There is another type of randomness which is of interest in the study of the properties of crystals. This we will call *vibrational randomness*. In a crystal each atom is vibrating about a given position and hence there is a randomness associated with the position of an atom at a given time. If we consider that each atom is moving in a cell, we should expect the vibrational randomness to be related to the volume of the cell. The larger the volume of the cell, the larger will be the randomness and hence the larger will be the entropy. The diameter of the cell would be expected to be proportional to the amplitude of vibration of the atom. This entropy contribution shall be designated by S_v.

Consider the previous discussion. Suppose that A and B had atomic sizes which were considerably different. Upon formation of a solid solution, because of the size difference, it would be difficult to pack the atoms

into a perfect array. The situation would appear similar to that shown
in Fig. 4.2. Therefore, in addition to the mixing entropy contribution to

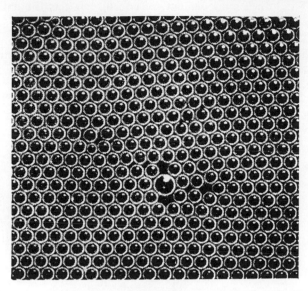

Fig. 4.2 Bubble-raft model of an impurity atom in a crystal. From L. Bragg and
J. F. Nye, *Proc. Roy. Soc.* (*London*), **A190**, 474 (1947).

randomness, there will be a vibrational contribution randomness associated with the process, since clearly the amplitude available for vibration
is greater than that in the perfect regions of the crystal. This will be
discussed in more detail in a later section.

4.3   POPULATION OF ENERGY STATES

Up to this point only mixing randomness has been considered in any
detail. Suppose now instead of being concerned with the entropy of a
mixture of various atomic species, we consider an entirely different
problem. Let us consider a molar volume of pure crystal. The N_0 atoms
in the crystal have a total energy E. All the atoms do not necessarily have
the same energy, however, since thermal fluctuations will occur in the
crystal. Let us consider, however, that discrete energy levels exist in the
crystal as shown in Fig. 4.3 and that atoms can only have these discrete
energies. In other words, an atom may exist with energy ϵ_0, ϵ_1, etc. but
may have no value in between. This, of course, corresponds to a quan-
tized state. The question then arises as to how many atoms occupy each

state. One would be tempted to argue that the crystal would seek a minimum energy: all atoms having energy ϵ_0 and the total energy being given by $E_0 = N_0\epsilon_0$. Such an argument, of course, neglects the entropy consideration. The energy states corresponding to ϵ_0, ϵ_1, ϵ_2, ... are distinguishable from one another, and the atoms occupying state ϵ_0 are distinguishable from those in state ϵ_1, etc. If all the atoms were in state ϵ_0, the number of ways of mixing $\mathcal{W}$ would be equal to one and hence S

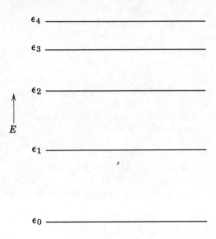

Fig. 4.3   Quantized energy levels.

would be equal to zero. As we determined previously, the equilibrium state corresponds to a maximum value of S and hence leads to an occupancy of states of higher energy than ϵ_0. Consider that in levels ϵ_0, ϵ_1, ϵ_2, ..., ϵ_r there are n_0, n_1, n_2, ..., n_r atoms. Then S is given by

$$S = k \ln \mathcal{W}$$

or

$$S = k \ln \frac{N_0!}{n_0!\, n_1!\, n_2! \cdots n_r!} \tag{4.8}$$

Applying Stirling's approximation to the case for large values of n_i, we find

$$S = -k \sum_{i=0}^{r} n_i \ln \frac{n_i}{N_0} \tag{4.9}$$

The total energy of the system is expressed as

$$E = \sum_{i=0}^{r} n_i \epsilon_i \tag{4.10}$$

The internal energy is constant, however, if our crystal is at a constant temperature and volume. Thus E is independent of the value of n_i and

$$dE = 0 = \sum_{i=0}^{r} \epsilon_i \, dn_i \qquad (4.11)$$

Since at equilibrium S is a maximum, $dS = 0$, or

$$dS = 0 = -k \sum_{i=0}^{r} \left(1 + \ln \frac{n_i}{N_0}\right) dn_i \qquad (4.12)$$

Furthermore, the number of atoms is constant so

$$N_0 = \sum_{i=0}^{r} n_i \qquad (4.13)$$

and

$$0 = \sum_{i=0}^{r} dn_i \qquad (4.14)$$

Substituting equation 4.14 into 4.12, we find

$$dS = 0 = -k \sum \ln \frac{n_i}{N_0} \, dn_i \qquad (4.15)$$

From equation 4.15 we see that the maximum S depends on several variables $(n_0, n_1, n_2, \ldots, n_r)$, but these variables are connected by equations 4.11 and 4.14. Such a condition is called a constrained maximum, and techniques for the mathematical treatment of constrained maxima have been developed by Lagrange.[1]

Applying these techniques, we obtain a set of equations

$$\ln \frac{n_0}{N_0} - \lambda_1 - \lambda_2 \epsilon_0 = 0$$

or

$$\ln \frac{n_1}{N_0} - \lambda_1 - \lambda_2 \epsilon_1 = 0$$

$$\ln \frac{n_i}{N_0} - \lambda_1 - \lambda_2 \epsilon_i = 0$$

In these equations λ_1 and λ_2 are constants known as Lagrangian multipliers. Rearranging one of these equations we find

$$\frac{n_i}{N_0} = \exp(\lambda_1) \exp(\lambda_2 \epsilon_i) \qquad (4.16)$$

[1] See any text on advanced calculus for full treatment of constrained maxima.

Since $\Sigma(n_i/N) = 1$, we find from equation 4.16

$$\sum \frac{n_i}{N_0} = 1 = \exp(\lambda_1) \sum \exp(\lambda_2\epsilon_i)$$

and thus

$$\exp(\lambda_1) = \frac{1}{\sum \exp(\lambda_2\epsilon_i)}$$

Therefore

$$\frac{n_i}{N_0} = \frac{\exp(\lambda_2\epsilon_i)}{\sum \exp(\lambda_2\epsilon_i)} \tag{4.17}$$

The coefficient λ_2 may now be evaluated quite readily. Let us transfer for example dn atoms from energy state ϵ_1 to energy state ϵ_2 in a reversible fashion. An entropy change dS will result, and using equations as obtained from 4.9 and 4.14 we find

$$dS = -k\left[-\ln\frac{n_1}{N_0} + \ln\frac{n_2}{N_0}\right]dn \tag{4.18}$$

Substitution for n_1 and n_2 from equation 4.17 we find

$$dS = -\lambda_2 k(\epsilon_2 - \epsilon_1)\,dn \tag{4.19}$$

The internal energy will change an amount dE equal to

$$dE = (\epsilon_2 - \epsilon_1)\,dn \tag{4.20}$$

If the system is at constant volume,

$$dE = DQ \tag{4.21}$$

from the first law and thus, from substitution of equations 4.20 and 4.21 into 4.19, we have

$$dS = -k\lambda_2 DQ \tag{4.22}$$

From the second law of thermodynamics, for a reversible process

$$dS = \frac{DQ}{T} \tag{4.23}$$

Comparison of equations 4.22 and 4.23 shows that

$$\lambda = -kT$$

Therefore the fraction of particles n_i/N_0 occupying energy state ϵ_1 is given by

$$f_i = \frac{n_i}{N_0} = \frac{\exp[-\epsilon_i/kT]}{\sum_i \exp[-\epsilon_i/kT]} \tag{4.24}$$

The denominator of equation 4.24 is known as the *partition function* $\mathscr{Z}$.

$$\mathscr{Z} = \sum_i \exp\left[-\epsilon_i/kT\right] \tag{4.25}$$

The numerator in equation 4.24 is known as the Boltzmann factor.

Illustration

Most solid state reactions such as diffusion involve an activated state. That is to say that an atom, in moving from one site to another, must pass over an energy barrier of height ΔE as shown in Fig. 4.4. The average

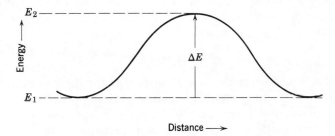

Fig. 4.4   Illustration of the activated state in diffusion.

energy of an atom in a normal lattice is E_1. In most cases, the energy levels arc so close to one another that a continuous curve may be used to approximate the path as shown in Fig. 4.4. The partition function $\mathscr{Z}$ instead of being given by a sum is expressed as

$$\mathscr{Z} = \int_0^\infty \exp\left(-E/kT\right) dE = kT \tag{4.26}$$

For our calculation, not only those with energy E_2 between $E_2 + dE$ will be able to move over the barrier, but those with any higher energy as well. Assuming the energy to be a continuum, the probability that an atom will have an energy between E and $E + dE$ is given by 4.24 as

$$f(E)\, dE = \frac{\exp\left(-E/kT\right) dE}{\displaystyle\int_0^\infty \exp\left(-E/kT\right) dE} \tag{4.27}$$

Thus the probability that it will have an energy between E_2 and $E = \infty$ is

$$f(E > E_2) = \int_{E_2}^\infty f(E)\, dE = \frac{\displaystyle\int_E^\infty \exp\left(-E/kT\right) dE}{\displaystyle\int_0^\infty \exp\left(-E/kT\right) dE}$$

and

$$f(E > E_2) = \exp\left(-E_2/kT\right) \tag{4.28}$$

Similarly the fraction of atoms having an energy between E_1 and ∞ is given by

$$f(E > E_1) = \int_{E_1}^{\infty} f(E)\, dE = \frac{\int_{E_1}^{\infty} \exp(-E/kT)\, dE}{\int_{0}^{\infty} \exp(-E/kT)\, dE}.$$

and

$$f(E > E_1) = \exp(-E_1/kT) \qquad (4.29)$$

The energy E_1 corresponds to the ground state of the atom. The fraction of atoms in the excited state, f^*, corresponds to $E > E_2$, and will be given by the ratio of 4.28 to 4.29, or

$$f^* = \exp(-\Delta E/kT) \qquad (4.30)$$

where ΔE is known as the activation energy for the process. Actually equation 4.30 is not completely rigorous since it was assumed that the number of states available at any energy is independent of the energy. This is not actually so and entropy considerations must be taken into account.[1] When this is done equation 4.30 becomes

$$f^* = \exp[-(F_2 - F_1)/kT] = \exp(-\Delta F/kT)$$
$$= \exp \Delta S/k \, \exp(-\Delta E/kT) \qquad (4.31)$$

where F_2 and F_1 are the free energies associated with energies E_2 and E_1 respectively. Equation 4.31 is very important and we shall refer to it throughout the book. From this equation, it is seen that the fraction of particles in a high energy state increases exponentially as the temperature increases and decreases exponentially as the activation energy increases. This equation explains the reason for the exponential increase in the rate of chemical and physical reactions as the temperature is increased, since the fraction of particles in the excited state, and consequently the number of particles able to react, increases in the same way.

4.4   HEAT CAPACITY OF SOLIDS

If heat is absorbed by a solid at constant volume, the temperature increases, of course, by the ratio $(\partial E/\partial T)_V$, known as the heat capacity. The question then arises as to what the nature of this heat capacity is. Why is it different for different substances and why does it change with temperature? There are two principle mechanisms for the absorption of heat by a solid: one through atomic vibrations and the other through

[1] See for example, J. C. Slater, *Introduction to Chemical Physics*, McGraw-Hill, New York, 1939.

increased kinetic energy of electrons. The latter factor is not particularly important for most substances at ordinary temperatures, according to quantum mechanics, since only a small fraction of electrons near the Fermi surface are excited. As a result the principle mechanism of energy absorption is through the lattice vibrations. This may lead to some understanding of the heat capacity, which, as mentioned earlier, is zero at $T = 0$, proportional to T^3 at low temperatures, and approaches a constant $3R$ at high temperatures. In addition to shedding light on this particular problem, some experience will be gained in handling the Boltzmann expression derived in the last section.

Let us consider that the crystal is composed of a system of atoms which vibrate as harmonic oscillators all with the same frequency v. Following Einstein, we shall assume that each oscillator has three degrees of freedom with regard to its direction of vibration. Thus a system of N_0 oscillators in a three-dimensional crystal corresponds to $3N_0$ linear oscillators. From quantum theory we find that the energy of an oscillator of frequency v is

$$E = (n + \tfrac{1}{2})hv \tag{4.32}$$

where n is an integer and h is Planck's constant. The heat capacity of the crystal C_V is given by $(\partial E/\partial T)_V$, but before differentiating, the average energy of the system of $3N$ oscillators must be determined. This is given by

$$\bar{E} = 3\sum n_i E_i \tag{4.33}$$

where n_i, the number of atoms in state E_i, is expressed by the Boltzmann factor, equation 4.24. Before using equation 4.24, however, the partition function must be evaluated.

$$\mathscr{Z} = \sum_i \exp\left[-E_i/kT\right] \tag{4.34}$$

This may readily be done by substitution of equation 4.32 into 4.34

$$\mathscr{Z} = \sum_{n=0}^{\infty} \exp\left[-(n + \tfrac{1}{2})hv/kT\right]$$

and upon expansion

$$\mathscr{Z} = \exp\left(-\frac{hv}{2kT}\right)\left[1 + \exp\left(-\frac{hv}{kT}\right) + \exp\left(-\frac{2hv}{kT}\right) + \cdots\right]$$

The term in brackets [ ] may be put into the form

$$\left\{1 + \exp\left(-\frac{hv}{kT}\right) + \left[\exp\left(-\frac{hv}{kT}\right)\right]^2 + \cdots\right\}$$

which is of the form $(1 + x + x^2 + \cdots)$. This sum is equal to

$$\frac{1}{1 - x}$$

Therefore

$$\mathscr{Z} = \frac{\exp(-h\nu/2kT)}{1 - \exp(-h\nu/kT)} \tag{4.35}$$

The analysis of the problem may be simplified by consideration of the relation between the partition function and the Helmholz free energy F. By definition, of course,

$$F = E - TS$$

and substituting equation 4.9 and 4.10, we have

$$F = \sum n_i E_i + kT \sum n_i \ln \frac{n_i}{N_0} \tag{4.36}$$

The relation between n_i and E_i may be obtained from the Boltzmann equation. Solving for E_i

$$E_i = -kT \ln \frac{n_i}{N_0} - kT \ln \mathscr{Z}$$

and substitution into 4.36 gives per particle

$$F = -kT \ln \mathscr{Z} \tag{4.37}$$

This is a very useful equation in the general application of statistical mechanics. We may express other thermodynamic functions in terms of $\mathscr{Z}$ also. For example, in the case of entropy

$$-S = \left(\frac{\partial F}{\partial T}\right)_V$$

Upon substitution of equation 4.37 we find

$$S = k \ln \mathscr{Z} + \frac{kT}{\mathscr{Z}}\left(\frac{\partial \mathscr{Z}}{\partial T}\right)_V \tag{4.38}$$

Also since

$$E = F + TS$$

we have

$$E = \frac{kT^2}{\mathscr{Z}}\left(\frac{\partial \mathscr{Z}}{\partial T}\right)_V \tag{4.39}$$

The heat capacity is given by $C_V = (\partial E/\partial T)_V$. For the case of simple harmonic oscillators being considered here,

$$C_V = k\left(\frac{h\nu}{kT}\right)\frac{\exp(h\nu/kT)}{[\exp(h\nu/kT) - 1]^2} \tag{4.40}$$

Equation 4.40 expresses the heat capacity per oscillator. There are $3N_0$ oscillators in a mole of crystals, so C_V per mole of substance is

$$C_V = 3Rx^2 \frac{e^x}{(e^x - 1)^2} \qquad (4.41)$$

where

$$x \equiv \frac{h\nu}{kT}$$

This equation was derived by Einstein and is known as the Einstein function. C_V, plotted as a function of temperature according to this equation, is shown in Fig. 4.5.

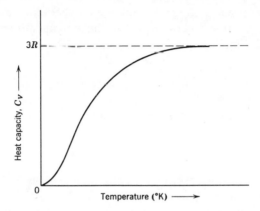

Fig. 4.5 Heat capacity as a function of temperature for a system of harmonic oscillators.

The agreement between experimental and calculated C_V values is only semiquantitative. At a temperature of $0°K$, C_V is predicted to be equal to zero, and at high temperatures to approach $3R$, in agreement with experiment. At intermediate temperatures however, the agreement is not satisfactory. The reason for this was recognized by Einstein as being related to the assumption that all oscillators have the same frequency. Debye analyzed the same problem by assuming that the crystal has a whole spectrum of frequencies from ν_1 to ν_m, where ν_m represents the maximum frequency allowed. The distribution of frequencies depends on the temperature. As the temperature is increased the distribution of frequencies is moved toward the upper end. Ultimately at some temperature called the *Debye temperature*, θ, virtually all frequencies will be close to ν_m, consequently above $T = \theta$, the Einstein picture again becomes essentially valid. The expression arrived at by Debye from analysis of the modes of vibration in the crystal is

$$C_V = \frac{36R}{x^3} \int_0^x \frac{y^3\,dy}{e^y - 1} - \frac{9xR}{e^x - 1} \tag{4.42}$$

where

$$y = \frac{h\nu}{kT} \quad \text{and} \quad x = \frac{h\nu_m}{kT}$$

At low temperatures equation 4.42 simplifies to

$$C_V \cong 78\left(\frac{k}{h\nu_m}\right)^3 T^3 = CT^3 \tag{4.43}$$

This relationship is found to be in agreement with experimental observation for many systems, as mentioned in an earlier chapter. This situation corresponds to large values of x. At high temperatures where $x \ll 1$, equation 4.42 simplifies to

$$C_V \cong 3R$$

again in basic agreement with experiment. By use of equation 4.43, experimental values of the constant C may be obtained directly for a crystal, and hence the Debye temperature may be calculated, since

$$\theta = \frac{h\nu_m}{k}$$

If the Debye picture were completely accurate, values of C obtained from equation 4.42 using experimental heat capacity data should be constant for a given substance. This is not found to be true, however, for most materials, but rather the calculated Debye temperature θ varies to some extent with the temperature of the experiment. Nonetheless this model

TABLE 4.1
Debye Temperature of Various Elements[a]

Substance	θ (°K)	Substance	θ (°K)	Substance	θ (°K)
Be	1160	Co	445	Al	418
Mg	406	Ni	456	In	109
Fe	467	Pd	275	Tl	89
La	132	Cu	339	C (diamond)	(2000)
Ti	278	Ag	225	Si	658
Zr	270	Au	165	Ge	366
V	273	Zn	308	Pb	94.5

[a] From C. Kittel, *Introduction to Solid State Physics*, Second Edition, John Wiley and Sons, New York, 1956.

appears to be a reasonably accurate picture of the vibrational specimen in solids. Some representative values of θ are listed in Table 4.1 for various substances. From this table it is observed that at room temperature most substances are above the Debye temperature and hence most atoms have frequencies near ν_m.

4.5 VIBRATIONAL ENTROPY

Let us consider the vibrational entropy contribution to a crystal at elevated temperatures. For this situation $x \ll 1$ and most frequencies are close to ν_m. Consequently, it will be a valid approximation to use the Einstein approach. As we have shown earlier the entropy of an oscillator is given by

$$S = k \ln \mathscr{L} + kT \left(\frac{\partial \ln \mathscr{L}}{\partial T} \right)_V \tag{4.44}$$

where

$$\mathscr{L} = \frac{\exp(-h\nu/2kT)}{1 - \exp(-h\nu/kT)}$$

Expanding $\mathscr{L}$ in an infinite series,

$$\mathscr{L} = \frac{1 - (h\nu/2kT) + \frac{1}{2}(h\nu/2kT)^2 + \cdots}{(h\nu/kT) - \frac{1}{2}(h\nu/kT)^2 + \cdots}$$

At high temperatures $h\nu/kT \ll 1$, and hence high order terms in the infinite series may be neglected. Thus

$$\mathscr{L} \cong \frac{kT}{h\nu} \tag{4.45}$$

Assuming ν to be independent of temperature at high temperatures, the vibrational entropy per oscillator is found by substituting 4.45 into 4.44:

$$S = k \left(\ln \frac{kT}{h\nu} + 1 \right)$$

Since a gram-atom of crystal has $3N$ oscillators, the entropy per gram-atom is

$$S = 3R \left(\ln \frac{kT}{h\nu} + 1 \right) \tag{4.46}$$

Suppose now that the oscillators are changed from frequency ν to ν'. The entropy change associated with this process is, from 4.46,

$$\Delta S = 3R \ln \left(\frac{\nu}{\nu'} \right) \tag{4.47}$$

Thus if the frequency is lowered, ΔS will be positive.

Consider now the case of a defect in a crystal lattice such as an impurity atom or vacancy. A high vibrational frequency is associated with large effective force constants between atoms in the lattice. A defect causes a local disturbance as shown schematically in Fig. 4.2 for a foreign atom of the wrong size. This will have an effect on the vibrational frequencies of atoms in the vicinity of the defect, and in general will result in a reduction of v, giving a positive vibrational entropy associated with the defect.

An interesting application has been pointed out by Lumsden[1] for tin. Tin exists in two allotropic modifications: below 13°C, gray tin (diamond cubic structure) is stable and above 13°C, white tin (tetragonal structure) is stable. It will also be recalled from Section 3.1 that gray tin would appear to be the most stable modification, since on conversion of white tin to gray tin, heat is *evolved*. This implies that the atoms in gray tin are in a lower energy state and therefore would be more tightly bound. In addition the modulus or force constant between atoms would be expected to be larger in the case of gray tin than white tin. The question then arises as to why gray tin converts to the more unstable tetragonal structure. The answer of course comes from the consideration of the free energy of the transformation which is for the reaction

$$\text{gray tin} = \text{white tin}$$
$$\Delta G = \Delta H - T \Delta S$$

For the process to proceed spontaneously, ΔG must be negative. The quantity ΔH is positive, so ΔS must be a positive quantity. The question then occurs as to why ΔS is positive. The answer has already been partially given. The more stable gray tin structure would correspond to a situation where the force constants between atoms are probably strong. This means that the restoring force on an atom removed somewhat from equilibrium will be high and hence the vibrational frequency will be large. Thus from equation 4.47 we see that ΔS for the reaction will be positive. At low temperatures, the $T \Delta S$ term is small and hence the enthalpy term predominates, giving gray tin as the stable structure. At high temperatures $T \Delta S$ is large, and thus white tin is stable. It is seen therefore that the entropy term is the monitor of stable structures and that allotropes stable at high temperatures will always be those having lower vibrational frequencies than the modifications occurring at lower temperatures.

[1] J. Lumsden, *Thermodynamics of Alloys*, Institute of Metals, London, 1952.

chapter 5

The Third Law of Thermodynamics

5.1 BACKGROUND OF THE THIRD LAW

Perhaps the history of the third law may be placed in proper perspective by consideration of the actual need for a third law. The third law, unlike the first two laws, introduces no new concepts, but rather clarifies some of the existing ones. The principal quantity of interest to us will be the free energy function, hence, it would naturally be desirable if this could readily be obtained by standard thermal techniques. By use of a calorimeter, we can obtain the enthalpy, ΔH, for a reaction and since this can be measured at various temperatures, we may obtain ΔC_P, since $\Delta C_P = (\partial \Delta H/\partial T)_P$. The quantity ΔS for a reaction, however, cannot be obtained directly from these thermal measurements. To illustrate the problem, let us consider the reaction

$$A(T_1) = B(T_1)$$

The entropy of the reaction ΔS is equal to $(S_B - S_A)$ at T_1. Let us break the reaction into three steps, namely

$$
\begin{aligned}
&(1)\ A(0°K) = B(0°K) \qquad \Delta S_1 \\
&(2)\ B(0°K) = B(T_1) \qquad \Delta S_2 \\
&(3)\ A(T_1)\ \ = A(0°K) \qquad \Delta S_3
\end{aligned}
$$

The reaction of interest is equal to the sum of these three steps. The entropy of our reaction is therefore equal to $(\Delta S_1 + \Delta S_2 + \Delta S_3)$. In Chapter 3 we determined that

$$\Delta S_2 = \int_0^{T_1} \frac{(C_p)_B}{T}\, dT$$

and

$$\Delta S_3 = \int_{T_1}^{0} \frac{(C_P)_A}{T}\, dT$$

which shows that the entropies of these steps can be determined from thermal measurements. We are still lacking ΔS_1, however, which is equal to $[(S_B)_0 - (S_A)_0]$, the difference of the entropies of the components themselves at $0°K$, so we are, on the surface at least, as badly off as before. In the latter half of the nineteenth century, LeChatelier and G. N. Lewis attacked the problem of determining entropies at $T = 0$ without complete

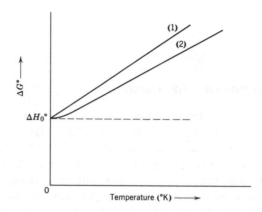

Fig. 5.1 Possible ways for $\Delta G°$ to approach $\Delta H°$ at temperature near $0°K$. Curve 1, $\Delta S \neq 0$ as $T \to 0$; curve 2, $\Delta S = 0$ as $T \to 0$.

success. In 1902 F. W. Richards made a large step toward solving the problem. From his work, he found that as $T \to 0°K$, ΔG approached the value of ΔH. This in itself is no real contribution, since by definition

$$\Delta G = \Delta H - T\,\Delta S$$

and the quantity $T\,\Delta S \to 0$ as $T \to 0$ if ΔS is finite. Thus $\Delta G \to \Delta H$ as $T \to 0$. There was some indication from his work, however, that the slope of ΔG versus T approached zero as $T \to 0$. Since we found in the last chapter that

$$-\Delta S = \left(\frac{\partial\,\Delta G}{\partial T}\right)$$

this suggested that ΔS itself $\to 0$ as $T \to 0$. The question then is in connection with the shape of the curve of ΔG versus T near $0°K$. Is it like curve 1 on Fig. 5.1, or like curve 2? Several other workers attacked the problem and the culmination was reached by Nernst in 1906 in what is known as the Nernst Heat Theorem, the essence of which is

$$\Delta S = 0 \quad \text{at} \quad T = 0°K$$

This general statement means that the entropies of substances must approach the same value at $0°K$. It does not mean that $(S_B)_0$ and $(S_A)_0$ are equal to zero themselves, but only that they are the same. Since, for the purpose of calculating ΔS for reactions, we may choose any standard state, we shall arbitrarily choose $(S_B)_0 = (S_A)_0 = 0$ as our reference state. Thus we shall be able to calculate "absolute" entropies of components from heat capacity data at any temperature from the relation

$$S_T = \int_0^T \frac{C_P}{T} \, dT + S_0 \qquad (5.1)$$

since S_0 is considered to be zero.

The criterion that ΔS for a reaction $\to 0$ as $T \to 0$ must be applied with some discretion, however. It was proposed by Planck that the Nernst heat theorem only applied to pure crystalline solids. This statement is too restrictive in view of the recent advances made in the quantum mechanical understanding of gases, which show that the Nernst heat theorem holds even for gases. Perhaps one of the best statements of the third law is the following, which is due to Sommerfeld.[1]

As the temperature of a system tends to absolute zero its entropy tends to a constant value S_0 which is independent of pressure, state of aggregation, etc.

The reader will note that it is stated that the entropy tends to zero. To illustrate, consider the problem of a solid solution. At an elevated temperature, let us assume that the solution is stable. Two things may occur upon cooling.

(a) The maximum solubility of one constituent in a crystal generally decreases as the temperature decreases and in fact becomes equal to zero at $T = 0$. Hence precipitation of the solute will be feasible.

(b) Many solutions tend to order themselves with respect to the arrangement of atoms on the lattice site at lower temperatures. It has been suggested that an ordered structure is the equilibrium structure for all solid solutions at very low temperatures.

If complete precipitation or ordering occurs, the third law would hold because $\ln \mathscr{W} = 0$ and hence $S = 0$, but since at low temperatures atomic rearrangement becomes difficult, a metastable structure could be "frozen in." The entropy of this sytem is not zero, since there will be a randomness or configurational entropy contribution as calculated in Chapter 4. For

---

[1] A. Sommerfeld, *Thermodynamics and Statistical Mechanics*, Springer, Berlin, 1956.

the third law to hold, process (a) above need not occur but process (b) should. In other words the solution need not be in equilibrium with its surroundings but only in *internal equilibrium*. Before applying the third law to components of a reaction, it should be ascertained that the individual components are in internal equilibrium.

5.2 DEDUCTIONS FROM THE THIRD LAW

Heat Capacity at $0°K$

Starting with the definition

$$\Delta G = \Delta H - T \Delta S$$

and, taking the total differential, we have

$$d \Delta G = d \Delta H - T d \Delta S - \Delta S \, dT$$

Dividing through by dT at constant pressure gives

$$\left(\frac{\partial \Delta G}{\partial T}\right)_P = \left(\frac{\partial \Delta H}{\partial T}\right)_P - T \left(\frac{\partial \Delta S}{\partial T}\right)_P - \Delta S$$

At $T = 0$, $\Delta S = 0$, and the product

$$T \left(\frac{\partial \Delta S}{\partial T}\right)_P = 0$$

if the term $(\partial \Delta S/\partial T)_P$ is finite. Since

$$-\left(\frac{\partial \Delta G}{\partial T}\right)_P = \Delta S$$

which is zero at $T = 0$, we find that

$$\Delta C_P = 0 \quad \text{at} \quad T = 0$$

Applying the same reasoning to the equation

$$G = H - TS$$

we find that the heat capacities of the components themselves become zero at $T = 0$. Thus

$$C_P = 0 \quad \text{at} \quad T = 0°K$$

Experimentally this is confirmed as discussed in Chapter 4.

Thermal Expansion Coefficient at 0°K

Since, according to the third law, the entropy of all substances approaches a common value S_0 at 0°K, this implies that the value of S_0 is not a function of any other variables such as V or P. Thus at 0°K

$$\left(\frac{\partial S}{\partial P}\right)_T = 0$$

and from one of Maxwell's relations we know

$$-\left(\frac{\partial S}{\partial P}\right)_T = \left(\frac{\partial V}{\partial T}\right)_P$$

Thus

$$\left(\frac{\partial V}{\partial T}\right)_P = 0$$

at 0°K. By definition

$$\left(\frac{\partial V}{\partial T}\right) \equiv \alpha V$$

and since V is not expected to go to zero as $T \to 0$, α must approach 0. Experimental evidence confirms the approach of α to zero as $T \to 0$.

The compressibility, however, does not go to zero as $T \to 0$.

Besides showing that the heat capacity and thermal expansion coefficient approach zero at $T \to 0$, the third law shows that it is impossible to attain the absolute zero of temperature by any finite process. One may approach arbitrarily close to zero, however.

5.3 APPLICATIONS OF THE THIRD LAW

As pointed out earlier, the third law enables entropies of reactions to be uniquely determined from thermal properties (i.e., heat capacities) alone. Thus the entropy change in bringing a substance from 0°K to T at 1 atmosphere is given by

$$S_T^\circ = \int_0^T \frac{C_P}{T}\, dT$$

In actuality this is a ΔS term, but, since S_0 is assumed to be zero, the form above will be used. Thus, in order to calculate S_T°, considerable integration of low temperature heat capacity data must be performed. Conveniently, tables of S_T° are available. In most tables T is chosen as 298°K. Integration from 298°K is relatively easy since standard tabulations of high temperature C_P data are available, as discussed in Chapter 2. Several sources of data are available, among which are (a) *Metallurgical*

Thermochemistry by Kubashewski and Evans; (b) *U.S. Bureau of Mines Bulletin* 477 (1950) by K. K. Kelley; and (c) *Table of Selected Values of Chemical Thermodynamic Properties* of the National Bureau of Standards. Some values of S_{298}° are listed in Table 5.1.

TABLE 5.1
Absolute Entropies of Some Substances[a]

Substance	S_{298}°(cal/mole degree)	Substance	S_{298}°(cal/mole degree)
Ag(s)	10.20 ± 0.05	Graphite(s)	1.361 ± 0.005
AgCl(s)	23.0 ± 0.1	H(g)	27.4 ± 0.01
Al(s)	6.77 ± 0.05	$H_2(g)$	31.21 ± 0.02
Au(s)	11.32 ± 0.05	MgO(s)	6.55 ± 0.15
B(s)	1.4 ± 0.05	MnO(s)	14.3 ± 0.2
$BCl_3(l)$	49.2 ± 2.0	$MnSiO_3(s)$	21.3 ± 0.2
$BCl_3(s)$	69.3 ± 0.5	$O_2(g)$	49.02 ± 0.01
BeO	3.37 ± 0.05	Si(s)	4.5 ± 0.05
Diamond(s)	0.583 ± 0.005	Sn(gray)	10.7 ± 0.1
Fe(s)	6.49 ± 0.03	Sn(white)	12.3 ± 0.1
Ge(s)	10.1 ± 0.2		

[a] From O. Kubaschewski and E. Evans, *Metallurgical Thermochemistry*, Third Edition, Pergamon, London, 1958.

To illustrate the third law, let us calculate ΔS° for the following reaction at 298°K.

$$2Al(s, 298) + \tfrac{3}{2}O_2(g, 298, 1\ atm) = Al_2O_3(s, 298)$$

To calculate, break the reaction into the following steps algebraically, and add the entropies for each step. The sum is equal to the desired reaction.

(1) $2Al(s, 0°K) + \tfrac{3}{2}O_2(g, 0°K, 1\ atm) = Al_2O_3(s, 0°K)$ ΔS_1°

(2) $2Al(s, 298) = 2Al(s, 0°K)$ $-2(S_{298}^\circ - S_0^\circ)_{Al}$

(3) $\tfrac{3}{2}O_2(g, 298°K, 1\ atm) = \tfrac{3}{2}O_2(g, 0°K, 1\ atm)$ $-\tfrac{3}{2}(S_{298}^\circ - S_0^\circ)_{O_2}$

(4) $Al_2O_3(s, 0°K) = Al_2O_3(s, 298)$ $(S_{298}^\circ - S_0^\circ)_{Al_2O_3}$

$$\Delta S^\circ = \Delta S_1^\circ - 2(S_{298}^\circ - S_0^\circ)_{Al} - \tfrac{3}{2}(S_{298}^\circ - S_0^\circ) + (S_{298}^\circ - S_0^\circ)_{Al_2O_3}$$

and since

$$S_0^\circ = 0 \quad \text{and} \quad \Delta S_1^\circ = 0$$

$$\Delta S^\circ = 2(S_{298}^\circ)_{Al} - \tfrac{3}{2}(S_{298}^\circ)_{O_2} + (S_{298}^\circ)_{Al_2O_3}$$

Hence

$$\Delta S^\circ = -2(6.77) - \tfrac{3}{2}(49.02) + 12.2 = -74.87\ \text{e.u.}$$

Suppose we are interested in the same reaction at a different temperature, 1000°K,

$$2\text{Al}(l, 1000) + \tfrac{3}{2}\text{O}_2(g, 1 \text{ atm}, 1000) = \text{Al}_2\text{O}_3(s, 1000)$$

Note that Al has undergone a phase change at 933°K. We have the reaction at 298°K so let us start from there and repeat the procedure just discussed using C_P data.

(1) $2\text{Al}(s, 298) + \tfrac{3}{2}\text{O}_2(g, 1 \text{ atm}, 298) = \text{Al}_2\text{O}_3(s, 298)$ $\Delta S_1^{\circ} = -74.87$ e.u.

(2) $\quad 2\text{Al}(s, 933) = 2\text{Al}(s, 298)$ $\quad -2(S_{933}^{\circ} - S_{298}^{\circ})_{\text{Al}} = 2\displaystyle\int_{933}^{298} \frac{C_P}{T} dT$

(3) $\quad 2\text{Al}(l, 933) = 2\text{Al}(s, 933)$ $\quad \Delta S_2^{\circ} = -2\dfrac{\Delta H_f}{933}$

(4) $\quad 2\text{Al}(l, 1000) = 2\text{Al}(l, 933)$ $\quad -2(S_{1000}^{\circ} - S_{933}^{\circ})_{\text{Al}} = 2\displaystyle\int_{1000}^{933} \frac{C_P}{T} dT$

(5) $\quad \tfrac{3}{2}\text{O}_2(g, 1 \text{ atm}, 1000) = \tfrac{3}{2}\text{O}_2(g, 1 \text{ atm}, 298)$

$$-\tfrac{3}{2}(S_{1000}^{\circ} - S_{298}^{\circ}) = \tfrac{3}{2}\int_{1000}^{298} \frac{C_P}{T} dT$$

(6) $\quad \text{Al}_2\text{O}_3(s, 298) = \text{Al}_2\text{O}_3(s, 1000)$

$$(S_{1000} - S_{298})_{\text{Al}_2\text{O}_3} = \int_{298}^{1000} \frac{C_P}{T} dT$$

$$2\text{Al}(l, 1000) + \tfrac{3}{2}\text{O}_2(g, 1000) = \text{Al}_2\text{O}_3(s, 1000) \qquad \Delta S^{\circ}$$

Using the equations expressing C_P as a function of T, ΔS° can readily be calculated by summation.

5.4 OTHER METHODS OF OBTAINING ΔS° FOR A REACTION

Some methods used for studying the thermodynamics of reactions yield ΔG directly from experimental data. In particular we might cite the use of emf measurements. Generally, ΔG may be obtained at several different temperatures, and since we know that

$$\Delta S^{\circ} = -\left(\frac{\partial \Delta G^{\circ}}{\partial T}\right)_P$$

ΔS° can be readily determined from the slope of the ΔG° versus T curve.

Another technique which is useful primarily for gases is based on statistical mechanical principles. We have already seen something of these principles. This is a very useful technique and should be included as one of the methods available for entropy determinations.

In summary, we find that three basic methods are available for obtaining entropy data for reactions:

(a) Use of the third law.
(b) Direct determination of ΔG as a function of T.
(c) Statistical mechanical procedures.

It is generally desirable to have a wide variety of general techniques available for the determination of thermodynamic properties, since often the characteristics of particular components in a reaction are such as to make some procedures relatively unfavorable.

chapter 6

Relation between Thermodynamic and Physical Properties

6.1 RICHARDS' RULE AND TROUTON'S RULE

A little reflection will show that one would expect a direct relation between thermodynamic properties and the physical properties of the substances themselves. One tends, for example, to associate an exothermic reaction with stability and the converse for an endothermic reaction. Stability in this sense might be reflected in a high melting point, volume contraction, high modulus of elasticity, etc. These properties are, of course, only manifestations of the fundamental binding energies between the atoms themselves in the crystals. It is, therefore, of interest to compare experimental thermodynamic properties with certain physical properties in order to see how far these qualitative concepts can be carried.

Two empirical relations are familiar to the reader. An empirical relation between the energy of vaporization of a crystal and the boiling temperature has been found: this is known as Trouton's rule. Similarly, a relation between the heat of fusion and the melting temperature of a substance has been observed: this is known as Richards' rule. Such relations would be expected. The heat of vaporization, ΔH_v, for example, is the energy input needed to dissociate the crystal into free atoms or molecules. Similarly the boiling point should be directly related to the thermal energy needed to obtain complete dissociation of the crystal; the higher the boiling point, the stronger the binding forces between atoms in the crystal. The constant of proportionality proposed by Trouton is 21. Thus

$$\Delta S_v = \frac{\Delta H_v}{T_{\text{b.p.}}} = 21 \tag{6.1}$$

59

Similarly, the melting temperature should reflect the binding forces in a crystal, since melting introduces disorder into the crystal and a high binding energy between atoms would tend to oppose the introduction of disorder. Richards' rule is

$$\Delta S_f = \frac{\Delta H_f}{T_{\text{m.p.}}} = 2 \tag{6.2}$$

The usefulness of such empirical rules lies in the ability to predict reasonably well, properties of heretofore uninvestigated materials of interest. Thus, correlations form an important aspect of physical science. Also when detailed atomic models or theories of crystals are proposed, these empirical correlations may be used as a test of the validity of these detailed models. Such theories must predict that such correlations would be found. Very often the correlations themselves suggest detailed atomic theories.

6.2 ESTIMATION OF HEAT CAPACITIES OF CRYSTALS

As a first approach, if no heat capacity data exist for a particular crystal, recourse may be made to the *Dulong-Petit rule*, which states that at high temperatures (generally in the vicinity of room temperature)

$$C_V = 3R \quad \text{or} \quad 6 \text{ cal/mole degree}$$

In an earlier chapter the following relation was derived between C_P and C_V.

$$C_P = C_V + \frac{\alpha^2 V T}{\beta}$$

The term $\alpha^2 V T/\beta$ is generally of the order of 0.5 cal/mole degree for crystals, and thus according to the Dulong-Petit relation one would expect $C_P \cong 6.5$ cal/mole degree. This rule is very approximate since some crystals have lower values of heat capacities and many have larger. Diamond, for example, with extremely strong interatomic bonds, has a value of C_P in the vicinity of 4 cal/mole degree.

Very often an approach known as the *Neumann-Kopp rule* may be applied with reasonable success for the estimation of heat capacities of compounds formed from elements in the solid or liquid states. This approximation considers the value ΔC_P for a reaction in which a compound is formed. Thus for the reaction

$$x A(s) + y B(s) = A_x B_y(s)$$

According to the Neumann-Kopp rule

$$(C_P)_{A_x B_y} = x(C_P)_A + y(C_P)_B \tag{6.3}$$

This, of course, says that the heat capacity of a compound is the sum of those of the elements forming the compound. A test of this rule is shown in Table 6.1 in which predictions of the Neumann-Kopp rule are compared

TABLE 6.1

Test of Neumann-Kopp Rule at 300°K

Compound A_xB_y	$x(C_P)_A$	$y(C_P)_B$	Sum (cal/mole degree)	C_P (experimental) (cal/mole degree)
Ni_2Si	12.6	4.8	17.4	16.8
PbS	6.33	5.45	11.78	11.83
Ni_3Sn	18.87	6.31	25.18	23.84
Sb_2S_3	12.1	16.4	28.5	28.2

with actual values for some substances at 300°K. It can be seen from this table that agreement is generally excellent.

At first glance, it might appear that the compounds have high heat capacities compared with the elements from which they were formed. It might be worthwhile at this point to point out that this is not the case. For example, consideration of Sb_2S_3 shows that one mole of compound actually consists of two moles of antimony and three moles of sulfur. There are thus $5N_0$ atoms in a mole of Sb_2S_3 whereas, of course, there are only N_0 atoms in a mole of Sb or a mole of S. The heat capacity C_P for N_0 atoms or a gram-atom of Sb_2S_3 is equal to only $28 \times (1/5)$ or 5.6 cal/gram-atom degree. In later chapters we shall be principally concerned with quantities defined in terms of the gram-atom. In this case x and y will represent fractions and the Neumann-Kopp rule may be restated as follows:

The heat capacity of a gram-atom of a solid phase may be considered to be the weighted sum of the heat capacities of the elements forming the phase.

6.3 ENTROPIES OF FUSION

Richards' rule does not hold particularly well for a wide variety of substances. Trouton's rule holds surprisingly well on the other hand. The value of ΔS_v is within the limits of 20–25 e.u. for a wide variety of substances in excellent agreement with the Trouton's rule value of 21.

In Table 6.2 are listed some values of ΔS_f calculated from experimental values of ΔH_f and $T_{m.p.}$. These should be compared with the Richards' rule value of 2. The reason for the large values of the entropies of fusion for the intermetallic compounds listed in Table 6.2 is easily understood, since the configurational or mixing entropy in the solid state for the compound is zero, whereas the liquid solution is always quite random. No

TABLE 6.2

Some Entropies of Fusion

Compound	ΔS_f (cal/gm-atom degree)	Compound	ΔS_f (cal/gm-atom degree)
Pb	2.0	V_2O_5	2.35
Si	6.7	CCl_4	0.48
NaCl	3.2	CdSb	5.25
MgO	3.0	$CuAl_2$	3.48
FeO	2.3	AuSn	4.43

ordered compounds exist in the liquid state. To see what the configurational entropy contribution could be per gram-atom of compound, consider the following reaction which occurs upon melting of a compound.

$$(1) \qquad \frac{1}{x+y} A_x B_y(s) = \frac{x}{x+y} A(l) + \frac{y}{x+y} B(l) \qquad \Delta S_1{}^\circ$$

This reaction can be broken into two hypothetical steps:

$$(2) \qquad \frac{1}{x+y} A_x B_y(s) = \frac{1}{x+y} A_x B_y(l) \qquad \Delta S_2{}^\circ$$

$$(3) \qquad \frac{1}{x+y} A_x B_y(l) = \frac{x}{x+y} A(l) + \frac{y}{x+y} B(l) \qquad \Delta S_3{}^\circ$$

Reaction 2 corresponds to a hypothetical melting process whereby the compound retains its ordered structure in the liquid state. Reaction 3 corresponds to disordering of the compound in the liquid state to form a random solution. For the case of reaction 2, the entropy will result from a vibrational change but not from a mixing contribution such as for the melting of an element. Thus $\ln \mathscr{W} \simeq 0$. For reaction 3, however, according to equation 4.7,

$$\Delta S_3{}^\circ = -R\left[\frac{x}{x+y} \ln\left(\frac{x}{x+y}\right) + \frac{y}{x+y} \ln\left(\frac{y}{x+y}\right)\right]$$

Calculation of ΔS_3 for CdSb, $CuAl_2$, and AuSn give 1.37, 1.26, and 1.37 cal/gm-atom degree respectively. Values of ΔS_1 are listed in Table 6.2 and since $\Delta S_1{}^\circ = \Delta S_2{}^\circ + \Delta S_3{}^\circ$, we find $\Delta S_2{}^\circ$ by subtraction, $\Delta S_2{}^\circ$ is found to be 3.88, 2.22, and 3.06 cal/gm-atom degree for CdSb, $CuAl_2$, and AuSn respectively. These values are much closer to the Richards' rule value of 2.

With regard to the entropy of fusion for the elements, there appears to be a proportionality between ΔS_f° and atomic number. This relation is shown in Fig. 6.1 for Group IV elements. The fundamental parameter in

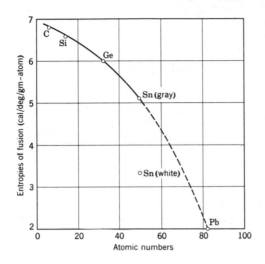

Fig. 6.1 Relation between entropy of fusion and atomic number. From O. Kubaschewski and E. Evans, *Metallurgical Thermochemistry*, Second Edition, Pergamon, London, 1955.

this case is probably not atomic number but binding energy since the binding energy of the crystals also shows the same relation to atomic number as does ΔS_f°.

6.4 HEATS OF FORMATION OF COMPOUNDS

Relation to Cation Atomic Number

There appears to be a relation between the heat of formation, ΔH_f°, of compounds and the atomic number of the metallic component, similar to that of the entropy of fusion, ΔS_f°. In Fig. 6.2 are shown some values of ΔH_f° for chlorides and oxides as a function of atomic number. Looking at the series Li, K, Rb, Cs, it will be seen that the dependence upon atomic number has the opposite sign for chlorides as for oxides. The value of ΔH_f° tends to increase with atomic number for the chlorides and to decrease for the oxides.

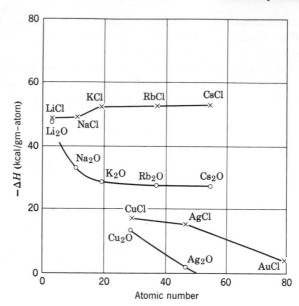

Fig. 6.2 Relation between heat of formation of compounds and cation atomic number. ○ = oxides; × = chlorides. From O. Kubaschewski and E. Evans, *Metallurgical Thermochemistry*, Second Edition, Pergamon, London, 1955.

Relation to Molar Volume

It will be recalled that, although useful, the atomic size of a component is a rather variable quantity. The size of an atom in a crystal depends to a large extent upon its immediate environment. Perhaps the classic example of this point is the relation between interatomic spacing between carbon atoms in a hydrocarbon and the number of covalent bonds shared by the atoms. The stronger the bond is, the smaller the apparent atomic size is. Similarly in a crystal, the interatomic distance between atoms would be expected to depend markedly upon the affinities between atoms. We should therefore expect a relation between the molar volume of a crystal and the heat of formation of the crystal. A large negative value of ΔH_f°, which means that energy is evolved upon formation of the crystal, implies a large affinity between atoms in the crystal. To illustrate that such a relation exists, let us consider a wide variety of compounds covering oxides, halides, nitrides, and intermetallic compounds which crystallize with either the NaCl or the CsCl structure. We will take as our reference volume the atomic value of the elements in the pure state. Thus, knowing the crystal structure of a particular compound, a hypothetical unit cell volume V' or molar volume may be calculated, assuming that the atoms have the same size in the compound as in the pure form, by just adding the volumes of the pure constituents. This might be expected to be the case if the binding energy of the atoms in the compound is the average of those in the pure form. This hypothetical volume V' may be compared with the actual cell volume or molar volume V determined by x-ray or specific gravity measurements. The difference $\Delta V = (V - V')$ will be compared with ΔH_f°. This volume charge ΔV corresponds to the following reaction:

$$x\text{A} + y\text{B} = \text{A}_x\text{B}_y \qquad \Delta V \text{ and } \Delta H_f^\circ$$

In order to calculate the hypothetical volume V of a unit cell of A_xB_y, the atomic volumes of most components were obtained from the lattice parameter measurements of elements in the close-packed state. For nitrogen, oxygen, and sulfur, however, atomic volumes of 5.0, 9.0, and 14.5 Å^3 were used respectively. A graph of ΔV versus ΔH_f° is shown in Fig. 6.3, where it is seen that an excellent correlation exists. The compounds for which $\Delta H_f^\circ \sim 0$ show little volume contraction, as would be expected. In the case of very exothermic reactions, considerable contraction occurs.

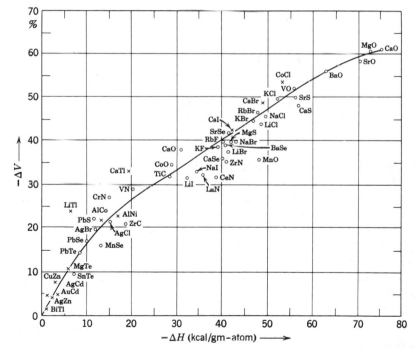

Fig. 6.3   Heat evolution and volume contraction upon formation of compounds of simple structural type. ○ = NaCl type; × = CsCl type. From O. Kubaschewski and E. Evans, *Metallurgical Thermochemistry*, Second Edition, Pergamon, London, 1955

Born-Haber Cycle

Enthalpies of formation for ionic compounds may be calculated from certain experimental data by use of what is called the Born-Haber cycle. To illustrate this procedure consider the following reaction:

$$Na(s, 298) + \tfrac{1}{2}Cl_2(g, 1 \text{ atm}, 298) = NaCl(s, 298) \qquad \Delta H_f^\circ$$

Let us put the metallic component into the gas phase, dissociate the Cl_2 molecule, transfer an electron from a sodium atom to a distance of infinity, transfer an electron from infinity to a Cl atom, and then combine the $Na^+ + Cl^-$ ions to form a crystal. Our reaction of interest will consist of the following five steps, all at the same temperature.

(1) $Na(s) = Na(g, 1 \text{ atm})$ $\qquad \Delta H_1 = \Delta H_s =$ heat of sublimation

(2) $\tfrac{1}{2}Cl_2(g, 1 \text{ atm}) = Cl(g, 1 \text{ atm})$ $\qquad \Delta H_2 = D =$ dissociation energy

(3) $Na(g, 1 \text{ atm}) = Na^+(g, 1 \text{ atm}) + e(\infty)$ $\qquad \Delta H_3 = I =$ ionization energy

(4) $Cl(g, 1 \text{ atm}) + e(\infty) = Cl^-(g, 1 \text{ atm})$ $\qquad \Delta H_4 =$ electron affinity

(5) $Na^+(g, 1 \text{ atm}) + Cl^-(g, 1 \text{ atm}) = NaCl(s)$ $\qquad \Delta H_5 =$ lattice energy

---

$$Na(s) + \tfrac{1}{2}Cl_2(g, 1 \text{ atm}) = NaCl(s) \qquad \Delta H_f^\circ = \sum_1^5 \Delta H_i$$

The quantity ΔH_1 is the enthalpy of sublimation, ΔH_s, and is readily available in the literature as determined from vapor pressure measurements. Similarly ΔH_2, the enthalpy of dissociation, is available experimentally for diatomic gases. The term ΔH_3 is called the *ionization energy* and can be determined from optical measurements. The ionization energies for a large number of electrons in an atom are available. If a doubly charged ion were needed for the reaction, another reaction would have to be considered in which a second electron is removed. This is called the second ionization energy. The quantity ΔH_4 is known as the *electron affinity* and is determined by the reverse procedure of measuring the ionization energy of a Cl^- ion. The term ΔH_5 is known as the *lattice energy* and may be calculated using a theory proposed by Born, which is described below.

In the case of an ionic crystal, the forces holding the ions together in the crystal are coulombic in nature. Thus, the energy between two univalent ions separated at a distance x is

$$E_a = \pm \frac{e^2}{x}$$

where e is the electronic charge. According to our convention, the negative sign refers to unlike ions (attraction) and the positive term refers to like ions (repulsion). In the case of a crystal, a given ion is not affected by only one ion but by many. For example, in the NaCl structure, a sodium ion has 6Cl$^-$ nearest neighbors at a distance x, 12Na$^+$ second nearest neighbors at $\sqrt{2}\,x$, 8Cl$^-$ third nearest neighbors at $\sqrt{3}\,x$, 6Na$^+$ fourth nearest neighbors at $2\,x$, etc. Thus, the net coulombic energy of this Na$^+$ ion in the crystal is the sum of these repulsive and attractive interactions:

$$E_a = -\frac{e^2}{x}\left[6 - \frac{12}{\sqrt{2}} + \frac{8}{\sqrt{3}} - \frac{6}{2} + \cdots\right]$$

or

$$E_a = -\frac{\mathscr{A}e^2}{x}$$

where $\mathscr{A}$ is equal to the sum in brackets and is known as the *Madelung constant*. $\mathscr{A}$ is 1.748, 1.763, 1.638, and 1.641 for the NaCl, CsCl, zinc-blende, and wurtzite structures respectively. When the ions approach each other closely a strong repulsive interaction E_r occurs. This repulsive term is not as easy to calculate as the attractive term. In order to evaluate this term Born assumed an exponential relation of the type

$$E_r = \frac{B}{x^n}$$

where B and n are constants for a given system. The total lattice energy for N_0 positive ions and N_0 negative ions is

$$E_l = N_0[E_a + E_r] = N_0\left(-\frac{\mathscr{A}e^2}{x} + \frac{B}{x^n}\right) \tag{6.4}$$

The quantity E_l, as a function of x, is shown schematically in Fig. 6.4 as well as the E_a and E_r terms individually. The equilibrium atom spacing will be x_0, where $dE_l/dx = 0$. In order to obtain values for the constants B and n in the repulsive term, appeal must be made to experiment. One of these parameters can be eliminated by use of the fact that the equilibrium spacing occurs when $dE_l/dx = 0$. Differentiating equation 6.4 with respect to x, setting equal to zero, and solving for B, we find

$$\left(\frac{dE_l}{dx}\right)_{x=x_0} = N_0\left[\frac{\mathscr{A}e^2}{x^2} - \frac{nB}{x^{n+1}}\right] = 0$$

and thus

$$B = \frac{\mathscr{A}e^2 x_0^{n-1}}{n} \tag{6.5}$$

Substituting equation 6.5 into 6.4, we find

$$(E_l)_{x=x_0} = - \frac{N_0 \mathscr{A} e^2}{x_0}\left(1 - \frac{1}{n}\right) \qquad (6.6)$$

Strictly speaking, this calculation is only valid at $T = 0°$K, since the equilibrium spacing x_0 is governed not by the point where the energy is a minimum but where the free energy is a minimum. In order to make a

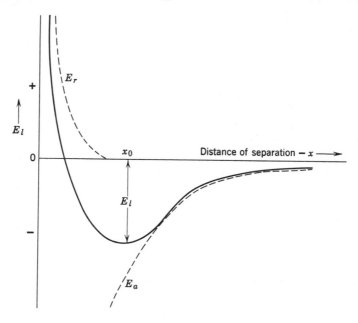

Fig. 6.4   Lattice energy of a crystal as a function of separation of the ions. E_r is the repulsive contribution and E_a is the attractive contribution.

calculation at $T > 0°$K, the entropy term TS_l would have to be considered. This contribution is far more difficult to evaluate than the energy contribution.

The only coefficient now remaining to be evaluated is n, and it remains to find a relation between this and some experimental function. It would seem reasonable to expect the repulsive contribution to E_l to be related to the compressibility of the crystal since the main factors entering into the compressibility result from the repulsive interaction between ions. Therefore, let us examine this point further by considering the compressibility at $T = 0°$K. By definition

$$\beta \equiv - \frac{1}{V}\left(\frac{\partial V}{\partial P}\right)_T$$

Placing the restriction of constant temperature,

$$dP = -\frac{dV}{\beta V}$$

Let V_0 be the volume at zero pressure and therefore the pressure required to make a small change in the volume from V_0 to V' is given by

$$P \cong -\frac{V' - V_0}{\beta V_0} \tag{6.7}$$

The work performed by the solid during the compression from V_0 to V' is

$$W = \int_{V_0}^{V'} P \, dV$$

and, substituting equation 6.7,

$$W \cong -\frac{1}{\beta} \int_{V_0}^{V'} \left(\frac{V' - V_0}{V_0}\right) dV$$

Recalling that V_0 is a constant we find upon integration that

$$W = -\frac{(V' - V_0)^2}{2\beta V_0} \tag{6.8}$$

Consider now the internal energy change ΔE_l upon compression:

$$\Delta E_l = E_l' - (E_l)_{x=x_0}$$

It will be recalled that E_l, a state property, may be considered to be a function of any two state variables. The temperature is constant at $T = 0°K$, so therefore pressure and volume are the obvious variables. P has been expressed in terms of V by relation 6.7 and thus we may express

$$E_l = f(V)$$

It is convenient at this point to introduce *Taylor's theorem* which states that, if a function $f(x)$ has continuous derivatives in the range of interest, then

$$f(x) = f(x_0) + (x' - x_0)\left[\frac{df(x)}{dx}\right]_{x=x_0} + \frac{1}{2!}(x' - x_0)^2\left[\frac{d^2f(x)}{dx^2}\right]_{x=x_0} + \cdots$$

In our case $E_l' = f(V)$, and expanding this about $V = V_0$,

$$E_l' = (E_l)_{V=V_0} + (V' - V_0)\left(\frac{dE_l}{dV}\right)_{V=V_0} + \tfrac{1}{2}(V' - V_0)^2\left(\frac{d^2E_l}{dV^2}\right)_{V=V_0} + \cdots \tag{6.9}$$

At the equilibrium volume V_0, $(dE_l/dV)_{V=V_0} = 0$. The energy change of the crystal, $[E_l' - (E_l)_{V=V_0}]$, is therefore given by

$$E_l' - (E_l)_{V=V_0} \cong \tfrac{1}{2}(V' - V_0)^2 \left(\frac{d^2 E_l}{dV^2}\right)_{V=V_0} \tag{6.10}$$

if high order terms are neglected. This is justified if $(V' - V_0) \ll V_0$. Using the first law of thermodynamics, $dE = T\, dS - P\, dV$, but $T = 0°K$, and hence

$$dE = -P\, dV \quad \text{or} \quad \Delta E = -W$$

Therefore, equating 6.10 to 6.8 we find

$$\frac{1}{\beta} = V_0 \left(\frac{d^2 E_l}{dV^2}\right)_{V=V_0} \tag{6.11}$$

From equation 6.11 it is seen that the compressibility of a crystal is inversely proportional to the curvature of the energy versus distance curve at the minimum. For a crystal, the molar volume is related to the interatomic distance x by

$$V = CN_0 x^3 \tag{6.12}$$

where C is a constant which depends only on crystal structure. Since

$$\frac{dE}{dV} = \left(\frac{dE}{dx}\right)\left(\frac{dx}{dV}\right)$$

we find, using 6.12, that

$$\frac{dE}{dV} = \frac{1}{3N_0 C x_0^2}\left(\frac{dE}{dx}\right)$$

Similarly, the second derivative

$$\left(\frac{d^2 E}{dV^2}\right)_{V=V_0} = \frac{1}{9C^2 N_0^2 x_0^2}\left[-\frac{4\mathscr{A}e^2}{x_0^5} + \frac{n(n+3)B}{x_0^{n+4}}\right] \tag{6.13}$$

We have derived an expression for B in equation 6.5, and substituting this into equation 6.13, and then 6.13 into 6.11, we find that

$$n = 1 + \frac{9C x_0^4}{\beta e^2 \mathscr{A}} \tag{6.14}$$

Thus n can readily be evaluated from extrapolation of β and x_0 to $T = 0°K$. The quantity n would be expected to vary with the number of electrons in a given atom. For elements with high atomic numbers n would be expected to be larger than for elements with low atomic numbers. Indeed Pauling has determined that n is related to the closed shell configuration of a given ion. For an ion having the closed shell configuration of He, Ne, Ar, Kr, and Xe, n is found to be 5, 7, 9, 10, and 12 respectively. When ions having two different configurations make up a crystal the average should be taken. Thus, for LiF, the average n is 6, since n for Li^+ is 5 and for F^- is 7.

In order to obtain ΔH_5 two more steps are needed. We have evaluated E_l at $T = 0°K$. In order to be rigorous this must be converted into an enthalpy term, which is then brought up to $298°K$ from $0°K$. These corrections are second order terms for our purposes of checking the Born-Haber theory, however, so will be ignored. In Table 6.3 are listed values

TABLE 6.3

Comparison of Theoretical and Experimental Values of $\Delta H_f°$ (in kcal/mole)

Compound	ΔH_1	ΔH_2	ΔH_3	ΔH_4	ΔH_5	$\Delta H_f°$(calc)	$\Delta H_f°$(exptl)
LiCl(s)	38.3	29.0	125.8	−87.3	−193.5	−87.7	−96.9
NaCl(s)	25.7	29.0	120.0	−87.3	−184.5	−97.1	−98.7
KCl(s)	21.0	29.0	101.6	−87.3	−163.6	−99.3	−104.2
RbCl(s)	20.0	29.0	97.8	−87.3	−159.0	−99.5	−102.9
LiBr(s)	38.3	26.6	125.8	−82.0	−182.1	−73.4	−83.4
NaBr(s)	25.7	26.6	120.0	−82.0	−173.0	−82.7	−86.4
KBr(s)	21.0	26.6	101.6	−82.0	−156.8	−89.6	−93.7
LiI(s)	38.3	25.5	125.8	−75.7	−170.7	−56.8	−64.8
NaI(s)	25.7	25.5	120.0	−75.7	−161.4	−65.9	−69.2
KI(s)	21.0	25.5	101.6	−75.7	−150.0	−77.6	−78.3

of $\Delta H_f°$ calculated according to the Born-Haber cycle, together with experimentally determined values for a variety of compounds. The agreement is quite good between calculated and experimental values.

chapter 7

Free Energy of Heterogeneous Reactions

7.1 PHASE TRANSITIONS CLASSIFIED ACCORDING TO ORDER

It is convenient to classify transitions according to which derivative of the free energy first shows a discontinuity. Obviously for any phase transition the free energy G is continuous since at the equilibrium temperature $G_\alpha = G_\beta$ for the reaction

$$\alpha = \beta$$

We have shown that

$$\left(\frac{\partial G}{\partial T}\right)_P = -S$$

$$\left(\frac{\partial G}{\partial P}\right)_T = V$$

$$\frac{\partial\left(\dfrac{G}{T}\right)}{\partial\left(\dfrac{1}{T}\right)} = H$$

If a transition occurs with a discontinuity in any of these first derivatives of the free energy, it is called a *first order transition*. Most of the transitions of interest to us are this type. As examples we may list: (a) melting, (b) evaporation, and (c) allotropic transformations. All of these are observed to show a discontinuity in ΔS, ΔV, and ΔH at the transition temperature. An example of G as a function of T is shown for a first order transition in Fig. 7.1. Obviously, if the first derivative is discontinuous, all higher order derivatives are discontinuous also.

Some transformations are continuous with regard to their first derivatives. These would show no discontinuity with regard to entropy volume or enthalpy. In other words the volume of β at the transformation

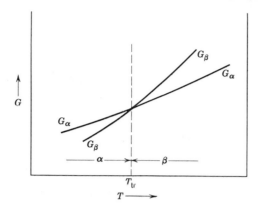

Fig. 7.1 Illustration of a first order transition.

temperature is equal to the volume of α. If such a transformation is discontinuous in its second derivatives of the free energy function, it would be signified as second order. Thus the quantities

$$\left(\frac{\partial^2 G}{\partial T^2}\right)_P = -\left(\frac{\partial S}{\partial T}\right)_P = -\frac{C_P}{T}$$

$$\left(\frac{\partial^2 G}{\partial P^2}\right) = \left(\frac{\partial V}{\partial P}\right)_T = -\beta V$$

$$\left(\frac{\partial H}{\partial T}\right)_P = C_P$$

would become discontinuous.

The transformation from the ferromagnetic to the paramagnetic state is considered as an example of a second order transition. The free energy functions for the α and β phases for a transition of this type are shown in Fig. 7.2. In principle it is possible to have higher order transitions where the first discontinuous derivatives would, for example, be

$$\left(\frac{\partial^2 G^3}{\partial T^3}\right)_P \quad \text{or} \quad \left(\frac{\partial^2 G^4}{\partial T^4}\right)_P$$

It becomes difficult experimentally to distinguish the exact order of a high order transition, however. In fact, as an example it has not been completely decided whether or not the order-disorder transformation in alloys is first order or second order.

As mentioned earlier, most transformations to be discussed here are first order transitions.

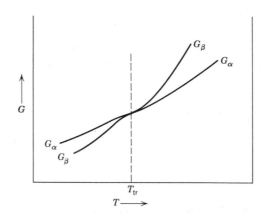

Fig. 7.2   Illustration of a second order transition.

7.2 INFLUENCE OF EXTERNAL PRESSURE ON TRANSITION TEMPERATURE

Consider a general phase transition of a pure substance from α to β at a constant temperature and pressure:

$$\alpha = \beta$$

If the temperature happens to be the equilibrium transition temperature, ΔG for the reaction is zero. By definition

$$\Delta G = G_\beta - G_\alpha$$

and thus when α is in equilibrium with β, $G_\beta = G_\alpha$. Differentiating both sides we see that at equilibrium

$$dG_\beta = dG_\alpha \tag{7.1}$$

Since the reaction is considered to be performed reversibly, we may use the relation derived previously that

$$dG = V\, dP - S\, dT$$

Therefore

$$dG_\alpha = V_\alpha\, dP - S_\alpha\, dT$$

$$dG_\beta = V_\beta\, dP - S_\beta\, dT$$

In view of equation 7.1 we find upon rearranging that

$$\frac{dP}{dT} = \frac{S_\beta - S_\alpha}{V_\beta - V_\alpha}$$

or

$$\frac{dP}{dT} = \frac{\Delta S}{\Delta V} \tag{7.2}$$

Since the reaction is proceeding at constant temperature and pressure

$$\Delta S = \int_\alpha^\beta \frac{DQ}{T} = \int_\alpha^\beta \frac{dH}{T} = \frac{\Delta H}{T}$$

where ΔH is the enthalpy change of the transition. Substituting in equation 7.2, we find

$$\frac{dP}{dT} = \frac{\Delta H}{T\,\Delta V} \tag{7.3}$$

This relation is known as the *Clapeyron* equation. From this relation we see that a change of transition temperature dT equal to $(T\,\Delta V/\Delta H)\,dP$ results upon a pressure change dP. If the change in the phase transition temperature is small compared with T, ΔV, ΔH, and T may be considered constant and

$$\Delta T = \left(\frac{T\,\Delta V}{\Delta H}\right)\Delta P \tag{7.4}$$

This may be seen by carrying out the integration rigorously, expanding in an infinite series and neglecting high order terms.

Illustration

Problem. Calculate the change in the transition temperature of the reaction

$$Sn(gray) = Sn(white)$$

if the gray tin phase is contained by a pressure of 100 atmospheres.

Solution. From the literature we find that $\Delta H = 500$ cal/mole. The equilibrium transformation temperature is $286°K$, the atomic weight, M, is 118.7, and the densities of gray tin and white tin are 5.75 and 7.28 gm/cm³ respectively. The molar volume change is therefore

$$\Delta V = M\left(\frac{1}{\rho_{white}} - \frac{1}{\rho_{gray}}\right) = -4.35 \text{ cm}^3/\text{mole}$$

Substituting into equation 7.4 and using the relation that one liter-atmosphere $= 24.2$ cal, we have

$$\Delta T = \frac{286°K \times (-4.35 \times 10^{-3} \text{ liter})(100 - 1) \text{ atm } (24.2)}{500 \text{ cal/mole}}$$

$$\Delta T = -5.95°K$$

TABLE 7.1
The Effect of Pressure on the Melting Point of Solids[a]

Substance	$T_{m.p.}$ (°K)	ΔH_f (cal/gm)	ΔV $(V_l - V_s)$ (cm³/gm)	ΔT for 1000 atm	
				calc	obs
H_2O	273.2	79.8	−0.0906	−7.5	−7.4
Acetic acid	289.8	44.7	+0.01595	+25.0	+24.4
Tin	505	14.0	+0.00389	+3.40	+3.28
Bismuth	544	12.6	−0.00342	−3.56	−3.55

[a] From H. M. Strong, *Am. Scientist*, **48**, 58 (1960).

Application of significant pressures sometimes results in the formation of phases which could not be obtained by thermal means alone. An example is the transition of graphite to diamond which occurs only at extremely high pressure and temperature. In general, the metastable structures induced by the application of high pressures are found to be more close packed than the initial structure.

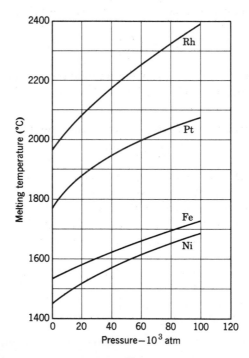

Fig. 7.3 The experimental fusion curves of iron, nickel, platinum, and rhodium. From H. M. Strong, *Am. Scientist*, **48**, 58 (1960).

The effect of pressure upon transformation temperature depends upon the sign of ΔV and ΔH in equation 7.4. Consider the fusion process for example. The heat of fusion is always positive, but the volume change upon fusion may be positive or negative. For metallic elements crystallizing in the close-packed structures, ΔV is positive upon fusion and so the melting point is increased upon increase in pressure. For elements crystallizing with open structures, ΔV is often negative upon fusion and so the melting point is lowered upon application of pressure according to equation 7.4. In Table 7.1 the influence of pressure on the melting point is shown for a variety of solids. Actual values of ΔT are compared with values calculated from equation 7.4. The agreement is excellent.

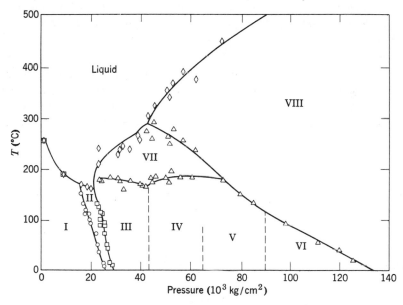

Fig. 7.4 Phase diagram of bismuth. From H. M. Strong, *Am. Scientist*, **48**, 58 (1960).

In the application of equation 7.4 to the data in Table 7.1, it is assumed that ΔH and ΔV are constant. Thus the dependence of ΔT upon pressure should be linear. Such an assumption is approximately valid at low pressures, since one would not expect ΔV or ΔH to be strongly dependent upon pressure for most substances. At high pressures, however, things may be considerably different. ΔV for example will tend to become closer to zero as the pressure increases. From equation 7.4, it is seen that this will tend to diminish the effect of pressure on melting point. This effect is shown in Fig. 7.3 for a variety of elements.

As mentioned earlier, high pressures may cause metastable phases to appear which normally are not observed. In the case of bismuth, for example, at one atmosphere pressure, only one solid phase is present but as the pressure is increased, six new solid phases may appear at room temperature, each stable over a range in pressure. The phase diagram of bismuth is shown in Fig. 7.4 (1 kg/cm² = 0.97 atm). Phase I is the phase normally observed at ordinary pressures.

7.3   TRANSITION FROM CONDENSED PHASE TO VAPOR PHASE

Suppose that the β phase in Section 7.1 represents a vapor in equilibrium with its condensed pure phase. For this particular case the Clapeyron equation can be put into a more useful form. The ΔV term in equation 7.3 is defined as $V_\beta - V_\alpha$. When β is a gas at normal pressures

$$V_\beta \gg V_\alpha$$

Therefore ΔV may be approximated by V_β. Further, the pressures of the vapors of interest here are generally very low. This means that the gas molecules are sufficiently far apart for little interaction to occur between them. As a result the perfect gas law will apply and the molar volume of β is given by

$$V_\beta = \frac{RT}{p} \tag{7.5}$$

where p represents the partial pressure of β. Substitution into 7.3 yields

$$\frac{dp}{dT} = \frac{\Delta H p}{RT^2}$$

Dividing through by p and multiplying by dT,

$$\frac{dp}{p} = \frac{\Delta H}{RT^2} dT$$

or

$$\frac{d \ln p}{d(1/T)} = -\frac{\Delta H}{R} \tag{7.6}$$

Upon integration we find therefore that

$$\ln p = -\frac{\Delta H}{RT} + \ln A \tag{7.7}$$

where $\ln A$ is the integration constant. Thus it is seen that the vapor pressure of a substance increases exponentially with temperature. In Fig. 7.5 the equilibrium pressure or vapor pressure of a substance is shown, schematically, as a function of $1/T$. The slope at any temperature is equal to $-\Delta H/R$ according to equation 7.6. ΔH is known as the heat of sublimation, ΔH_s for solids, and is somewhat dependent upon temperature because of the heat capacity difference of α and β.

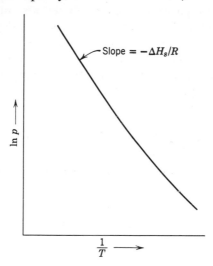

Fig. 7.5 Vapor pressure as a function of temperature.

Writing equation 7.7 in exponential form,

$$p = A \exp \left[- \frac{\Delta H_s}{RT} \right] \qquad (7.8)$$

we see the strong exponential dependence of the vapor pressure upon temperature. In Table 7.2 values of the heat of sublimation are listed for

TABLE 7.2

Heats of Sublimation in kcal/mole (at $T_{m.p.}$)^a

Substance	ΔH_s	Substance	ΔH_s
Ag	65.4	Li	38.3
Al	75.3	MoO_3	61.0
Al_2I_6	27.9	BeO	145.5
Au	88.7	Zn	30.25
Fe	88.7	V	119.9
Ge	90.0	Si	85 (est)
Mo	134.5	Ni	498.5

^{a} From Kubaschewski and Evans, *Metallurgical Thermochemistry*, Third Edition, Pergamon, London, 1958.

a variety of substances. These were measured at melting points of the substances.

If ΔH_s were independent of temperature, only two constants would need to be known in order to determine p at any temperature: A and ΔH_s. Because of the heat capacity difference between a substance in the condensed form and in the vapor form, the temperature dependence of ΔH_s must be taken into account for p to be evaluated accurately. This is particularly important since a small error in ΔH_s will result in a large error in p because of the occurrence of ΔH_s in the exponent. As a result of this temperature dependence of ΔH_s, $\ln p$ is generally expressed in the following form for convenience in evaluation.

$$\ln p = \frac{a}{T} + b \log T + cT + d$$

Some values of the constants are tabulated in Table 7.3 for a variety of substances.

TABLE 7.3
Vapor Pressure Constants of Several Substances (in mm Hg)[a]

Substance	a	b	$c \times 10^3$	d	Temperature Range (°K)
Ag(s)	−14,710	−0.755	—	11.66	298–m.p.
Ag(l)	−14,260	−1.055	—	12.23	m.p.–b.p.
BeO(s)	−34,230	−2	—	18.50	298–m.p.
Ge(s)	−20,150	−0.91	—	13.28	298–m.p.
Mg(s)	−7,780	−0.855	—	11.41	298–m.p.
Mg(l)	−7,550	−1.41	—	12.79	m.p.–b.p.
NaCl(s)	−12,440	−0.90	−0.46	14.31	298–m.p.
Si(s)	−18,000	−1.022	—	12.83	1200–m.p.

[a] From Kubaschewski and Evans, *Metallurgical Thermochemistry*, Third Edition, Pergamon, London, 1958.

7.4 EFFECT OF EXTERNAL PRESSURE APPLIED TO A CONDENSED PHASE UPON ITS VAPOR PRESSURE

Suppose that our condensed phase system of interest is placed in a chamber as shown in Fig. 7.6. If the chamber is evacuated, the only vapor in the chamber will be that of component B, at pressure p at temperature T. This problem was discussed in the last section. Suppose now that the temperature is held constant but we admit an inert gas at pressure P. The question then arises: How does the vapor pressure p of a substance depend upon the external pressure P applied to the system?

Since B in the vapor phase is presumed to be in equilibrium with B in the condensed phase

$$dG_{\text{cond}} = dG_{\text{gas}}$$

Let us now change the external pressure by dP. Since this is done reversibly we may use the equation

$$dG = V\,dP - S\,dT$$

and since T is constant

$$dG_{\text{cond}} = V_{\text{cond}}\,dP$$

The pressure change dP of the inert gas will effect a pressure change dp in the vapor pressure of B. This will result in a free energy change of the gas given by

$$dG_{\text{gas}} = V_{\text{gas}}\,dp$$

Since

$$dG_{\text{cond}} = dG_{\text{gas}}$$

we find

$$\frac{dp}{dP} = \frac{V_{\text{cond}}}{V_{\text{gas}}} \tag{7.9}$$

Assuming the gaseous B to be perfect, $pV = RT$ and

$$\frac{dp}{dP} = \frac{pV_{\text{cond}}}{RT} \tag{7.10}$$

From equation 7.9, it is seen that dp/dP is small, since $V_{\text{cond}} \ll V_{\text{gas}}$. A typical ratio of $V_{\text{cond}}/V_{\text{gas}}$ is 10 cm^3/10^5 cm^3 or 10^{-4}. Thus a change in P of the order of an atmosphere will result in a change in vapor pressure

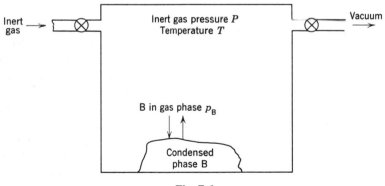

Fig. 7.6

of the order of 10^{-4} atm in this case. Very large external pressures could, of course, result in noticeable changes in vapor pressure. Therefore we are safe in considering the vapor pressure of a phase to be dependent only on temperature at ordinary pressures.

7.5 STANDARD FREE ENERGY OF REACTIONS

One of the most important thermodynamic quantities we will be concerned with is knowledge of the standard free energy of a reaction, $\Delta G°$. In earlier chapters we have discussed methods for obtaining $\Delta H°$ and $\Delta S°$ at any given temperature. Since

$$\Delta G° = \Delta H° - T \Delta S°$$

it is easy to calculate $\Delta G°$ at a given temperature if $\Delta H°$ and $\Delta S°$ are known. It will be recalled that the superscript (°) refers to all components of the reaction being in their standard states at the given temperature and at one atmosphere pressure. It should be noted that, even though $\Delta H°$ and $\Delta S°$ are not strongly dependent upon temperature, $\Delta G°$ is because of the occurrence of the $T \Delta S°$ term.

In the discussion of heat capacities it was pointed out that the heat capacity is conveniently expressed as an empirical function of temperature. This means, therefore, that $\Delta H°$, $\Delta S°$, and hence $\Delta G°$ can be conveniently expressed as empirical functions of temperature. For the more common reactions, this labor has been performed for us and convenient tabulations of $\Delta G°$ as functions of temperature exist in the literature.[1] For less common reactions, however, the investigator must often do his own calculations using values of $\Delta H°_{298}$, $S°_{298}$, and heat capacity data.

A sample of the type of data available is shown in Table 7.4 expressed in the form

$$\Delta G° = a + bT \log T + cT$$

For accurate calculations at a variety of temperatures the use of $\Delta G°$ data as a function of temperature in the empirical form shown in Table 7.4 is useful. For many applications, where more approximate answers are sufficient, particularly when comparisons between the oxidizing or reducing powers of various components are of interest, it is more convenient to plot $\Delta G°$ for the various materials as a function of temperature. Such plots for a variety of oxides and sulfides are shown in Figs. 7.7 and 7.8.

In observing Fig. 7.7 it will be noted that three scales appear to the right and bottom of the figure. These are labeled CO/CO_2 ratio, H_2/H_2O ratio, and p_{O_2} respectively. The three scales refer to the following types of reactions using the oxidation of titanium as an example:

(1) $Ti(s) + 2CO_2(g) = TiO_2(s) + 2CO(g)$ $K = \left(\dfrac{p_{CO}}{p_{CO_2}}\right)^2$

[1] For example, Kubaschewski and Evans, *Metallurgical Thermochemistry*, Third Edition, Pergamon, London, 1958.

TABLE 7.4

Standard Free Energies of Reactions[a]

$$\Delta G^\circ = a + bT \log T + cT \text{ (in cal)}$$

Reaction	a	b	c	$\pm$kcal	Temperature Range (°K)
$2Al(s) + \frac{3}{2}O_2(g, 1\text{ atm}) = Al_2O_3(s)$	-400,810	-3.98	87.64	3	298–923
$2Al(l) + \frac{3}{2}O_2(g, 1\text{ atm}) = Al_2O_3(s)$	-405,760	-3.75	92.22	4	923–1800
$2Be(s) + O_2(g) = 2BeO$	-286,900	-3.32	56.1	10	298–1557
$Ca(s) + Si(s) = CaSi(s)$	-36,000	—	-0.5	4	298–1123
$2CaO(s) + SiO_2(s) = Ca_2SiO_4$	-30,200	—	-1.2	2.5	298–1700
$2Co(s) + C = Co_2C(s)$	3,950	—	-2.08	5	298–1200
$Fe(s) + \frac{1}{2}O_2(g) = FeO(s)$	-62,050	—	14.95	3	298–1642
$\frac{1}{2}Ge(s) + \frac{1}{2}GeO(g) = GeO(g, 1\text{ atm})$	-54,600	-6.9	62.0	4	298–860
Graphite = diamond	-310	—	1.13	0.2	298–1500
$La(s) + \frac{1}{2}N_2(g) = LaN(s)$	-72,100	—	25.0	9	298–1000
$2MgO(s) + SiO_2(s) = Mg_2SiO_4(s)$	-15,120	—	0.0	2	298–1700
$MnO(s) + SiO_2(s) = MnSiO_3(s)$	-5,920	—	3.0	4	298–1600
$Mo(s) + O_2(g) = MoO_2(s)$	-140,100	-4.6	55.8	6	298–1300
$Na_2O(s) + SiO_2(s) = Na_2SiO_3$	-55,550	—	1.40	8	298–1361
$Ti(s) + 2Cl_2(g, 1\text{ atm}) = TiCl_4(g, 1\text{ atm})$	-180,700	-1.8	34.65	3	298–1700
$Si(s) + O_2(g, 1\text{ atm}) = SiO_2(s)$	-210,600	-3.0	52.22	3	298–1700

[a] From Kubaschewski and Evans, *Metallurgical Thermochemistry*, Third Edition, Pergamon, London, 1958.

The activity of pure titanium is 1 and hence does not appear in the expression for K.

(2) $Ti(s) + 2H_2O(g) = TiO_2(s) + 2H_2(g)$ $K = \left(\dfrac{p_{H_2}}{p_{H_2O}}\right)^2$

(3) $Ti(s) + O_2(g) = TiO_2(s)$ $K = \dfrac{1}{p_{O_2}}$

If the metals and oxides are in their pure stable states, the equilibrium constants are related to these three quantities as shown above. These scales enable one to calculate the equilibrium CO/CO_2 ratio, H_2/H_2O ratio, or the p_{O_2} between a pure metal and its oxide at any temperature. This is done by the case of reaction (3) for example by running a straight edge from the point marked O on the extreme left hand side of the diagram through the value of $\Delta G°$ for the oxidation of titanium at the temperature of interest to the p_{O_2} scale. At 1600°C, we find $p_{O_2} \simeq 10^{-16}$ atm. This of course means that if a piece of titanium is situated at 1600°C in an atmosphere (or vacuum) where the partial pressure of oxygen is greater than 10^{-16} atm, oxidation will occur. If the pressure is below 10^{-16} atm, oxidation will not occur but the oxide, if present, will be reduced. Similarly by performing the same operation using the points marked C and H, equilibrium values of p_{CO}/p_{CO_2} and p_{H_2}/p_{H_2O} of 4×10^4 and 10^4 are obtained respectively.

This type of graphical representation can also be used for evaluating the relative stability of various oxides in contact with metals. The more negative the free energy, the more stable the oxide will be. As a result we see from the figure that $Ti(s)$ will reduce $SiO_2(s)$ at 1000°C but $Cr(s)$ will not. This follows since the curves are all calculated on the basis of one mole of O_2 participating in the reaction. For our former example of Ti metal in contact with $SiO_2(s)$, we have at 1000°C from the figure

$Ti(s) + O_2(g, 1 atm) = TiO_2(s)$		$\Delta G° = -161$ kcal
$SiO_2 = Si(s) + O_2(g, 1 atm)$		$\Delta G° = 154$ kcal

$Ti(s) + SiO_2(s) = Si(s) + TiO_2(s)$ $\Delta G° = -7$ kcal

Thus the standard free energy change is -7 kcal, and if pure titanium is placed in contact with pure SiO_2, the SiO_2 will be reduced. This could be calamitous if pure titanium is desired since the elemental silicon from the reaction will tend to dissolve in the titanium and contaminate it. From the figure we see that if the titanium is held in Al_2O_3 crucibles, this reduction will not occur.

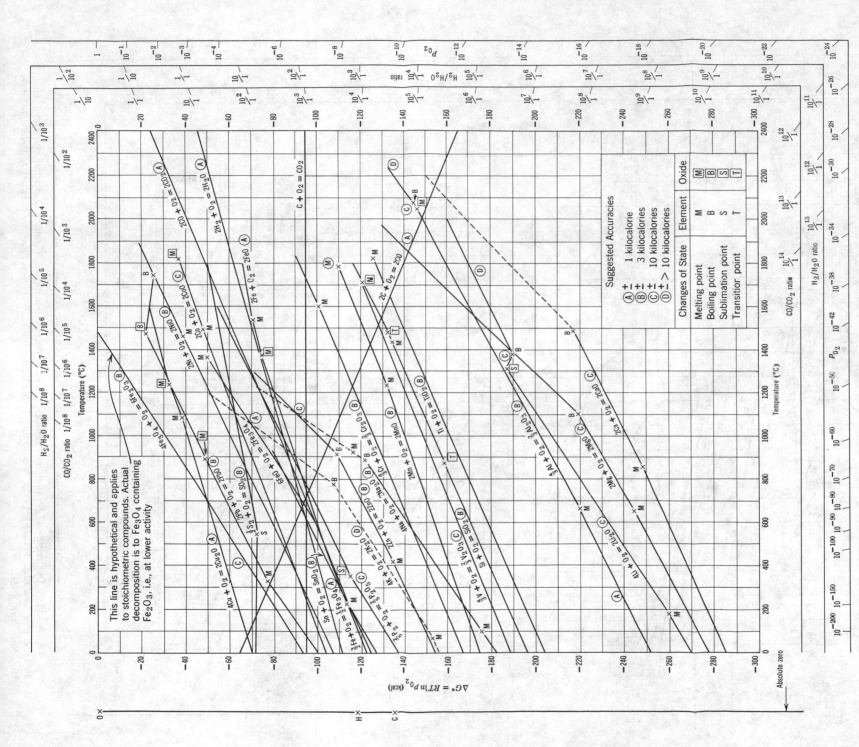

Fig. 7.7 Standard free energy of formation of oxides as a function of temperature. From F. D. Richardson and J. H. E. Jeffes, *J. Iron Steel Inst.*, **160**, 261 (1948). Modified by L. S. Darken and R. W. Gurry, *Physical Chemistry of Metals*, McGraw-Hill, New York, 1953.

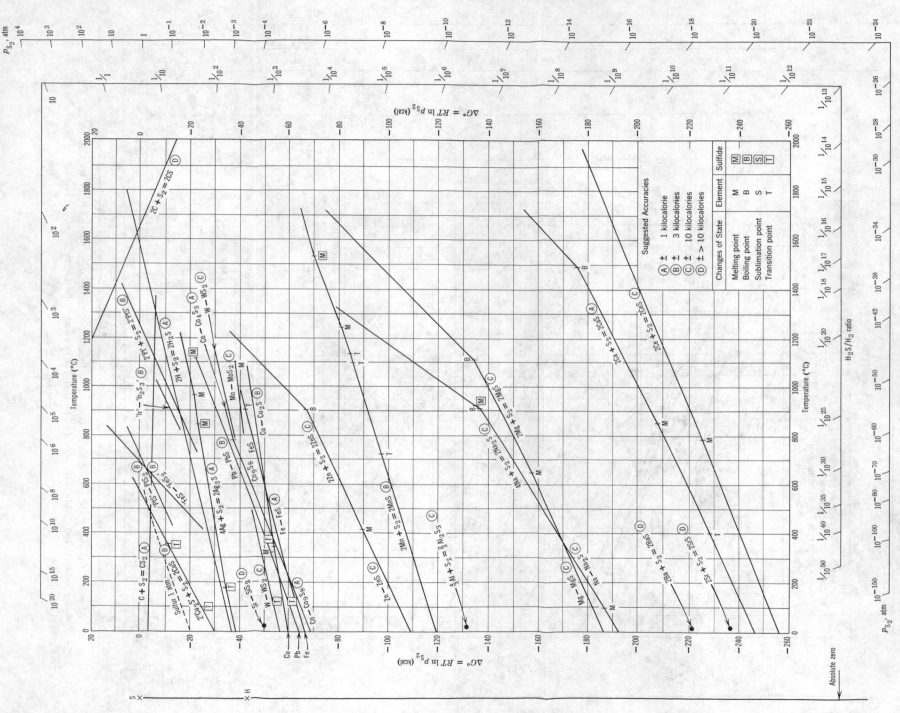

Fig. 7.8 Standard free energy of formation of sulfides as a function of temperature. From F. D. Richardson and J. H. E. Jeffes, *J. Iron Steel Inst.*, **171**, 167 (1952). Modified by L. S. Darken and R. W. Gurry, *Physical Chemistry of Metals*, McGraw-Hill, New York, 1953.

For reactions involving sulfides, Fig. 7.8 is applicable. The equilibrium values of p_{S_2} and the H_2S/H_2 ratio between metal and its sulfide may be obtained in the same way as discussed for oxides.

Since $\Delta G°$ is a state property, individual reactions can be added together to give the $\Delta G°$ for a reaction not listed in the table, as discussed in connection with $\Delta H°$ and $\Delta S°$.

Perhaps it should be emphasized at this point that the sign of $\Delta G°$ for a particular reaction can be used only as a criterion of spontaneity if all substances are in their standard states. The real significance of $\Delta G°$ lies not in connection with the predictability of spontaneity but in connection with equilibrium constant calculations as will be discussed next.

Consider an isothermal reaction between solid phases in their standard states with a free energy change $\Delta G_1°$.

$$aA(s) + bB(s) = cC(s) + dD(s) \qquad \Delta G_1°$$

Each of these components is in equilibrium with its own vapor at its particular partial pressure. As a result we may convert the above reaction of interest to one involving gaseous components at their equilibrium pressures, $p_i°$, as follows:

(1) $\qquad aA(s) + bB(s) = cC(s) + dD(s) \qquad \Delta G_1°$

(2) $\qquad aA(g, p_A°) = aA(s) \qquad \Delta G_2 = 0$

(3) $\qquad bB(g, p_B°) = bB(s) \qquad \Delta G_3 = 0$

(4) $\qquad cC(s) = cC(g, p_C°) \qquad \Delta G_4 = 0$

(5) $\qquad dD(s) = dD(g, p_D°) \qquad \Delta G_5 = 0$

Sum: $\quad aA(g, p_A°) + bB(g, p_B°) = cC(g, p_C°) + dD(g, p_D°) \quad \Delta G_6 = \Delta G_1°$

The free energy changes associated with reactions 2 through 5 are zero because $p_A°$, $p_B°$, $p_C°$, and $p_D°$ are chosen so as to be the equilibrium values for pure components. As a result a reaction between gaseous components in equilibrium with their solids gives the standard free change $\Delta G_1°$. If one of the components were stable in the gaseous state at the temperature T, however, then in order for ΔG_6 to be equal to $\Delta G°$, it would have to be at one atmosphere pressure.

Let us now change the values of $p_A°$, $p_B°$, $p_C°$, and $p_D°$ to new values p_A^e, p_B^e, p_C^e, and p_D^e. These values will be chosen so that the reaction will be in equilibrium and hence the free energy change of the reaction will be equal to zero. Thus

(7) $\quad aA(g, p_A^e) + bB(g, p_B^e) = cC(g, p_C^e) + dD(g, p_D^e) \qquad \Delta G_7 = 0$

In order to convert reaction (6) to reaction (7), the partial pressure of each component must be changed from p_i° to p_i^e. To evaluate the free energy change due to such a pressure change we will use

$$dG = V \, dp - S \, dT$$

Assuming T constant and considering the vapor to be ideal $(pV = RT)$ we find

$$dG = RT \, d \ln p \tag{7.11}$$

or upon integration

$$\Delta G = RT \ln \frac{p_i^e}{p_i^{\circ}} \tag{7.12}$$

Thus, starting with reaction (6) we obtain

(6) $aA(g, p_A^{\circ}) + bB(g, p_B^{\circ}) = cC(g, p_C^{\circ}) + dD(g, p_D^{\circ}) \quad \Delta G_6 = \Delta G_1^{\circ}$

and converting each component to p_i^e

(8) $\quad a A(g, p_A^e) = a A(g, p_A^{\circ}) \qquad \Delta G_8 = aRT \ln \dfrac{p_A^{\circ}}{p_A^e}$

(9) $\quad b B(g, p_B^e) = b B(g, p_B^{\circ}) \qquad \Delta G_9 = bRT \ln \dfrac{p_B^{\circ}}{p_B^e}$

(10) $\quad c C(g, p_C^{\circ}) = c C(g, p_C^e) \qquad \Delta G_{10} = cRT \ln \dfrac{p_C^e}{p_C^{\circ}}$

(11) $\quad d D(g, p_D^{\circ}) = d D(g, p_D^e) \qquad \Delta G_{11} = dRT \ln \dfrac{p_D^e}{p_D^{\circ}}$

---

(7) $aA(g, p_A^e) + bB(g, p_B^e) = cC(g, p_C^e) + dD(g, p_D^e) \qquad \Delta G_7 = 0$

The free energy change for this reaction is of course zero since it is at equilibrium.

Upon summation of the free energy changes,

$$\Delta G_7 = 0 = \Delta G_6 + \Sigma \Delta G_i$$

Substituting and putting the coefficients a, b, c, and d inside the logarithms yields

$$0 = \Delta G_1^{\circ} + RT \ln \left[\frac{(p_C^e/p_C^{\circ})^c (p_C^e/p_D^{\circ})^d}{(p_A^e/p_A^{\circ})^a (p_B^e/p_B^{\circ})^b} \right] \tag{7.13}$$

The bracketed expression inside the logarithm is called the equilibrium constant K for the reaction. Rearranging we find

$$\Delta G^{\circ} = -RT \ln K \tag{7.14}$$

It should be noted from 7.13 that K is a dimensionless quantity regardless of the values of a, b, c, and d.

The general quantity p_i/p_i° is defined as the *activity*, a_i, of component i for the case of ideal vapors. Thus

$$K = \frac{(a_C^e)^c \cdot (a_D^e)^d}{(a_A^e)^a \cdot (a_B^e)^b} = \frac{\prod (a_i^e)^{n_i} \text{ (for products)}}{\prod (a_i^e)^{n_i} \text{ (for reactants)}} \quad (7.15)$$

where a_A^e, a_B^e, a_C^e, and a_D^e represent the activities when the reactants and products are in equilibrium.

From the definition of a_i,

$$a_i \equiv \frac{p_i}{p_i^\circ} \quad (7.16)$$

we see that p_i is a variable and p_i° is fixed at a given temperature, since it is the vapor pressure of pure component. Thus substituting 7.16 into 7.11, we see that

$$dG = RT \, d \ln a_i \quad (7.17)$$

and integrating

$$G_i - G_i^\circ = RT \ln (a_i/a_i^\circ) \quad (7.18)$$

Equation 7.18 must not be confused with equation 7.14. Equation 7.18 might be thought of as a fundamental thermodynamic equation whereas 7.14 might be thought of as a mathematical accident.

Equation 7.14 shows that from knowledge of the standard free energy change of a reaction, which has nothing to do with the reaction at equilibrium, the relation between the quantities themselves at equilibrium is obtained. The value of the activities depends, of course, on p_i° which in turn depends on our choice of standard states. Thus far, we have used the pure condensed phase as standard state, if this is stable at the temperature of interest. If the stable form is a gas, then it is considered that the standard state is 1 atm pressure. From the definition of activity, it is seen that the activity of the pure stable substance in the considered form is equal to one by definition and for a stable ideal gas is equal to the pressure itself measured in atmospheres. In dealing with solutions it is sometimes more convenient to change the standard state. Thus the equation to obtain ΔG° is changed and also p_i° will be changed.

Equation 7.11 is valid for gaseous components only if the vapor components themselves behave ideally. If this is not the case, p in equation 7.11 must be corrected for nonideality. This is done by use of what is called the *fugacity*. In most cases of interest to us, however, the partial pressures of solids and liquids are normally low enough for the gas to be considered as ideal.

Consider now the free energy change of our reaction (not the standard free energy) in which the components are at some arbitrary activity. This could occur, for example, if its components were in solution.

(1) $\qquad aA(a_A) + bB(a_B) = cC(a_C) + dD(a_D) \qquad \Delta G_1$

To evaluate let us begin with the reaction in which all components are in standard states, thus $a_i = 1$ for all components. The activities will then be reversibly changed from $a_i = 1$ to a_i and the free energy associated with each step will be calculated by use of equation 7.18. Thus

(2) $aA(a_A = 1) + bB(a_B = 1) = cC(a_C = 1) + dD(a_D = 1)$ $\Delta G°$

(3) $aA(a_A) = aA(a_A = 1)$ $\Delta G_3 = a(G_A° - G_A) = RT \ln \left(\dfrac{1}{a_A}\right)^a$

(4) $bB(a_B) = bB(a_B = 1)$ $\Delta G_4 = b(G_B° - G_B) = RT \ln \left(\dfrac{1}{a_B}\right)^b$

(5) $cC(a_C = 1) = cC(a_C)$ $\Delta G_5 = c(G_C - G_C°) = RT \ln a_C{}^c$

(6) $dD(a_D = 1) = dD(a_D)$ $\Delta G_6 = d(G_D - G_D°) = RT \ln a_D{}^d$

Upon summation of reactions (2) through (6), reaction (1) is obtained and

$$\Delta G_1 = RT \ln \left(\frac{a_C{}^c a_D{}^d}{a_A{}^a a_B{}^b}\right) + \Delta G° \tag{7.19}$$

Illustration 1

Problem. Consider the equilibrium reaction of pure solid CaSi at 1000°K with Ca and silicon dissolved in a solvent. Suppose that Ca initially has an activity of 0.5 in solution and CaSi is pure. What this means is that the vapor pressure of dissolved calcium is 0.5 times the vapor pressure of pure calcium at this temperature. Let us now find

(a) the activity of Si in equilibrium with Ca ($a = 0.5$) and CaSi(s).
(b) the partial pressure of Ca(g) in equilibrium with the dissolved Ca.
(c) the free energy of the reaction

$$\text{Ca } (a = 0.5) + \text{Si } (a = 0.4) = \text{CaSi } (a = 0.8)$$

(d) whether or not the reaction for (c) will proceed.

Solution. (a) Since we are interested in an equilibrium reaction we will use $\Delta G° = -RT \ln K$. From the literature $\Delta G°$ for the reaction at 1000°K is equal to $-41,000$ cal.

$$\text{Ca}(s) + \text{Si}(s) = \text{CaSi}(s)$$

Thus

$$\ln K = \frac{41,000}{(1.986)1000} = 20.6$$

and

$$K = \frac{a_{CaSi}}{a_{Ca} a_{Si}} = 8.92 \times 10^8$$

Since CaSi exists as a pure stable phase, $a_{CaSi} = 1$, and it was given that $a_{Ca} = 0.5$. Thus on substitution, we find that the equilibrium activity of Si is

$$a_{Si} = 2.24 \times 10^{-9}$$

If the activity of silicon in solution were initially higher, CaSi would precipitate until equilibrium was reached.

(b) It is given that $a_{Ca} = 0.5$. Since $a_i = p_i/p_i^\circ$ we can obtain p_{Ca} if the value of p_i° can be obtained. Since our standard state for Ca is pure solid at $1000°K$, p_{Ca}° is simply the vapor pressure for pure Ca at $1000°K$. From the literature $p_{Ca}^\circ = 0.11$ mm Hg, and thus on substituting $p_{Ca} = 0.055$ mm Hg. Thus the solution has an equilibrium pressure of calcium of 0.055 mm Hg.

(c) We are not concerned with equilibrium constants in this part. The free energy for a reaction of this type is given by equation 7.19. Upon substitution we find

$$\Delta G = (1.986)(1000) \ln \frac{0.8}{(0.5)(0.4)} - 41,000 = -38,240$$

(d) Since ΔG is negative, the reaction as written is thermodynamically possible.

Illustration 2

Problem. Calculate the standard free energy change $\Delta G°$ of the following reaction at $1000°K$.

$$Ca(a = 0.9) = Ca(a = 0.5)$$

Solution. $\Delta G°$ is calculated by measuring the free energy change of both reactants and products in their standard states. Since calcium is solid at $1000°K$, the standard state for both reactants and products is pure solid Ca as indicated and thus

$$\Delta G° = 0, \quad K = 1$$

Illustration 3

Problem. Calculate the free energy change ΔG of the following reaction at $1000°K$.

$$Ca(a = 0.9) = Ca(a = 0.5)$$

Solution.

$$\Delta G = RT \ln \frac{a_{(product)}}{a_{(reactant)}} = RT \ln \frac{0.5}{0.9}$$

$$\Delta G = -1168 \text{ cal}$$

The equilibrium constant concept and its relation to free energy is one of the most important relationships of thermodynamics. Let us now consider the variation of K with temperature.

In an earlier chapter we found that

$$\frac{\partial(\Delta G/T)}{\partial(1/T)} = \Delta H$$

Substitution of the relation $\Delta G° = -RT \ln K$ into the equation above yields

$$\frac{\partial \ln K}{\partial(1/T)} = -\frac{\Delta H°}{R} \qquad (7.20)$$

From equation 7.20, it can be seen that the value of K varies markedly with temperature. As a result a shift of a rather small amount in temperature may markedly affect the direction of reaction. Whether or not K increases or decreases as the temperature increases depends upon the sign of $\Delta H°$ for the reaction. This quantity, of course, may be either negative or positive.

Let us now consider the effect of an error in $\Delta G°$ upon K. Rewriting $\Delta G° = -RT \ln K$ we obtain

$$\ln K = -\frac{\Delta G°}{RT}$$

Holding the temperature constant and differentiating we obtain

$$\frac{dK}{K} = -\frac{d \Delta G°}{RT}$$

or

$$\frac{\Delta K}{K} \cong \frac{\Delta(\Delta G°)}{RT} \qquad (7.21)$$

A typical value of the experimental error in $\Delta G°$ is ± 2000 cal. At $1000°K$, this would lead to an error in K given by

$$\frac{\Delta K}{K} \cong \pm \frac{2000}{2000} = 100\%$$

A typical value of $\Delta G°$ is 50,000 cal; thus a 4% error in $\Delta G°$ can lead to a 100% error in K. It is clear therefore that extreme accuracy in obtaining free energy data is needed if they are used in equilibrium constant calculations. For many other cases to be discussed in later chapters, this accuracy is not needed.

chapter 8

Solutions

8.1 PARTIAL MOLAL QUANTITIES

Up to the present, all of the discussion of thermodynamic properties has centered around pure materials. Very rarely, however, are we concerned with pure materials. Rather, we are interested in solutions defined in the broad sense. We may be concerned with a mixture of A and B atoms or a solution consisting of one type of atom and defects such as lattice vacancies, interstitials, or dislocations. As a result, we are concerned with the thermodynamic properties of a particular component in a solution. Such a property is called a *partial molal quantity* or more conveniently, partial molar quantity. A given component will have a partial molal volume, entropy, energy, enthalpy, and free energy associated with it. Physically speaking, the partial molal quantities are not difficult to understand. For the purpose of illustration, let us consider the volume, since it is the easiest to visualize. Suppose we have a quantity of solution consisting of two types of molecules. This solution has a definite volume. This volume may be thought to consist of the volume occupied by A molecules and the volume occupied by B molecules. The volume occupied by a mole of A is designated the partial molal volume of A. In order to put it on the basis of a standard amount of material, the volume is referred to one mole of the given component. To formulate mathematically, consider a solution at a fixed temperature and pressure. In this case the only variable will be those relating to composition. In this chapter, the superscript ($\cdot$) will be used to refer to a property of pure component. Let the volume of solution be V', consisting of n_1 moles of component 1, n_2 moles of component 2, etc. Then since $V' = f(n_1, n_2, \ldots)$ we have

$$dV' = \left(\frac{\partial V'}{\partial n_1}\right)_{T\,P,n_2,n_3,\,\ldots} dn_1 + \left(\frac{\partial V'}{\partial n_2}\right)_{T,P,n_1,n_3,\,\ldots} dn_2 + \cdots \quad (8.1)$$

Similar equations could be written for the free energy G', enthalpy H', etc. Comparing equation 8.1 with the verbal definition of a partial molal volume, we see that the partial molal volume of component i, designated as $\bar{V}_i$ is given by

$$\bar{V}_i = \left(\frac{\partial V'}{\partial n_i}\right)_{T,P,n_j} \tag{8.2}$$

Thus

$$dV' = \bar{V}_1 \, dn_1 + \bar{V}_2 \, dn_2 + \cdots \tag{8.3}$$

$$dG' = \bar{G}_1 \, dn_1 + \bar{G}_2 \, dn_2 + \cdots \tag{8.4}$$

$$dH' = \bar{H}_1 \, dn_1 + \bar{H}_2 \, dn_2 + \cdots \tag{8.5}$$

In these operations it should be emphasized that the composition has been kept constant. This may be experimentally accomplished in one of two ways. If V' is small, dn_i moles may be added without changing composition, if dn_i is regarded as an infinitesimal. Similarly if dn_i is large, the composition may be kept approximately constant if V' is very large. Thus we see from equation 8.2, for example, that $\bar{V}_1$ may be found by adding an infinitesimal amount of component 1, dn_1, and observing the volume change dV'. Thus $\bar{V}_i$ is evaluated at a particular composition. At this composition $\bar{V}_i$ represents the actual molar volume of component in the solution. If the solution consists of n_i moles of component i, it follows therefore that the total volume equals the volume per mole of component 1 times the number of moles of component 1 in solution plus the volume per mole of component 2 in a solution of this composition times the number of moles of component 2, etc., or

$$V' = \bar{V}_1 n_1 + \bar{V}_2 n_2 + \cdots \tag{8.6}$$

Also

$$G' = \bar{G}_1 n_1 + \bar{G}_2 n_2 + \cdots \tag{8.7}$$

$$H' = \bar{H}_1 n_1 + \bar{H}_2 n_2 + \cdots \tag{8.8}$$

etc.

Differentiating equation 8.6 we obtain

$$dV' = \bar{V}_1 \, dn_1 + n_1 \, d\bar{V}_1 + \bar{V}_2 \, dn_2 + n_2 \, d\bar{V}_2 + \cdots \tag{8.9}$$

Comparison of equation 8.9 with 8.3 shows

$$n_1 \, d\bar{V}_1 + n_2 \, d\bar{V}_2 + \cdots = 0 \tag{8.10}$$

and similarly

$$n_1 \, d\bar{G}_1 + n_2 \, d\bar{G}_2 + \cdots = 0 \tag{8.11}$$

$$n_1 \, d\bar{H}_1 + n_2 \, d\bar{H}_2 + \cdots = 0 \tag{8.12}$$

$$n_1 \, d\bar{S}_1 + n_2 \, d\bar{S}_2 + \cdots = 0 \tag{8.13}$$

Instead of being concerned with an arbitrary amount of solution with volume V', free energy G', etc., it is generally convenient to consider a gram-atom of solution. By definition

$$V' = V(n_1 + n_2 + \cdots)$$

where V is the volume of solution per gram-atom. Dividing the equations by the number of gm-atoms of solution ($n_1 + n_2 + \cdots$) we find

$$V = \bar{V}_1 X_1 + \bar{V}_2 X_2 + \cdots \qquad (8.14)$$
$$G = \bar{G}_1 X_1 + \bar{G}_2 X_2 + \cdots \qquad (8.15)$$
$$H = \bar{H}_1 X_1 + \bar{H}_2 X_2 + \cdots \qquad (8.16)$$
$$S = \bar{S}_1 X_1 + \bar{S}_2 X_2 + \cdots \qquad (8.17)$$

and

$$dV = \bar{V}_1 \, dX_1 + \bar{V}_2 \, dX_2 + \cdots \qquad (8.18)$$
$$dG = \bar{G}_1 \, dX_1 + \bar{G}_2 \, dX_2 + \cdots \qquad (8.19)$$
$$dH = \bar{H}_1 \, dX_1 + \bar{H}_2 \, dX_2 + \cdots \qquad (8.20)$$
$$dS = \bar{S}_1 \, dX_1 + \bar{S}_2 \, dX_2 + \cdots \qquad (8.21)$$

and

$$X_1 \, d\bar{V}_1 + X_2 \, d\bar{V}_2 + \cdots = 0 \qquad (8.22)$$
$$X_1 \, d\bar{G}_1 + X_2 \, d\bar{G}_2 + \cdots = 0 \qquad (8.23)$$
$$X_1 \, d\bar{H}_1 + X_2 \, d\bar{H}_2 + \cdots = 0 \qquad (8.24)$$
$$X_1 \, d\bar{S}_1 + X_2 \, d\bar{S}_2 + \cdots = 0 \qquad (8.25)$$

where

$$X_i = \frac{n_i}{n_1 + n_2 + \cdots}$$

8.2 METHOD OF OBTAINING PARTIAL MOLAL QUANTITIES FROM MOLAR QUANTITIES

As an illustration, suppose that the volume per gram-atom of a binary solution is obtained as a function of composition and it is desired to obtain the partial molal volumes of the components. The molar volume of a binary solution of A and B as a function of composition is shown in Fig. 8.1. Let us consider a solution of composition which has a molar volume of V and find the values of $\bar{V}_A$ and $\bar{V}_B$ at this composition. Consider equation 8.18.

$$dV = \bar{V}_A \, dX_A + \bar{V}_B \, dX_B$$

Since

$$X_A + X_B = 1, \qquad dX_A = -dX_B$$

Thus

$$dV = (\bar{V}_B - \bar{V}_A) \, dX_B$$

Upon division by dX_B we obtain

$$\bar{V}_B = \bar{V}_A + \left(\frac{dV}{dX_B}\right) \tag{8.26}$$

By rearrangement of equation 8.14 we find

$$\bar{V}_A = \frac{V - \bar{V}_B X_B}{1 - X_B}$$

and substituting into equation 8.26 we find

$$\bar{V}_B = V + (1 - X_B)\left(\frac{dV}{dX_B}\right) \tag{8.27}$$

Similarly for $\bar{V}_A$,

$$\bar{V}_A = V - X_B\left(\frac{dV}{dX_B}\right) \tag{8.28}$$

Applying equations 8.27 and 8.28 to Fig. 8.1, we see that $\bar{V}_A$ and $\bar{V}_B$ are given by the intercepts of the tangent to the curve at $X_A = 1$ and $X_B = 1$

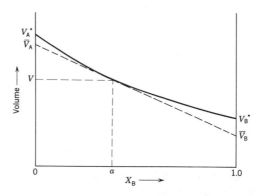

Fig. 8.1 Molar volume and partial molal volumes of a binary solution.

respectively for the composition of interest. The molar volumes for pure components are designated $V_A^\cdot$ and $V_B^\cdot$.

Identical equations for the free energy, enthalpy, energy, and entropy may be obtained.

8.3 METHOD OF OBTAINING ONE PARTIAL MOLAL QUANTITY FROM ANOTHER

Quite often from an experimental point of view it may be easy to obtain the partial molal quantity of one component as a function of composition but not that of the other component. Consider for example that $\bar{V}_A$ is known as a function of composition in the binary system A–B as shown in Fig. 8.2. The problem now is to obtain $\bar{V}_B$ as a function of composition. To do this consider equation 8.22.

$$X_A \, dV_A + X_B \, d\bar{V}_B = 0$$

Using the relation $(X_A + X_B) = 1$, and rearranging,

$$\int d\bar{V}_B = -\int \frac{(1 - X_B)}{X_B} \, d\bar{V}_A \qquad (8.29)$$

Let us find $\bar{V}_B$ at composition a shown in Fig. 8.2. To do this equation 8.29 must of course be integrated. In order to solve equation 8.29, the

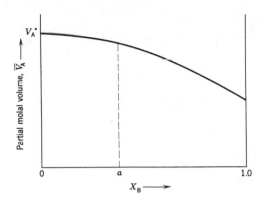

Fig. 8.2 Partial molar volume of one component of a binary system as a function of composition.

lower limit of integration should be evaluated at $X_B = 1$, since the term $(1 - X_B)/X_B$ in the integral is then equal to zero. Also on the left hand side, at the lower limit of integration,

$$\bar{V}_B = V_B{}^{\cdot}$$

Thus

$$\bar{V}_B - V_B{}^{\cdot} = -\int_{\bar{V}_A \text{ at } X_B = 1}^{\bar{V}_A \text{ at } X_B = a} \frac{(1 - X_B)}{X_B} \, d\bar{V}_A \qquad (8.30)$$

$\bar{V}_A$ is generally not put in analytical form, so a graphical method of obtaining $(\bar{V}_B - V_B{}^{\cdot})$ is used. From equation 8.30 we see that if Fig. 8.2 is replotted by plotting the quantity $(1 - X_B)/X_B$ versus $\bar{V}_A$, and integrating graphically between the value of $\bar{V}_A$, when $X_B = 1$ and $\bar{V}_A$ at $X_B = a$, the desired quantity is obtained. This is shown in Fig. 8.3. The quantity $(\bar{V}_B - V_B{}^{\cdot})$ is represented by the shaded area in Fig. 8.3.

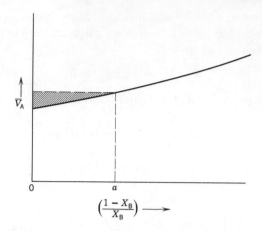

Fig. 8.3 Graphical method of obtaining one partial molar quantity from another.

The quantity V also may be obtained, since now both $\bar{V}_A$ and $\bar{V}_B$ are known from

$$V = X_A \bar{V}_A + X_B \bar{V}_B$$

8.4 SOME RELATIONS BETWEEN PARTIAL MOLAL QUANTITIES

Consider for example the equation

$$G' = H' - TS'$$

where G', H', and S' refer to the appropriate thermodynamic values for an arbitrary amount of solution. Keeping temperature and pressure constant, and differentiating, we obtain

$$dG' = dH' - T\,dS'$$

Dividing both sides by dn_i, keeping the other components the same and the temperature and pressure constant, we find

$$\left(\frac{\partial G'}{\partial n_i}\right) = \left(\frac{\partial H'}{\partial n_i}\right) - T\left(\frac{\partial S'}{\partial n_i}\right)$$

or

$$\bar{G}_i = \bar{H}_i - T\bar{S}_i$$

From this example it can be seen that the relation between partial molal thermodynamic quantities is exactly the same as the relations for pure components already derived. Thus

$$\left(\frac{\partial \bar{G}_i}{\partial T}\right)_{P,n_1,n_2,\ldots} = -\bar{S}_i$$

$$\left[\frac{\partial(\bar{G}_i/T)}{\partial(1/T)}\right]_{P,n_1,n_2,\ldots} = \bar{H}_i$$

$$\left(\frac{\partial \bar{G}_i}{\partial P}\right)_{T,n_1,n_2,\ldots} = \bar{V}_i$$

In future use the subscripts will be deleted in connection with partial derivatives. Their presence will be understood. Subtracting the appropriate equations for the relations for pure substances gives

$$\frac{\partial(\bar{G}_i - G_i^{\cdot})}{\partial T} = -(\bar{S}_i - S_i^{\cdot}) \tag{8.31}$$

$$\frac{\partial[(\bar{G}_i - G_i^{\cdot})/T]}{\partial(1/T)} = \bar{H}_i - H_i^{\cdot} \tag{8.32}$$

$$\frac{\partial(\bar{G}_i - G_i^{\cdot})}{\partial P} = \bar{V}_i - V_i^{\cdot} \tag{8.33}$$

The quantities on the right hand side of equations 8.31 and 8.33 are known as *relative partial molal* quantities. In the last chapter we derived

$$dG = RT\,d\ln a$$

where G and a represent the free energy and activity for a particular substance. For component i in solution

$$d\bar{G}_i = RT\,d\ln a_i$$

and since $a_i = 1$ for the pure component of free energy $G_i^{\cdot}$, we find upon integration that

$$\bar{G}_i - G_i^{\cdot} = RT\ln a_i \tag{8.34}$$

8.5 FREE ENERGY OF FORMATION OF A SOLUTION

Consider the formation of a gram-atom of solution from the pure components in their standard states:

$$X_A A\,(s) + X_B B\,(s) = (X_A, X_B) \qquad \Delta G_m$$

The free energy change associated with this is called the free energy of formation or more commonly the *free energy of mixing*. From the reaction we see that

$$\Delta G_m = G - X_A G_A^{\cdot} - X_B G_B^{\cdot} \tag{8.35}$$

Substitution of equation 8.15 into 8.35 yields

$$\Delta G_m = X_A(\bar{G}_A - G_A^{\cdot}) + X_B(\bar{G}_B - G_B^{\cdot}) \tag{8.36}$$

Substitution of equation 8.34 into 8.36 yields

$$\Delta G_m = RT(X_A \ln a_A + X_B \ln a_B) \tag{8.37}$$

Similarly we find for the heat of mixing and entropy of mixing

$$\Delta H_m = \sum_{n=1}^{n} X_i(\bar{H}_i - H_i^{\cdot}) \tag{8.38}$$

$$\Delta S_m = \sum_{n=1}^{n} X_i(\bar{S}_i - S_i^{\cdot}) \tag{8.39}$$

The equations derived thus far have been completely general. It is convenient at this point to consider some applications to specific types of solutions.

8.6 IDEAL SOLUTIONS

Most real solutions do not fall into this category, but it is a convenient base from which to start, since real solutions may be conveniently compared with ideal solutions. To illustrate an ideal solution, consider the vapor pressure of component i in a binary solution. When X_i is equal to 1, p_i obviously is equal to $p_i^{\cdot}$, the value for pure component i. When X_i is equal to 0, p_i is also equal to 0, since now no component i is present.

The question now arises as to how p_i varies with X_i between these two limits. An ideal solution is defined as a solution in which the vapor pressure of a component i is a linear function of composition:

$$p_i = X_i p_i^{\cdot} \tag{8.40}$$

This is known as Raoult's law and is illustrated in Fig. 8.4. Since $a_i = p_i/p_i^{\cdot}$ by definition, we find for an ideal solution that

$$a_i = X_i \tag{8.41}$$

Substituting equation 8.41 into equation 8.34, we find that

$$\bar{G}_i - G_i^{\cdot} = RT \ln X_i \tag{8.42}$$

Substituting 8.42 into 8.32 we find

$$R\left(\frac{\partial \ln X_i}{\partial(1/T)}\right) = \bar{H}_i - H_i^{\cdot} \tag{8.43}$$

Since $X_i \neq f(T)$ but is any value we choose, $(\bar{H}_i - H_i^{\cdot}) = 0$, and thus from 8.38 we see that for an ideal solution, the heat of mixing,

$$\Delta H_m = 0$$

indicating that no heat is absorbed or released upon formation of the solution.

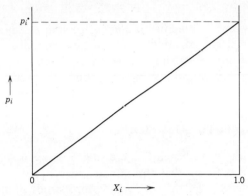

Fig. 8.4 Vapor pressure of a component in an ideal solution as a function of composition.

From equations 8.41 and 8.37 we see that for a binary solution

$$\Delta G_m = RT(X_A \ln X_A + X_B \ln X_B)$$

and, since at constant temperature,

$$\Delta G_m = \Delta H_m - T \Delta S_m$$

in view of the fact that

$$\Delta H_m = 0$$

we find

$$\Delta S_m = -R(X_A \ln X_A + X_B \ln X_B) \tag{8.44}$$

Equation 8.44 is identical with the equation derived in Chapter 4 by use of statistical concepts. Similarly, it is seen that for an ideal solution

$$\Delta V_m = 0$$

since

$$RT\left(\frac{\partial \ln X_i}{\partial P}\right) = 0$$

As a result

$$V = X_A V_A^{\cdot} + X_B V_B^{\cdot}$$

or in the case of the lattice parameter a of a solid solution

$$a = X_A a_A^{\cdot} + X_B a_B^{\cdot}$$

Thus Vegard's law holds across the entire composition range for an ideal solution. In summary, for an ideal solution

$$\Delta H_m = 0$$

$$\Delta V_m = 0$$

$$\Delta S_m = -R(X_A \ln X_A + X_B \ln X_B)$$

Thus the enthalpy and volume of an ideal solution are the same as those quantities for a mechanical mixture of various amounts of pure components. The entropy of mixing, however, is different. The equation shows that ΔS_m is positive and is symmetric about $X_A = X_B = 0.5$, where it is equal to 1.37 e.u.

8.7 NONIDEAL DILUTE SOLUTIONS

For a dilute solution, in general, the distance between solute atoms is large, and hence it is found that the interaction between solute atoms is small. In other words, the thermodynamic properties of the solute are additive. Thus we would expect that the solute vapor pressure of a solution containing two hundred solute atoms would be twice that containing one hundred solute atoms in the same volume of solution. Thus

$$p_i = bX_i$$

where b is a constant, the value of which depends on the nature of the solute and solvent. This is known as *Henry's law*. Note that the value of b is undefined. In fact it may have any value. From the definition of activity we find that for the solute

$$a_B = \left(\frac{b}{p_B^{\,\circ}}\right)X_B \quad \text{or} \quad a_B = \gamma_B^{\,\circ}X_B \tag{8.45}$$

The general term γ is called an *activity coefficient*. For an ideal solution we see that $\gamma_B = 1$. The quantity $\gamma_B^{\,\circ}$ may be less than one or greater than one for solute in a nonideal solution, but for a given solute it is independent of concentration when the solute concentration is small.

It is of interest at this point to consider the activity of solvent atoms in a solution where the activity of the solute follows Henry's law.

Let us consider equation 8.23.

$$X_A \, d\bar{G}_A + X_B \, d\bar{G}_B = 0$$

From equation 8.34 we see that

$$d\bar{G}_i = RT \, d \ln a_i$$

Substitution of equation 8.34 into 8.23 yields

$$X_A \, d \ln a_A + X_B \, d \ln a_B = 0 \tag{8.46}$$

Since $a_B = \gamma_B^\circ X_B$ where γ_B° is a constant,

$$d \ln a_B = d \ln X_B$$

and thus

$$d \ln a_A = - \frac{dX_B}{1 - X_B}$$

Integrating between the limits $X_B = 0$ and X_B gives

$$\int_{a=1}^{a} d \ln a_A = - \int_0^{X_B} \frac{dX_B}{(1 - X_B)}$$

and

$$\ln a_A = \ln X_A$$

$$a_A = X_B$$

As a generalization, therefore, it can be said that for a dilute solution in which the solute follows Henry's law, the solvent follows Raoult's law.

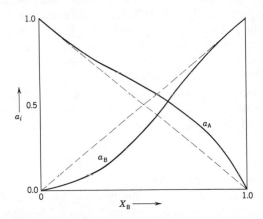

Fig. 8.5 Illustration of Henry's law and Raoult's law for a nonideal binary system. Dashed line represents ideal behavior.

At the other composition extreme when $X_A \ll 1$, component B will follow Raoult's law. For intermediate composition no simple relationship is valid and the shape of the curve depends upon the specific system. This is shown schematically in Fig. 8.5 for both components of a binary system. The composition range for which Henry's law is applicable for solute cannot be determined *a priori*. For one solution deviations may begin to be detected at 0.1 at % whereas in another solution the solute may follow

Henry's law up to 10 at % solute. As a generalization, it is perhaps safe to say that the greater the deviation of $\gamma_B{}^\circ$ from unity for a solute, the more restricted the composition range will be for which Henry's law applies. In a later chapter $\gamma_B{}^\circ$ will be interpreted in terms of more fundamental properties of the atoms in solution.

Applying equations 8.31, 8.32, and 8.33 to the solvent A in a dilute solution we find that

$$\bar{S}_A - S_A{}^\cdot = -R \ln X_A$$
$$\bar{H}_A - H_A{}^\cdot = 0$$
$$\bar{V}_A - V_A{}^\cdot = 0$$

For the solute B, $(\bar{H}_B - H_B{}^\cdot)$ and $(\bar{V}_B - V_B{}^\cdot)$ will not be equal to zero but will be constants *independent* of composition.

8.8 CONCENTRATED SOLUTIONS

Unfortunately no simple rules can be developed for the treatment of more concentrated solutions. The quantity γ_i is now a function of composition and the exact functional dependence must be determined for each system experimentally. In this range of composition (comprising about 90% of the phase diagram) considerable interaction between solute atoms occurs and the various partial molal quantitative are no longer independent of composition. The extent of interaction depends to a great extent upon the exact nature of solute and solvent.

Certain solutions (principally liquids) show a rather interesting phenomenon. The enthalpy of mixing of these solutions is different from zero but the entropy of mixing ΔS_m is the same as for an ideal solution. That is,

$$\Delta S_m = -R(X_A \ln X_A + X_B \ln X_B) \tag{8.44}$$

Such a solution is termed a *regular solution* and various simplifying relations between some of the thermodynamic quantities are obtained. Most solid solutions do not behave in this "regular" fashion but nonetheless, it becomes convenient to study how regular solutions behave as a step away from ideality. We shall consider these systems in more detail later. Briefly, however, since ΔS_m follows equation 8.44, ΔS_m will be parabolic with concentration and symmetric about $X_A = X_B = 0.5$. Similarly we shall show later that ΔH_m will also be symmetric about $X_A = X_B = 0.5$ and in fact can be expressed as

$$\Delta H_m = RTa' X_A X_B \tag{8.47}$$

where a' is a constant characteristic of the particular system at a given temperature and is proportional to T^{-1}.

More generally, however, ΔH_m and ΔS_m for most solid solutions are not given by such simple relations. For a moderately dilute solution it is convenient to write ΔH_m as a power series in X_B:

$$\Delta H_m = a'X_B + bX_B{}^2 + cX_B{}^2 + \cdots \qquad (8.48)$$

Using a relation similar to equation 8.27 we see that

$$\bar{H}_B = H + (1 - X_B)\frac{dH}{dX_B} \qquad (8.49)$$

From equation 8.16 we have

$$H = X_A\bar{H}_A + X_B\bar{H}_B$$

and also

$$\Delta H_m = H - X_A H_A{}^{\cdot} - X_B H_B{}^{\cdot}$$

Thus upon substitution in equation 8.49

$$\bar{H}_B = X_A H_A{}^{\cdot} + X_B H_B{}^{\cdot} + \Delta H_m + (1 - X_B)\frac{d(X_A H_A{}^{\cdot} + X_B H_B{}^{\cdot} + \Delta H_m)}{dX_B} \qquad (8.50)$$

Substitution of equation 8.48 into 8.50 yields

$$\bar{H}_B = X_A H_A{}^{\cdot} + X_B H_B{}^{\cdot} + a'X_B + bX_B{}^2 + cX_B{}^3 + \cdots +$$
$$(1 - X_B)(-H_A{}^{\cdot} + H_B{}^{\cdot} + a' + 2bX_B + 3cX_B{}^2 + \cdots)$$

or

$$\bar{H}_B - H_B{}^{\cdot} = a' + bX_B + (3c - b)X_B{}^2 + \cdots$$

Similarly for $\bar{H}_A$,

$$\bar{H}_A - H_A{}^{\cdot} = -bX_B{}^2 + \cdots$$

The quantity a represents the value of $(\bar{H}_B - H_B{}^{\cdot})$ in the composition range where the solute follows Henry's law, and has been interpreted to represent the interaction between solutes. A positive value of b represents a *repulsion* between like solute atoms, whereas a negative value of b represents an *attractive* interaction between the solute atoms in solution.

Perhaps it is appropriate to discuss here some of the general methods used to obtain thermodynamic data for solid solutions. One of the most useful methods is the e.m.f. technique whereby the electromotive force between a pure element and the element in solution is measured. Since

$$\Delta G = -n\mathscr{E}\mathscr{F} = (\bar{G}_i - G_i{}^{\cdot})$$

if the emf is measured between component i in solution and in the pure state, the activity of component i may be obtained since

$$\bar{G}_i - G_i{}^{\cdot} = RT \ln a_i$$

Since the composition is known the activity coefficient may readily be obtained. By measuring the emf as a function of temperature both $(\bar{H}_i - H_i^{\cdot})$ and $(\bar{S}_i - S_i^{\cdot})$ may be obtained since

$$\frac{\partial(\bar{G}_i - G_i^{\cdot})}{\partial T} = -(\bar{S}_i - S_i^{\cdot}) = -n\mathscr{F}\left(\frac{\partial\mathscr{E}}{\partial T}\right)$$

and

$$\frac{[(G_i - G_i^{\cdot})/T]}{\partial(1/T)} = (\bar{H}_i - H_i^{\cdot}) = -n\mathscr{F}\frac{\partial(\mathscr{E}/T)}{\partial(1/T)}$$

If these quantities are determined as a function of solution composition for one component of the binary system, the appropriate quantities may be determined for the other component by use of the procedures described

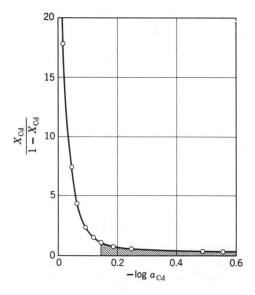

Fig. 8.6 Method of finding the activity of one component of a binary system if the other is known as a function of composition. Curve cannot be accurately integrated because $\log a_{Cd} \to -\infty$ as $X_{Cd} \to 0$. From L. S. Darken and R. W. Gurry, *Physical Chemistry of Metals*, McGraw-Hill, New York, 1953.

in Section 8.3. The emf technique is normally useful only at low temperatures, however, because of the difficulty in obtaining a suitable electrolyte at elevated temperatures.

Another technique, applicable when one of the components is rather volatile, is measurement of the equilibrium vapor pressure of this component over a solution containing this component. Since $a_i = p_i/p_i^{\cdot}$, the activity may be calculated. Since $(\bar{G}_i - G_i^{\cdot}) = RT \ln a_i$, the quantities

$(\bar{S}_i - S_i^{\cdot})$ and $(\bar{H}_i - H_i^{\cdot})$ may be obtained by measurements of a_i at various temperatures. If a_i is determined as a function of composition for a binary system, the activity of the other component may be obtained by use of the procedures described in Section 8.3. Actually some slight modification of these procedures is necessary in the case of activities. Starting with the basic equation

$$X_A \, d\bar{G}_A + X_B \, d\bar{G}_B = 0$$

or

$$X_A \, d\ln a_A + X_B \, d\ln a_B = 0 \tag{8.51}$$

If the activity of component B is known as a function of composition we may obtain a_A by integration

$$\ln a_A = \int_{a_A=1 \text{ at } X_B=0}^{a_A} d\ln a_A = -\int_{a_B=0}^{a_B} \frac{X_B}{(1-X_B)} \, d\ln a_B$$

The logical lower limit of integration to use is a_A at $X_B = 0$ and a_B at $X_B = 0$ since in this case $a_A = 1$ and $a_B = 0$. (Obviously $a_B = 0$ since $a_B = \gamma_B^{\circ} X_B$ and γ_B° is finite.) This creates a difficulty, however, since as $a_B \to 0$, $\ln a_B \to -\infty$ and thus the area under the curve of $X_B/(1-X_B)$ versus $\ln a_B$ cannot be accurately evaluated between the limits imposed, as shown in Fig. 8.6 for the Cd-Pb system. An easy path lies out of this difficulty however. By definition $a_i = \gamma_i X_i$, and substituting this relation into equation 8.51 we find

$$X_A \, d\ln \gamma_A + X_B \, d\ln \gamma_B + X_A \, d\ln X_A + X_B \, d\ln X_B = 0$$

Considering only the last two terms we see upon expansion that these equal

$$dX_A + dX_B$$

Since

$$X_A + X_B = 1$$
$$dX_A + dX_B = 0$$

and thus the equation simplifies to

$$X_A \, d\ln \gamma_A + X_B \, d\ln \gamma_B = 0$$

Since a_B is known as a function of composition, γ_B is also known as a function of composition. Thus we may determine γ_A by graphical integration

$$\ln \gamma_A = \int_{\gamma_A=1 \text{ at } X_B=0}^{\gamma_A} d\ln \gamma_A = -\int_{\gamma_B^{\circ}}^{\gamma_B} \frac{X_B}{(1-X_B)} \, d\ln \gamma_B$$

$$\tag{8.52}$$

At the lower limit of integration corresponding to $X_B = 0$, γ_B is the Henry's law activity coefficient $\gamma_B{}^\circ$ and as $X_B \to 0$, the solvent A follows Raoult's law and hence $\gamma_A = 1$. In Fig. 8.7 are shown the activity data for the Cd-Pb system plotted in this fashion.

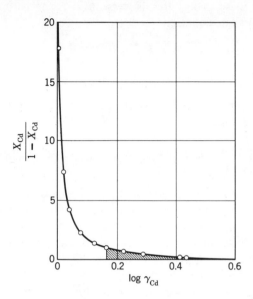

Fig. 8.7 Determination of γ_{Pb} from equation 8.52. From L. S. Darken and R. W. Gurry, *Physical Chemistry of Metals*, McGraw-Hill, New York, 1953.

A standard method for obtaining heat of mixing data is by use of a calorimetric method. A sample of solution is dropped into, say, liquid tin at a known temperature in a system of known heat capacity. If heat is evolved the temperature of the system will increase if the calorimeter is well insulated from its surroundings and vice versa for an endothermic process. Thus we have a reaction

Solid solution (X_A, X_B) = A and B in liquid Sn $\Delta H_i = C_P \, \Delta T_1$

where ΔH_i is the heat of the reaction and C_P is the heat capacity of the system. The same experiment is now performed for a mechanical mixture of A and B in the same proportion as in the solution with a resultant temperature change ΔT_2.

$$X_A A + X_B B = A \text{ and } B \text{ in liquid Sn} \qquad \Delta H_i = C_P \, \Delta T_2$$

By subtracting the former reaction, if the weights are kept in proportion, we have

$$X_A A + X_B B = \text{Solid solution } (X_A, X_B) \qquad \Delta H_m = (\Delta T_2 - \Delta T_1)C_P$$

For many solid systems, it is difficult to apply these techniques and hence complete thermodynamic data are available for only a small fraction of the possible systems. The available data are summarized by Kubaschewski and Evans.[1] One source of thermodynamic data comes from the phase diagrams of the systems themselves. In certain special cases much information may be gleaned from these diagrams. This topic forms the subject matter of Chapter 10.

8.9 EXCESS THERMODYNAMIC QUANTITIES

For many applications, it is of interest to know the deviation of thermodynamic quantities from those quantities in an ideal solution. As an example consider the partial molar free energy,

$$\Delta \bar{G}_i = \bar{G}_i - G_i^{\cdot} = RT \ln a_i = RT \ln \gamma_i + RT \ln X_i$$

For an ideal solution $\gamma_i = 1$ and thus

$$(\Delta \bar{G}_i)_{ideal} = RT \ln X_i$$

Defining the excess free energy as

$$\Delta \bar{G}_i^{xs} = \Delta \bar{G}_i - (\Delta \bar{G}_i)_{ideal}$$

we find

$$\Delta \bar{G}_i^{xs} = RT \ln \gamma_i \qquad (8.53)$$

For the case of the free energy of mixing we have

$$\Delta G_m^{xs} = \Delta G_m - (\Delta G_m)_{ideal}$$

and hence upon substitution

$$\Delta G_m^{xs} = RT[X_A \ln \gamma_A + X_B \ln \gamma_B] \qquad (8.54)$$

For the case of the enthalpy

$$(\Delta H_m)_{ideal} = 0$$

$$(\Delta \bar{H}_i)_{ideal} = 0$$

Therefore

$$\Delta H_m^{xs} = \Delta H_m \qquad (8.55)$$

and similarly

$$\Delta \bar{H}_i^{xs} = \Delta \bar{H}_i \qquad (8.56)$$

[1] Kubaschewski and Evans, *Metallurgical Thermochemistry*, Third Edition, Pergamon, London, 1958.

Similarly for the volume of mixing

$$(\Delta V_m)_{\text{ideal}} = 0$$

and

$$(\Delta \bar{V}_i)_{\text{ideal}} = 0$$

$$\Delta \bar{V}_m{}^{\text{xs}} = \Delta V_m \qquad (8.57)$$

and

$$\Delta \bar{V}_i{}^{\text{xs}} = \Delta \bar{V}_i \qquad (8.58)$$

The concept of an excess quantity is important, since, by definition, an ideal solution is one in which no net interaction between atoms occurs. The excess quantities reflect the type of interaction that occurs. From equation 8.53, for example, it can be seen that the activity coefficient of a particular component in solution is a measure of this interaction. If γ_i is 1, $\Delta \bar{G}_i{}^{\text{xs}}$ is zero. If $\gamma_i > 1$, $\Delta \bar{G}_i{}^{\text{xs}} > 0$. This is classified as positive deviation from Raoult's law. If $\gamma_i < 1$, $\Delta \bar{G}_i{}^{\text{xs}} < 0$ and is a negative deviation from Raoult's law. Generally, the former case, in which a given component has a higher activity that it would have in an ideal solution of the same composition, reflects itself in positive values of $\Delta \bar{V}_i{}^{\text{xs}}$ and $\Delta \bar{H}_i{}^{\text{xs}}$ as well. This indicates repulsive interaction between the components in solution whereas the latter situation reflects an attractive interaction.

chapter 9

The Quasichemical Approach to Solutions

9.1 INTRODUCTION

In principle, the interrelation of atoms in a condensed phase can be determined by solution of the Schrödinger equation. Unfortunately, the state of knowledge is such at present that this basic approach is not generally feasible. We therefore use more approximate methods of handling the problem of interaction of different types of atoms. We treat the atoms as having a discrete size, valence, and electronegativity. Thus, we have a *mechanical effect* or strain energy effect, a *valence effect* (or coulombic effect) and a *chemical effect* respectively. All of these will contribute to the energetics of the solution. The distinction between these effects is not clear-cut since they are all interrelated. An interesting and fruitful method of treating the energetics of crystals has evolved which is called the quasichemical approach. In this approach, atoms in a condensed phase are assumed to have a chemical bond between them. Thus, the energetics of formation of the crystal are handled by forming and breaking bonds of different energies. This theory treats only the chemical contribution to the energetics and ignores the others. This provides one serious limitation to the general applicability of the theory. Further, only nearest neighbor interactions are considered in the theory. The size effect obviously cannot be treated in this fashion since any distortion introduced in a crystal structure must extend over many interatomic distances, as is evident from Fig. 4.2. As a result the quasichemical approach cannot be expected to yield the correct answers if these other factors are important. On the other hand this approach is extremely valuable in understanding many phenomena, hence the reason for the inclusion in this text.

Consider a solution containing N_A atoms of type A and N_B atoms of type B. There will be three types of bonds to consider: (1) those between two nearest neighbor atoms of type A, (2) those between nearest neighbor atoms of type B, and (3) those between nearest neighbor atoms A and B as shown in Fig. 9.1. Each of these will have an enthalpy associated with it, H_{AA}, H_{BB}, and H_{AB} respectively. In a gram-atom of solution, there will

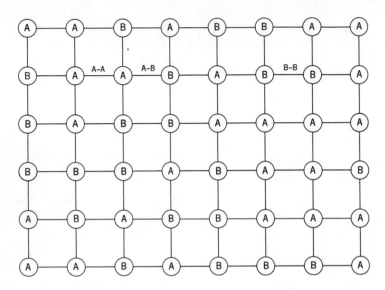

Fig. 9.1   Illustration of different types of bonds in a binary system.

be P_{AA} bonds of type A–A, P_{AB} bonds of type A–B, and P_{BB} bonds of type B–B. Thus the enthalpy of the solution will be given by

$$H = P_{AA}H_{AA} + P_{AB}H_{AB} + P_{BB}H_{BB} \qquad (9.1)$$

It is convenient to use dissociated atom pairs in the gaseous state as the standard state. Thus, as an example, the enthalpy H_{AA} would be associated with the following reaction.

Atom A(g) + Atom A(g) = A–A pair in solution H_{AA}

The next step is to evaluate P_{AA}, P_{AB}, and P_{BB}. Before attempting this, the treatment may be simplified by elimination of P_{AA} and P_{BB} as follows. The crystal contains N_A atoms of type A and each one of these has Z bonds where Z is the coordination number. Each A–B bond contains one atom of type A whereas each A–A bond contains two atoms of type A. Further, each atom is shared among Z bonds, thus the number of atoms of type A involved in A–B bonds is P_{AB}/Z and the number in type A–A bonds is $2P_{AA}/Z$. Since there are N_A atoms of type A,

$$N_A = P_{AB}/Z + 2P_{AA}/Z \qquad (9.2)$$

Similarly for atoms of type B

$$N_B = P_{AB}/Z + 2P_{BB}/Z \qquad (9.3)$$

Thus $P_{AA} + P_{BB}$ can be expressed in terms of P_{AB}, N_A, N_B, and Z, and substituting into equation 9.1

$$H = \tfrac{1}{2}ZN_A H_{AA} + \tfrac{1}{2}ZN_B H_{BB} + P_{AB}[H_{AB} - \tfrac{1}{2}(H_{AA} + H_{BB})] \quad (9.4)$$

Since absolute thermodynamic quantities are not measured, we are interested in knowing the enthalpy of a process, for example that of mixing, ΔH_m. This is given by the reaction

N_A atoms of type A(s) + N_B atoms of type B(s)

$$= (N_A + N_B) \text{ atoms in solution } \Delta H_m$$

and

$$\Delta H_m = H - H_A(N_A \text{ atoms of type A, pure}) - H(N_B \text{ atoms of type B, pure})$$

$$\Delta H_m = H - \text{enthalpy of pure A} - \text{enthalpy of pure B} \qquad (9.5)$$

Equation 9.4 gives the enthalpy for the solution. Consider that Z is the same for the two pure components. There are N_A atoms of component A in the pure state with Z neighbors. Each bond is counted twice in the summation process, however, and thus the total number of A–A bonds is $\tfrac{1}{2}ZN_A$. Similarly in the case of pure crystal B, the number of B–B bonds is $\tfrac{1}{2}ZN_B$. The enthalpies will be given by $\tfrac{1}{2}ZN_A H_{AA}$ and $\tfrac{1}{2}ZN_B H_{BB}$ respectively. If it is assumed as a first order approximation that H_{AA} and H_{BB} are parameters independent of atomic environment, these terms can be inserted into equation 9.5, yielding

$$\Delta H_m = P_{AB}[H_{AB} - \tfrac{1}{2}(H_{AA} + H_{BB})] \qquad (9.6)$$

Bonding enthalpies may be obtained for elements in the pure solid state by considering sublimation, for example,

$$N_A \text{ atoms in crystal} = N_A(g) \qquad \Delta H_s$$

The number of bonds in the crystal is $\tfrac{1}{2}ZN_A$ and the number in a mon-atomic gas is zero. If one mole of A atoms is considered,

$$-\Delta H_s = \tfrac{1}{2}ZN_0 H_{AA} \qquad (9.7)$$

In Table 9.1 are listed bond energies calculated by Pauling for a variety of pairs. Most of these were obtained from data in the gaseous state.

TABLE 9.1
Bond Energies (kcal/mole of bonds)[a]

Bond	Energy	Bond	Energy	Bond	Energy
C–C	−83.1	Bi–Bi	−25	C–Si	−69.3
Si–Si	−42.2	Se–Se	−44.0	Si–O	−88.2
Ge–Ge	−37.6	Te–Te	−33	Si–S	−54.2
O–O	−33.2	Br–Br	−46.1	Si–F	−129.3
Sn–Sn	−34.2	I–I	−36.1	Si–Cl	−85.7
P–P	−51.3	Si–H	−70.4	Si–Br	−69.1
As–As	−32.1	P–H	−76.4	Si–I	−50.9
Sb–Sb	−30.2	As–H	−58.6		

[a] From L. Pauling, *Nature of the Chemical Bond*, Third Edition, Cornell, Ithaca, 1960.

9.2 APPLICATION TO IDEAL AND REGULAR SOLUTIONS

For an ideal solution $\Delta H_m = 0$; therefore from equation 9.6

$$H_{AB} = \tfrac{1}{2}(H_{AA} + H_{BB})$$

Thus we see that a solution will behave ideally if the bond energy between unlike pairs is the arithmetic average of the bond energies between like pairs.

In the case of a regular solution it will be recalled that $\Delta H_m \neq 0$ but $\Delta S_m{}^{xs} = 0$. This latter restriction implies that the vibration entropy of elements remains unchanged upon transferring from the pure state to the solution and further that the mixing is completely random. As a result, P_{AB} can be readily evaluated from simple statistical considerations. Let us consider a gram-atom of solution. Thus $(N_A + N_B) = N_0$ and $X_A = N_A/N_0$ and $X_B = N_B/N_0$. The probability that an atom of type A will be on a given site is X_A. The probability that an atom of type B will be on a particular nearest neighbor site is X_B and the probability that both will be on their respective sites simultaneously is $X_A X_B$. Similarly, the probability that an atom of type B will be on the former site is X_B and the probability that an atom of type A will be on the latter site is X_A. The probability that they will be on their respective sites simultaneously is again $X_B X_A$. As a result the probability that two sites will be occupied by unlike atoms will be the sum, or $2X_A X_B$. The total number of bonds in the crystal is $\tfrac{1}{2}ZN_0$, therefore the number of A–B bonds will be equal to the total number of bonds multiplied by the probability that a bond will be of the A–B type. Thus

$$P_{AB} = 2X_A X_B \cdot \tfrac{1}{2}ZN_0 = X_A X_B Z N_0 \tag{9.8}$$

Substitution of equation 9.8 into equation 9.6 yields

$$\Delta H_m = X_A X_B Z N_0 [H_{AB} - \tfrac{1}{2}(H_{AA} + H_{BB})] \tag{9.9}$$

Defining Ω as

$$\Omega = Z N_0 [H_{AB} - \tfrac{1}{2}(H_{AA} + H_{BB})] \tag{9.10}$$

we find that the heat of mixing is

$$\Delta H_m = X_A X_B \Omega \tag{9.11}$$

Since Ω is independent of composition according to the zeroth order approximation, ΔH_m is shown to be a parabolic function of composition in agreement with the statement made in Section 8.8.

If there is an attractive interaction between unlike atoms (large electronegativity difference for example), the A–B bond will be more stable than an A–A bond or B–B bond and hence Ω will be negative in sign, yielding a negative value of the heat of mixing. Conversely if there is a repulsive interaction between unlike atoms Ω will be positive and ΔH_m will also be positive.

If a strong attractive interaction between unlike atoms exists, ΔH_m can be made more negative by having short range order in the solution, which means *increasing* P_{AB} over the random value. This will tend to make the free energy of the solution more negative through reduction of the ΔH_m term. On the other hand, however, the mixing entropy will decrease, since $\mathscr{W}$, the number of ways of arranging atoms on the lattice, is less and thus increases the free energy. (This will be discussed more fully in a later section.) An optimum value of *short range order* will be attained, reflecting a balance between ΔH_m and the $T \Delta S_m$ contribution. In the case of a repulsive interaction, ΔH_m could be reduced by promoting clustering of like atoms or *decreasing* P_{AB} compared with the random value. This, also, will result in a decrease in $\mathscr{W}$, the number of ways of arranging atoms on the lattice, and hence a decrease in ΔS_m. Again an optimum degree of *clustering* will result, reflecting a balance between ΔH_m and ΔS_m in order to minimize ΔG_m. These examples reflect a fundamental conflict in thermodynamics. The system can achieve a maximum ΔS_m and hence a maximum $T \Delta S_m$ contribution to ΔG_m by the destruction of order but at the expense of the ΔH_m term, which would be minimum for an ordered system. Because in the expression

$$\Delta G_m = \Delta H_m - T \Delta S_m$$

the ΔS_m term is multiplied by T, the $T \Delta S_m$ term will be more important at elevated temperatures. As a result the degree of ordering or clustering in a system will decrease as the temperature is elevated.

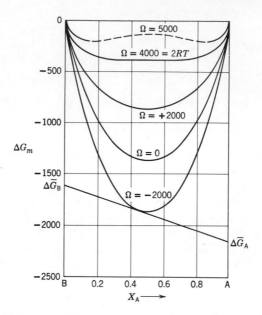

Fig. 9.2 Heat of mixing as a function of composition for a regular solution for various values of the interaction parameter, Ω. From O. J. Kleppa in *Liquid Metals and Solidification*, ASM, Cleveland, 1958.

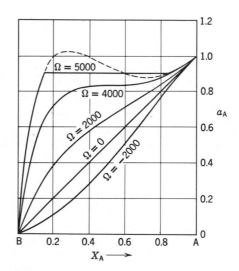

Fig. 9.3 Activity of component A in a regular solution as a function of the interaction parameter, Ω. From O. J. Kleppa in *Liquid Metals and Solidification*, ASM, Cleveland, 1958.

From this discussion it is evident that a regular solution for which $\Delta S_m{}^{xs} = 0$, will only be found at elevated temperatures in systems where Ω is a small quantity.

We may find $\Delta \bar{H}_A$ and $\Delta \bar{H}_B$, the relative partial molal enthalpies for a regular solution, from equation 9.11 by use of equation 8.28 (with enthalpy in place of volume). These are

$$\bar{H}_A - H_A{}^{\bullet} = \Delta \bar{H}_A = (1 - X_A)^2 \Omega \qquad (9.12)$$
$$\bar{H}_B - H_B{}^{\bullet} = \Delta \bar{H}_B = (1 - X_B)^2 \Omega \qquad (9.13)$$

Also, since $\Delta S^{xs} = 0$, using the same approach,

$$\bar{S}_A - S_A{}^{\bullet} = \Delta \bar{S}_A = -R \ln X_A$$
$$\bar{S}_B - S_B{}^{\bullet} = \Delta \bar{S}_B = -R \ln X_B$$

Since

$$\Delta \bar{G}_i = \Delta \bar{H}_i - T \Delta \bar{S}_i$$

we find that

$$\Delta \bar{G}_A = (1 - X_A)^2 \Omega + RT \ln X_A$$
$$\Delta \bar{G}_B = (1 - X_B)^2 \Omega + RT \ln X_B$$

and using the fact that

$$\Delta \bar{G}_i = RT \ln a_i = RT \ln \gamma_i + RT \ln X_i$$

we see that

$$\ln \gamma_A = (1 - X_A)^2 \Omega / RT \qquad (9.14)$$
$$\ln \gamma_B = (1 - X_B)^2 \Omega / RT \qquad (9.15)$$

Thus, for a regular solution, the activity coefficient is strongly related to the interaction parameter, Ω. As will be shown later, γ_i for a nonregular solution is also a function of $\Delta \bar{S}_i{}^{xs}$.

When the interaction between unlike atoms is attractive, Ω is negative and, hence $\ln \gamma_i$ is negative and $\gamma_i < 1$, giving negative deviation from Raoult's law. Conversely, when Ω is positive, $\gamma_i > 1$, giving positive deviation from Raoult's law. In Fig. 9.2 are shown values of ΔG_m at $1000°K$, as a function of composition for various values of Ω. It is observed that the function is symmetric, about $X_A = X_B = 0.5$. In Fig. 9.3 are shown values of a_A as a function of composition, and Ω at $1000°K$ as calculated from Fig. 9.2. From the equations derived, it may be seen that Henry's law is strictly an approximation. According to Henry's law, $\ln \gamma_i{}^{\circ}$ = constant when component i is dilute whereas from equation 9.14 we see that $\ln \gamma_i$ approaches a constant value, Ω / RT, asymptotically as $X_i \to 0$. Furthermore the validity of Raoult's law being applicable for the solvent in a solution where Henry's law is obeyed for the solute is also an approximation, since $\ln \gamma_i$ approaches zero asymptotically as X_i approaches unity, from equation 9.14.

9.3 NONREGULAR SOLUTIONS

Most solutions of interest fall into this class and the quasichemical approach is successful only in a qualitative sense. In some ordered phases, for example, structure will be such as to minimize or maximize P_{AB} according to whether repulsive or attractive interactions occur, as predicted by quasichemical theory. For many other phases, however, atom size also plays an important role in dictating the type of packing, since strain consideration may make an important contribution to ΔH_m. For this reason the quasichemical theory works most satisfactorily for liquid solutions, where strain energy considerations are not important.

For the case of nonregular solutions, Guggenheim and others have derived

$$P_{AB} = X_A X_B Z N_0 \{1 - X_A X_B [\exp(-2\Omega/ZRT) - 1]\} \qquad (9.16)$$

Expanding the exponential, in equation 9.16, and eliminating terms of higher order than the second, it is found that

$$\Delta H_m \cong X_A X_B \Omega (1 + X_A X_B 2\Omega/ZRT) \qquad (9.17)$$

$$\Delta S_m{}^{xs} \cong +X_A{}^2 X_B{}^2 \Omega^2/ZRT^2 \qquad (9.18)$$

$$\Delta G_m{}^{xs} \cong X_A X_B \Omega (1 + X_A X_B \Omega/ZRT) \qquad (9.19)$$

9.4 QUASICHEMICAL TREATMENT OF ORDER-DISORDER REACTIONS

Consider an alloy of composition 50 at % A and 50 at % B, which tends to form an ordered phase. That is, the A atoms tend to order themselves on one type of site, α, and B atoms tend to order themselves on another type of site, β, as shown in Fig. 9.4 for a body-centered cubic structure. Let us denote r_α as the fraction of α sites occupied by the right atoms (A atoms) and r_β equal the fraction of β sites occupied by the right atoms (B atoms) in an ordered system. The fraction of α sites occupied by wrong atoms (B atoms), w_α, will be given by

$$w_\alpha = 1 - r_\alpha$$

and the fraction of β sites occupied by wrong atoms (A atoms), w_β is given by

$$w_\beta = 1 - r_\beta$$

For complete order, $r_\alpha = r_\beta = 1$, and for complete randomness, the probability that an A site is occupied by an A atom is X_A, hence the fraction of α sites occupied by A atoms for complete disorder is X_A.

It is convenient to define a long range order parameter $\mathscr{S}$ in terms of disorder on the α sites as

$$\mathscr{S} \equiv \frac{r_\alpha - X_A}{1 - X_A} \tag{9.20}$$

or, considering disorder on the β sites,

$$\mathscr{S} = \frac{r_\beta - X_B}{1 - X_B} \tag{9.21}$$

From equations 9.20 and 9.21 we see that, for complete disorder, $\mathscr{S} = 0$ and, for complete order, $\mathscr{S} = 1$. For a state of order given by $0 \leq \mathscr{S} \leq 1$,

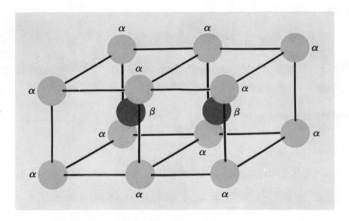

Fig. 9.4 Long range order on a B.C.C. lattice.

the fraction of A atoms on α sites is r_α. Considering N total sites, there are $(N/2)$ α sites and $(N/2)$ β sites. Thus, the total number of A atoms on α sites is $r_\alpha(N/2)$. Substituting in equation 9.20 for $X_A = X_B = \frac{1}{2}$ yields

$$\text{No. of A atoms on } \alpha \text{ sites} = \left(\frac{1 + \mathscr{S}}{4}\right) N$$

$$\text{No. of B atoms on } \beta \text{ sites} = \left(\frac{1 + \mathscr{S}}{4}\right) N$$

The fraction of B atoms on α sites is $(1 - r_\alpha)$ and the number of B atoms on α sites is $(1 - r_\alpha)N/2$. Upon substitution in equation 9.20, we find

$$\text{No. of A atoms on } \beta \text{ sites} = \left(\frac{1 - \mathscr{S}}{4}\right) N$$

$$\text{No. of B atoms on } \alpha \text{ sites} = \left(\frac{1 - \mathscr{S}}{4}\right) N$$

In the body-centered cubic crystal, β sites will be nearest neighbors to α sites. Let us now evaluate the number of A–A pairs, B–B pairs, and A–B pairs for an ordered structure with long range order parameter $\mathscr{S}$.

The probability that an A atom will be on an α site is r_α, and the probability that an A atom will be on a β site is $w_\beta = (1 - r_\beta)$. Each α site is surrounded by Z β sites, but each pair is counted twice, so the probability of an A–A pair is

$$Zr_\alpha(1 - r_\beta) = \frac{Z(1 + \mathscr{S})(1 - \mathscr{S})}{4} = \frac{Z(1 - \mathscr{S}^2)}{4}$$

The total number of pairs P_{AA} is the probability of an A–A pair times the number of A atoms or

$$P_{AA} = \frac{Z(1 - \mathscr{S}^2)}{4} \cdot \frac{N}{2} = (1 - \mathscr{S}^2)N \qquad (9.22)$$

since $Z = 8$. Similarly the total number of B–B pairs is found to be

$$P_{BB} = (1 - \mathscr{S}^2)N \qquad (9.23)$$

For a solution containing 50 at % A and 50 at % B, the number of AB pairs is

$$P_{AB} = 2(1 + \mathscr{S}^2)N \qquad (9.24)$$

From equation 9.1, the enthalpy for a gram-atom of solution is found to be

$$H = N_0(1 - \mathscr{S}^2)(H_{AA} + H_{BB}) + 2N_0(1 + \mathscr{S}^2)H_{AB} \qquad (9.25)$$

where H_{AA}, H_{BB}, and H_{AB} represent the enthalpies of an A–A bond, a B–B bond, and an A–B bond in the alloy, respectively. The configuration entropy is given by

$$S_{conf} = k \ln \mathscr{W}$$

where

$$\mathscr{W} = \frac{(N/2)!}{(\text{No. A atoms on } \alpha \text{ sites})! \, (\text{No. B atoms on } \alpha \text{ sites})!}$$
$$\times \frac{(N/2)!}{(\text{No. A atoms on } \beta \text{ sites})! \times (\text{No. B atoms on } \beta \text{ sites})!}$$

or

$$\mathscr{W} = \frac{(N/2)!}{\{[(1 + \mathscr{S})/4]N\}! \, \{[(1 - \mathscr{S})/4]N\}!}$$
$$\cdot \frac{(N/2)!}{\{[(1 - \mathscr{S})/4]N\}! \, \{[(1 + \mathscr{S})/4]N\}!}$$

Upon application of Stirling's approximation

$$S_{conf} = R\{\ln 2 - \tfrac{1}{2}[(1 + \mathscr{S}) \ln (1 + \mathscr{S}) + (1 - \mathscr{S}) \ln (1 - \mathscr{S})]\} \qquad (9.26)$$

In the limit of $\mathscr{S} = 0$, $S_{conf} = R \ln 2$, which is the entropy for a random solution given by an equation derived previously.

$$S_{conf} = -R[X_A \ln X_A + X_B \ln X_B] = R \ln 2 \qquad \text{for } X_A = X_B = \tfrac{1}{2}$$

In the limit of $\mathscr{S} = 1$, $S_{conf} = 0$ in agreement with what is expected for complete order.

The free energy of solution is

$$G = H - TS$$

and upon substitution

$$G = N_0(1 - \mathscr{S}^2)(H_{AA} + H_{BB}) + 2N_0(1 + \mathscr{S}^2)H_{AB}$$
$$+ RT\{\ln 2 - \tfrac{1}{2}[(1 + \mathscr{S}) \ln (1 + \mathscr{S}) + (1 - \mathscr{S}) \ln (1 - \mathscr{S})]\} + N_0 S_v^\circ$$
$$(9.27)$$

where S_v° represents the vibrational entropy per atom. The entropy, of course, is a maximum when $\mathscr{S} = 0$, or when there is complete randomness. If $\tfrac{1}{2}(H_{AA} + H_{BB}) > H_{AB}$, the enthalpy term will be reduced and an optimum value of $\mathscr{S}$ will be attained in order to make G a minimum.

As T increases, S_{conf} becomes more important relative to the enthalpy term, and hence $\mathscr{S}$ diminishes. At a critical temperature, T_c, $\mathscr{S}$ in fact becomes zero. In Fig. 9.5, G is shown schematically as a function of $\mathscr{S}$ at several representative temperatures. At low temperatures it is seen that a minimum in G will occur when the long range order parameter is close to one. As the temperature is increased the minimum in G will occur at lower values of $\mathscr{S}$ and finally, at T_c, a critical temperature, the minimum will appear when $\mathscr{S} = 0$. From Fig. 9.5, the equilibrium value of $\mathscr{S}$ may be calculated as a function of temperature. This is shown in Fig. 9.6.

The critical temperature T_c is governed by the relation between H_{AB} and $\tfrac{1}{2}(H_{AA} + H_{BB})$. The more stable the A–B bond is in relation to the average of the A–A and B–B bond energies, the higher T_c will be.

This problem may be treated analytically by consideration of equation 9.27. At any temperature $\mathscr{S}$ may be found by minimizing G with respect to $\mathscr{S}$. At the equilibrium value of $\mathscr{S}$, $\partial G/\partial \mathscr{S} = 0$, and

$$\frac{\partial G}{\partial \mathscr{S}} = \mathscr{S}[2H_{AB} - (H_{AA} + H_{BB})] + \frac{kT}{4} \ln \frac{(1 + \mathscr{S})}{(1 - \mathscr{S})} = 0 \quad (9.28)$$

The temperature T_c is defined as the lowest temperature for which $\mathscr{S}$ equals zero. To find T_c, equation 9.28 may not be solved directly, since the first term on the right hand side is multiplied by $\mathscr{S}$. To eliminate this problem, let us expand $\ln [(1 + \mathscr{S})/(1 - \mathscr{S})]$ in an infinite series and evaluate as $\mathscr{S} \to 0$. Doing this we find

$$\lim_{\mathscr{S} \to 0} \ln \frac{(1 + \mathscr{S})}{(1 - \mathscr{S})} = 2\mathscr{S} \qquad (9.29)$$

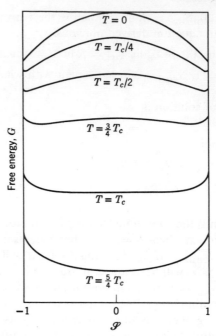

Fig. 9.5 Free energy of a solution versus long range order parameter $\mathscr{S}$. From J. C. Slater, *Introduction to Chemical Physics*, McGraw-Hill, New York, 1939.

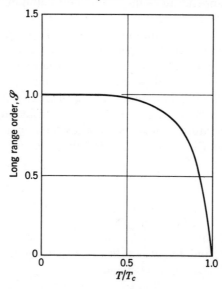

Fig. 9.6 Long range order parameter versus temperature for an AB solution. From C. Kittel, *Introduction to Solid State Physics*, Second Edition, Wiley, New York, 1956.

Substituting into equation 9.28, we obtain

$$T_c = -\frac{2[H_{AB} - (H_{AA} + H_{BB})]}{k} \qquad (9.30)$$

Thus, at any temperature different from T_c,

$$\ln\frac{(1 + \mathscr{S})}{(1 - \mathscr{S})} = \frac{2\mathscr{S}T_c}{T} \qquad (9.31)$$

At low temperature $\mathscr{S}$ is very close to 1, and as T increases toward T_c, $\mathscr{S}$ decreases very rapidly. This behavior is typical of a cooperative phenomenon. When order is perfect, it is difficult energetically to create disorder (to exchange A and B atoms). As disorder proceeds, however, the process becomes progressively easier from an energetic point of view and finally, in the case of complete disorder, the energy becomes zero for the exchange process. The disordering energy thus depends upon $\mathscr{S}$.

The theory of order-disorder as presented thus far has rested upon the assumption of quasichemical theory. From this theory we have found that long range order may occur only when $[H_{AB} - \frac{1}{2}(H_{AA} + H_{BB})] < 0$, as shown in equation 9.30. There is evidence, however, that order occurs where this criterion is not fulfilled, but where there is a considerable size difference between A and B atoms instead. Quasichemical theory of course considers only the chemical interaction of A and B atoms, and does not consider the strain energy of solution. When A and B atoms have considerably different sizes, the strain energy contribution to solution formation is large, and can be reduced if the atoms arrange themselves in an ordered fashion on the lattice.

Calculations similar to these may be done for components where $X_A \neq X_B \neq \frac{1}{2}$. In this case the critical temperature will be found to be lower for a given value of $[H_{AB} - \frac{1}{2}(H_{AA} + H_{BB})]$ than for the case where $X_A = 0.5$, and will appear as shown on Fig. 9.7 as a function of composition.

A similar analysis may be performed for other order-disorder systems, for example those containing 75 at % A and 25 at % B or 25 at % A and 75 at % B. An example of a structure in which order may occur is the face-centered cubic structure, where the face-centered sites are the α sites and the corner sites are the β sites (for the 75 at % A and 25 at % B alloy). Equilibrium values of $\mathscr{S}$ for this may be obtained as a function of temperature. The results for this system are considerably different from the results of Fig. 9.6, and are shown in Fig. 9.8. In this case, the long range order parameter is not zero at the critical temperature, but rather it drops discontinuously from a high value of $\mathscr{S}$ to a low value. Above T_c,

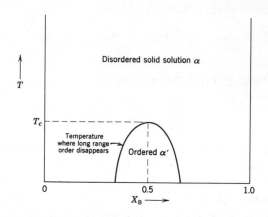

Fig. 9.7 Critical temperature for ordering as a function of composition.

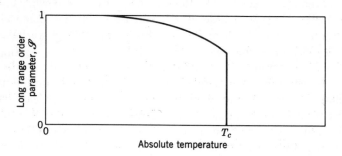

Fig. 9.8 Long range order parameter $\mathscr{S}$ for an A_3B alloy. From F. C. Nix and W. Shockley, *Revs. Mod. Phys.*, **10**, 1 (1938).

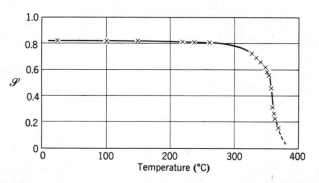

Fig. 9.9 Long range order parameter as a function of temperature for an alloy containing 80 at % Cu and 20 at % Au. From F. E. Jaumot and C. H. Sutcliffe, *Acta Met.*, **2**, 63 (1954).

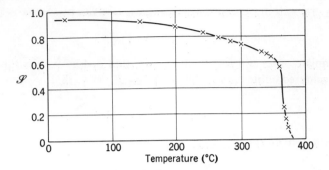

Fig. 9.10 Long range order parameter as a function of temperature for an alloy containing 70 at % Cu and 30 at % Au. From F. E. Jaumot and C. H. Sutcliffe, *Acta Met.*, **2**, 63 (1954).

$\mathscr{S}$ is zero. The long range order parameter has been obtained experimentally for alloys of Cu_3 Au over a range of temperature and composition.[1] In Figs. 9.9 and 9.10 are shown the experimental values of long range order parameter as a function of temperature for alloys containing 20 at % Au and 30 at % Au respectively. From observation of these figures, it is seen that the observed variation of long range order parameter with temperature is in basic agreement with the theoretical curves, Fig. 9.8.

9.5 QUASICHEMICAL TREATMENT OF SHORT RANGE ORDER

Short range order is probably common to most alloy systems, and is characterized in a quasichemical sense by a greater than random number of A–B pairs, P_{AB}, without the necessity of distinguishing between α and β sites as in the case of long range order. A quantitative theory of short range order, first obtained by Bethe,[2] was subsequently refined by other investigators. To treat the problem quantitatively, let us define a short range order parameter σ:

$$\sigma \equiv \frac{P_{AB} - (P_{AB})_{\text{random}}}{(P_{AB})_{\text{max}} - (P_{AB})_{\text{random}}} \tag{9.32}$$

In this equation P_{AB} represents the number of A–B pairs in the actual alloy; $(P_{AB})_{\text{random}}$ represents the number of A–B pairs which would exist in an alloy of the same composition if the solution were random; and $(P_{AB})_{\text{max}}$ represents the maximum number of A–B pairs which could exist if complete order occurred.

[1] F. E. Jaumot and C. H. Sutcliffe, *Acta Met.*, **2**, 63 (1954).
[2] H. Bethe, *Proc. Royal Soc.* (*London*), **A150**, 552 (1935).

For a gram-atom of solution, $(P_{AB})_{\text{random}}$ is given by

$$(P_{AB})_{\text{random}} = X_A X_B Z N_0 \tag{9.8}$$

For complete order, we see, from examination of Fig. 9.4 for the case of a body-centered cubic crystal, where $X_A = X_B = \frac{1}{2}$, that

$$(P_{AB})_{\text{max}} = \frac{Z N_0}{2} = 4 N_0$$

From equation 9.8 for this alloy

$$(P_{AB})_{\text{random}} = 2 N_0$$

Thus, upon substitution into equation 9.32, we find

$$\sigma = \frac{P_{AB}/N_0 - 2}{2} \tag{9.33}$$

and hence the number of A–B pairs is

$$P_{AB} = 2 N_0 (\sigma + 1) \tag{9.34}$$

Out of a total number of bonds $\frac{1}{2} Z N_0$, the fraction of bonds of the A–B A–B type is

$$f_{AB} = \frac{P_{AB}}{\frac{1}{2} Z N_0} = \frac{1}{2}(\sigma + 1) \tag{9.35}$$

Consequently the fraction of bonds which are like bonds is

$$(1 - f_{AB}) = \frac{1}{2}(1 - \sigma) \tag{9.36}$$

The enthalpy of an A–B bond is H_{AB}, the enthalpy of a B–B bond is H_{BB}, and the enthalpy of an A–A bond is H_{AA}. For a system with equal numbers of A and B atoms, $P_{AA} = P_{BB}$, and the average energy of like bonds is $\frac{1}{2}(H_{AA} + H_{BB})$. If $H_{AB} < \frac{1}{2}(H_{AA} + H_{BB})$, short range order will occur. To solve this problem quantitatively consider Fig. 9.11. The relative

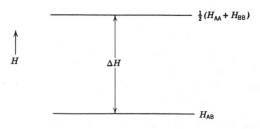

Fig. 9.11   Energy relation between unlike and like pairs.

probability of occupancy of the high energy state to that of the low energy state is given by Boltzmann statistics as derived in Section 4.3.

$$\frac{p_{\text{high energy state}}}{p_{\text{low energy state}}} = \exp\left(-\frac{\Delta H}{kT}\right)$$

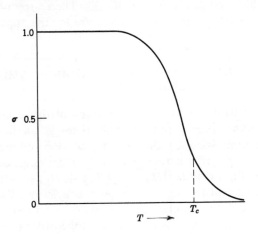

Fig. 9.12 Short range order parameter for an AB alloy as a function of temperature.

The probability of occupancy of the high energy state is the probability of a like bond which is the same as the fraction of total bonds which are like bonds.

$$p_{\text{high energy state}} = \frac{(P_{AA} + P_{BB})}{\frac{1}{2}ZN_0}$$

Similarly the probability of the low energy state or an unlike bond is

$$p_{\text{low energy state}} = f_{AB} = \frac{P_{AB}}{\frac{1}{2}ZN_0}$$

Substituting from equations 9.35 and 9.36 gives

$$\frac{(1-\sigma)}{(1+\sigma)} = \exp\left(-\frac{\Delta H}{kT}\right) \tag{9.37}$$

where

$$\Delta H = \frac{1}{2}(H_{AA} + H_{BB}) - H_{AB}$$

In Fig. 9.12, σ from equation 9.37 is plotted versus temperature for the case where ΔH is positive [$H_{AB} < \frac{1}{2}(H_{AA} + H_{BB})$]. In this case σ is positive, indicating short range order. If ΔH is negative σ will be negative and clustering will occur instead. In this figure, T_c, the critical temperature for long range order of this alloy is shown. It will be observed from Fig. 9.12 that σ does not equal zero at the critical temperature for long range order, but that short range order persists at elevated temperatures. It should be pointed out that the analysis of short range order does not depend at all upon the existence of long range order, but may exist in any system in which $H_{AB} < \frac{1}{2}(H_{AA} + H_{BB})$. There are no composition restrictions for short range order as there are for the appearance of long range order.

9.6 CORRELATION BETWEEN QUASICHEMICAL THEORY AND EXPERIMENTAL OBSERVATION

From the discussion in the earlier sections of this chapter, it is clear that quasichemical theory predicts that there is an intimate relation between the thermodynamic properties of a solution and the state of order. Both the long range order parameter and the short range order parameter are related to the quantity $[H_{AB} - \frac{1}{2}(H_{AA} + H_{BB})]$, which in turn is related to the heat of mixing. If this term is negative, the system has a preference for a large number of A–B pairs compared with complete randomness. If the term is positive, long range order is not favored but rather clustering will occur, so that the number of A–B pairs is less than found for random mixing. The state of order of many systems may be obtained experimentally from x-ray measurements. It will be of interest therefore to examine the experimental state of order both qualitatively and quantitatively in connection with the predictions of quasichemical theory for some systems.

Aluminium-Zinc System

The state of short range order has been examined experimentally for this system by Rudman and Averbach.[1] In this paper, as in the others to be discussed in this section, a definition of short range order somewhat different from that given by equation 9.32 is used. The short range order parameter is defined in a manner more consistent with experimental observations than is equation 9.32. To arrive at this expression, consider a B atom in the lattice surrounded by Z nearest neighbors in the first shell. If the solution is completely random the probability that an A atom would occupy a given site in this shell is simply X_A. For a solution exhibiting short range order or clustering, the probability of occupancy will be $p_1 \neq X_A$. The short range order parameter α_1 is defined as

$$\alpha_1 \equiv 1 - \frac{p_1}{X_A} \tag{9.38}$$

[1] P. S. Rudman and B. L. Averbach, *Acta Met.*, **2,** 576 (1954).

For complete randomness, $\alpha_1 = 0$; for short range order α_1 will be less than one; and for clustering α_1 will be greater than one. The reader should note that equation 9.32 is defined in such a manner that, for order, $\sigma > 1$ and, for clustering, $\sigma < 1$.

In Fig. 9.13 experimental values of α_1 are shown as a function of zinc content at 400°C. It is observed that α_1 is positive, indicating that clustering

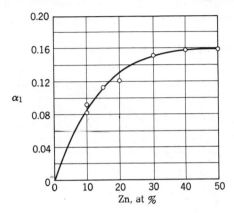

Fig. 9.13 Short range order in the Al–Zn system as a function of composition at 400°C. From P. S. Rudman and B. L. Averbach, *Acta Met.*, **2**, 576 (1954).

occurs, and it is also observed that clustering becomes more predominant as the zinc content is increased. The number of A–B pairs, P_{AB}, may be readily expressed in terms of α_1. Rearranging equation 9.38 we find

$$p_1 = X_A(1 - \alpha_1)$$

The average number of A atoms which surround a given B atom is $p_1 Z$, so therefore this is the number of A–B bonds per B atom on the average. The number of B atoms in a gram-atom of solution is $N_0 X_B$ and thus the total number of A–B pairs is

$$P_{AB} = Z N_0 X_A X_B (1 - \alpha_1) \tag{9.39}$$

A relation between P_{AB} and $[H_{AB} - \frac{1}{2}(H_{AA} + H_{BB})]$ for a nonrandom solution was given in equation 9.16 as

$$P_{AB} = X_A X_B Z N_0 \{1 - X_A X_B [\exp(-2\Omega/ZRT) - 1]\} \tag{9.16}$$

where

$$\Omega = Z N_0 [H_{AB} - \frac{1}{2}(H_{AA} + H_{BB})]$$

Thus, upon substitution of the experimental values of α_1 into equation 9.39 for a given composition, P_{AB} may be obtained. Upon substitution of the experimental value of P_{AB} into equation 9.16, Ω may be obtained.

Further, the relation between the enthalpy of mixing and Ω is,

$$\Delta H_m = X_A X_B \Omega \tag{9.11}$$

Thus, the relative enthalpy of mixing may be calculated from the short range order measurements and, if quasichemical theory is correct, this value should agree with the value of ΔH_m obtained by conventional thermodynamic methods. In the case of the aluminum-zinc system, ΔH_m

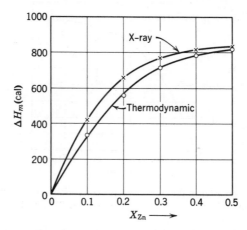

Fig. 9.14 Comparison between heat of mixing in the Al-Zn system calculated from x-ray measurements and direct thermodynamic methods. From P. S. Rudman and B. L. Averbach, *Acta Met.*, **2**, 576 (1954).

values have been determined as a function of composition by an emf technique.[1] In Fig. 9.14 is shown the comparison between ΔH_m values derived from quasichemical theory and values obtained by direct thermodynamic experiments. It is observed that the agreement is indeed excellent between the application of quasichemical theory and direct experiment. Qualitatively, of course, quasichemical theory predicts that a positive value of ΔH_m is associated with $\Omega > 0$ and hence a preference for like bonds over unlike bonds. It might be pointed out that aluminum and zinc atoms are almost identical in size and thus strain energy will not be important.

Gold-Nickel System

The phase diagram for the gold-nickel system is shown in Fig. 9.15 and is characterized by a miscibility gap. The occurrence of a miscibility gap

---

[1] J. E. Hilliard, B. L. Averbach, and M. Cohen, *Acta Met.*, **2**, 621 (1954).

is associated, according to quasichemical theory, with a preference of like neighbors over unlike neighbors. Thus Ω would be expected to be greater than zero and it would be expected that clustering would result.

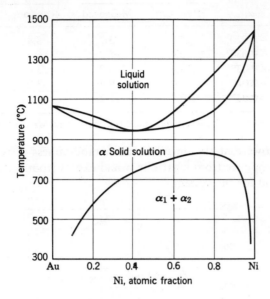

Fig. 9.15 Gold-nickel phase diagram.

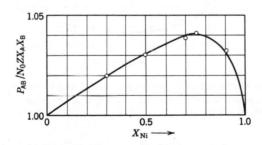

Fig. 9.16 Short range order parameter in the Au-Ni system. (Measured number of unlike neighbors)/(unlike neighbors in random solution); Au-Ni solid solutions; quenched from 900°C. From P. A. Flinn, B. L. Averbach, and M. Cohen, *Acta Met.*, **1**, 664 (1953).

For this system, however, the short range order parameter appears to be slightly negative, as shown in Fig. 9.16, indicating the presence of short range order. In Table 9.2 values of the average number of gold atoms surrounding each nickel and vice versa, as calculated from equation 9.38, are tabulated, as well as the same quantities for a random solution.

TABLE 9.2
Average Nearest Neighbor Identities in Gold-Nickel Alloys[a]

X_{Ni}	α_1	No. Ni atoms surr. Au		No. Au atoms surr. Ni	
		Random	Measured	Random	Measured
0.30	−0.020	3.6	3.7	8.4	8.7
0.50	−0.030	6.0	6.2	6.0	6.2
0.70	−0.038	8.4	8.7	3.6	3.7
0.75	−0.040	9.0	9.4	3.0	3.1
0.90	−0.032	10.8	11.2	1.2	1.24

[a] From P. A. Flinn, B. L. Averbach, and M. Cohen, *Acta Met.*, **1**, 664 (1953).

Table 9.2 shows that the deviation from randomness is very small but nonetheless opposite from what one would expect from the type of phase diagram found for the system.

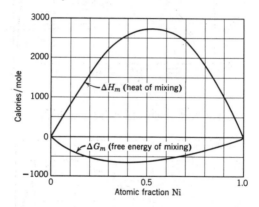

Fig. 9.17 Experimental values of the heat of mixing and free energy of mixing in the Au-Ni system as a function of composition. From B. L. Averbach, P. A. Flinn, and M. Cohen, *Acta Met.*, **2**, 92 (1954).

In Fig. 9.17 is shown a plot of the heat of mixing in the gold-nickel system as measured thermodynamically versus composition. It is observed from this figure that ΔH_m is a large positive quantity in agreement with what would be expected from the phase diagram but in disagreement with the apparent existence of short range order as found from x-ray measurements.

The question arises, therefore, as to why quasichemical theory applies so well to a system such as aluminum-zinc but appears to fail for a system such as gold-nickel. The reason for the behavior may lie in the size relations between the two components of the binary system. As emphasized before, the enthalpy of a solid solution consists not only of a chemical term but also of a very important strain term, resulting from the placement of a wrong-sized atom on a lattice site. Therefore, in order to derive an Ω value and relate this to α_1, the strain energy contribution to the heat of mixing must first be subtracted from the total value of the heat of mixing. For the gold-nickel system, a large atomic size disparity exists, and hence ΔH_m is probably composed principally of strain energy, which is always positive in sign. In the case of the aluminum-zinc system, the atomic sizes of the two components are almost identical. ΔH_m consists almost wholly of the chemical term and thus is readily amenable to the application of quasichemical theory.

chapter 10

Equilibrium between Phases of Variable Composition

10.1 CHEMICAL POTENTIAL

Consider very large amounts of two phases, both of which contain component A as shown in Fig. 10.1. Component A in the α phase will have an activity a_α, and in the β phase it will have an activity a_β. Let us

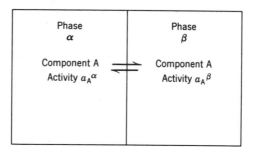

Fig. 10.1

transfer a gram-atom of A from α to β at a constant temperature without changing composition. The original quantities of A and B are so large that the composition is changed only infinitesimally. The reaction is

$$A(a^\alpha) = A(a^\beta) \qquad \Delta G$$

Component A in β will have a partial molar free energy given by

$$\bar{G}_A{}^\beta = G_A{}^\cdot + RT \ln a_A{}^\beta$$

and in α it will be given by

$$\bar{G}_A{}^\alpha = G_A{}^\cdot + RT \ln a_A{}^\alpha$$

The free energy of the reaction will be given by

$$\Delta G = RT \ln \frac{a_A{}^\beta}{a_A{}^\alpha} \tag{10.1}$$

The quantity $\bar{G}_i$ is commonly referred to as the *chemical potential*, and is often designated by the symbol μ_i. This terminology will be used in the remaining chapters.

If $a_A{}^\beta < a_A{}^\alpha$ the reaction above will proceed spontaneously since in this case $\Delta G < 0$. Conversely if $a_A{}^\alpha < a_A{}^\beta$ the reverse reaction will occur since similarly $\Delta G \to 0$ by such a reaction. When the composition has finally changed so that equilibrium is attained, $\Delta G = 0$ and therefore $a_A{}^\alpha = a_A{}^\beta$. Generally, the composition of A in the two phases will not be equal, since there will be a difference in the activity coefficient of A in the two phases. The procedure just outlined is often used for obtaining activity coefficient data for a component in one phase, when the activity coefficient of the component is known in the other phase as a function of composition. This is, in general, only applicable to liquids, because reaction rates involving solids are usually too slow for determining equilibrium accurately. From the preceding derivation it is seen that it is important that the activities of component A in both phases are referred to the same standard state or the $G_A{}^\cdot$ terms will not cancel out.

Illustration

Liquid A and liquid B are insoluble in each other. The thermodynamic properties of element C in A have been measured and it is found that A and C form a regular solution with the heat of mixing at 1000°K equal to

$$\Delta H_m = 500 X_A X_C$$

The other thermodynamic properties may be readily obtained, since for a regular solution $\Delta S_m{}^{xs} = 0$. Since

$$\Delta G_m{}^{xs} = \Delta H_m{}^{xs} - T \Delta S_m{}^{xs}$$

and we know that $\Delta H_m{}^{xs} = \Delta H_m$

$$\Delta G_m{}^{xs} = \Delta H_m$$

for a regular solution.

Since

$$\bar{H}_i - H_i{}^\cdot = \Delta H_m + (1 - X_i) \frac{\partial \Delta H_m}{\partial X_i}$$

we find

$$(\bar{H}_C - H_C^{\cdot}) = 500(1 - X_C)^2$$

From equation 8.53 we see that

$$\Delta \bar{G}_C^{xs} = RT \ln \gamma_C^A = \Delta \bar{H}_C = (\bar{H}_C - H_C^{\cdot})$$

or

$$\ln \gamma_C^A = \frac{500(1 - X_C)^2}{RT}$$

At 1000°K

$$\gamma_C^A = \exp[0.252(1 - X_C)^2]$$

When element C is added to a vessel containing liquids A and B as separate layers, it is found, at equilibrium, that phase A contains 10 at % C whereas phase B contains 20 at % B. The activity of C in A may be found since γ_C^A is known, and

$$a_C^A = \gamma_C^A X_C^A = (1.25)(0.1) = 0.125$$

since at equilibrium

$$a_C^A = a_C^B = 0.125$$

and

$$\gamma_C^B = 0.625$$

10.2 SOLUBILITY OF ONE COMPONENT IN ANOTHER PHASE

B Is Soluble in A but A Is Insoluble in B

Let us consider this simple case first for the purposes of illustrating the principles. Component B is considered to be soluble to the extent of $X_{B(sat)}^{\alpha}$ in α at a given temperature T_1, but A has an infinitesimal solubility in B. Such a situation might be represented by the phase diagram shown in Fig. 10.2. Thus at equilibrium at T_1, for any composition X_B where $X_{B(sat)}^{\alpha} < X_B < 1$, pure B will be in equilibrium with B in the α phase at composition $X_{B(sat)}^{\alpha}$, or for the reaction

$$B(s) = B(X_{B(sat)}^{\alpha}) \quad \Delta G = 0 \tag{10.2}$$

Thus

$$\mu_B^{\cdot} = \mu_{B(sat)}^{\alpha}$$

and

$$a_B^{\cdot} = a_{B(sat)}^{\alpha}$$

Since pure B is defined as the standard state, $a_B^{\cdot} = 1$, and thus $a_{B(sat)}^{\alpha} = 1$. If the α solution is dilute, component B may be assumed to follow Henry's law, and as a result γ_B° may be evaluated since

$$a_{B(sat)}^{\alpha} = 1 = \gamma_B^{\circ} X_{B(sat)}^{\alpha}$$

and hence

$$\gamma_B{}^\circ = \frac{1}{X^\alpha_{B(sat)}} \tag{10.3}$$

We may gain information about the shape of the solvus line of α as a function of temperature for this type of phase diagram. Unfortunately equation 10.2 for the solution reaction is not too useful from this point

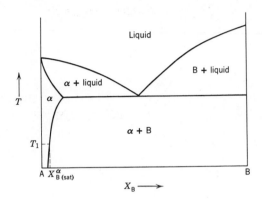

Fig. 10.2   Phase diagram for case where B is soluble in A but A is insoluble in B.

of view, since ΔG is zero. As a result let us consider a different solution equation. Let component B be transferred from the pure state to some arbitrary composition in α, say $X_B = 0.01$, instead of to $X^\alpha_{B(sat)}$. Thus

$$B(s) = B(X_B = 0.01) \qquad \Delta G_1$$

Let us now evaluate ΔG_1. From our basic thermodynamics

$$\Delta G_1 = \mu_B - \mu_B{}^\bullet = RT \ln \frac{a_B}{a_B{}^\bullet} \tag{10.4}$$

$a_B{}^\bullet = 1$ as before, and $a_B = \gamma_B{}^\circ (0.01)$. Substitution into equation 10.3 yields

$$a_B = \frac{0.01}{X^\alpha_{B(sat)}}$$

Thus from equation 10.4

$$(\mu_B - \mu_B{}^\bullet) = RT \ln (0.01) - RT \ln X^\alpha_{B(sat)}$$

We know that

$$\frac{\partial(\mu_i/T)}{\partial(1/T)} = \bar{H}_i$$

Therefore

$$\frac{\partial(\mu_B/T)}{\partial(1/T)} - \frac{\partial(\mu_B^*/T)}{\partial(1/T)} = \bar{H}_B - H_B^* = -R\left(\frac{\partial \ln X_{B(sat)}^\alpha}{\partial(1/T)}\right)$$

or

$$\frac{\Delta\bar{H}_B}{R} = -\left(\frac{\partial \ln X_{B(sat)}^\alpha}{\partial(1/T)}\right)$$

or

$$X_{B(sat)}^\alpha = A \exp\left(-\Delta\bar{H}_B/RT\right) \tag{10.5}$$

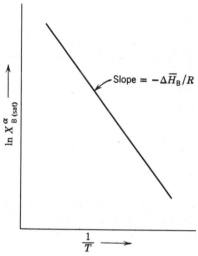

Fig. 10.3   Solvus line on phase diagram of Fig. 10.2 plotted according to equation 10.5.

From reaction 10.2, it is seen that $\Delta\bar{H}_B$ corresponds to the enthalpy expended in transferring pure B to the dilute solution. This is the relative partial molal enthalpy. For a dilute solution in which the solute is following Henry's law, $\Delta\bar{H}_B$ is independent of composition. It is clear that, if the phase diagram for an actual system is of the type shown in Fig. 10.2, $\Delta\bar{H}_B$ may be obtained from the solvus line. $\Delta\bar{H}_B$, as for most enthalpies of solid state reactions, is virtually independent of temperature. Experimentally, when $\ln X_{B(sat)}^\alpha$ is plotted versus $1/T$, a line very close to being straight is obtained, with a slope equal to $-\Delta\bar{H}_B/R$, as shown by equation 10.5. This is shown schematically in Fig. 10.3. Generally $\Delta\bar{H}_B$ is positive for solid solutions, so $X_{B(sat)}^\alpha$ increases with T. This discussion illustrates the first example of the use of binary phase diagrams for obtaining thermodynamic data.

The problem treated above may be approached from the statistical mechanical point of view, which will yield more information about the nature of the constant A. Let us consider a gram-atom of solution consisting of N_A atoms of component A and N_B atoms of component B. Thus $X_A = N_A/N_0$ and $X_B = N_B/N_0$. An atom of B has a vibrational entropy in the pure state of S_v. When the B atom is put into solution it will undergo a vibrational entropy change to S_v', resulting in a change per atom of ΔS_v. Further, there will be a configurational entropy change given by $\Delta S_m = k \ln (\mathscr{W}'/\mathscr{W})$. In the pure state $\mathscr{W} = 1$ and in the alloy

$$\mathscr{W}' = \frac{N_0!}{N_B! N_A!}$$

It has been shown that the entropy of mixing for a gram-atom of solution is given by

$$\Delta S_m = -N_0 k [X_A \ln X_A + X_B \ln X_B]$$

The partial molal mixing entropy $\Delta \bar{S}_B$ per gram-atom of B is given by

$$\Delta \bar{S}_{B(m)} = -N_0 k \ln X_B$$

and hence the mixing change per atom of B is

$$\Delta \bar{S}_c = -k \ln X_B$$

Thus the initial entropy change per atom of B is the sum of the vibrational and mixing terms:

$$\Delta \bar{S}_B = -k \ln X_B + \Delta \bar{S}_v$$

In addition, upon transfer of an atom from pure B to the solution, there is an enthalpy change $\Delta \bar{H}_B$. The chemical potential change per atom is given by

$$\mu_B - \mu_B{}^\bullet = \Delta \bar{H}_B - T \Delta \bar{S}_B$$

or

$$\mu_B - \mu_B{}^\bullet = \Delta \bar{H}_B + kT \ln X_B - T \Delta \bar{S}_v \qquad (10.6)$$

At equilibrium of course $\mu_B = \mu_B{}^\bullet$ for composition $X_{B(sat)}^\alpha < X_B < 1$, and the mole fraction of B in α is $X_{B(sat)}^\alpha$. As a result we find upon rearrangement of 10.6 that

$$X_{B(sat)}^\alpha = \exp (\Delta \bar{S}_v/k) \exp (-\Delta \bar{H}/kT) \qquad (10.7)$$

Comparing equation 10.7 with 10.5, we see that the integration constant A is equal to $\exp (\Delta \bar{S}_v/k)$. Taking the logarithm of both sides of equation 10.7,

$$\ln X_{B(sat)}^\alpha = \frac{\Delta \bar{S}_v}{k} - \frac{\Delta \bar{H}_B}{kT}$$

we see that if ln $X^{\alpha}_{B(sat)}$ is plotted versus $1/T$ as in Fig. 10.3, and extrapolated to $1/T = 0$, the second term on the right hand side becomes zero and the intercept of ln $X^{\alpha}_{B(sat)}$ at this point is equal to $\Delta \bar{S}_v/k$.

Thus, application of simple statistical mechanics provides a method of evaluating the vibrational entropy of a solute in a solution relative to the value of the pure solute. In Fig. 10.4 are shown solubility data of solutes in aluminum plotted in this way. These systems, however, involve an

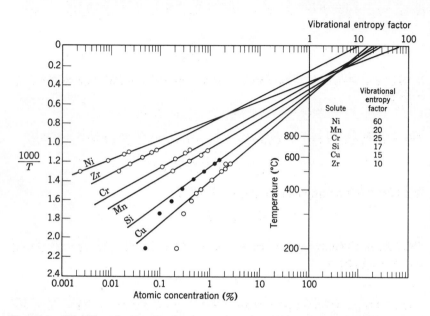

Fig. 10.4 Solubility of solutes in aluminum plotted according to equation 10.7 so as to obtain relative partial molar heats of solution and relative partial molar entropy charges. From C. Zener in *Thermodynamics in Physical Metallurgy*, ASM, Cleveland, 1950.

equilibrium between α solid solution and an intermediate phase. It will be noted that, in general, the larger the value of $\Delta \bar{H}_B$, the higher is the value of $\Delta \bar{S}_v$. This is understandable since often the most important contribution to the heat of solution is associated with the strain energy contribution, and hence a large value of $\Delta \bar{H}_B$ is associated with a large misfit of solute into the crystal, which lowers the vibrational frequencies of neighboring solute atoms and results in a positive contribution to $\Delta \bar{S}_v$. It is evident however, from examination of Fig. 10.4, that a small error in slope will result in a very large error in $\Delta \bar{S}_v$.

Freedman and Nowick[1] have considered this problem in more detail,

[1] J. F. Freedman and A. S. Nowick, *Acta Met.*, **6**, 176 (1958).

and have applied it to simple eutectic systems of the type shown in Fig. 10.2. Actually they modified equation 10.7 somewhat, since it is only applicable to systems for which the solute follows Henry's law. For most systems the upper limit of applicability is about 1 at % solute. Since many of the systems investigated had solubilities greater than this, equation

TABLE 10.1

Relative Partial Molal Enthalpies-Vibrational Entropies for Simple Eutectic Systems[a]

Solvent	Solute	$\Delta \bar{S}_v/k$	$\Delta \bar{H}_B/k$
Cu	Ag	1.4	4790
Ag	Cu	1.4	3960
Ag	Pb	2.5	4320
Al	Si	1.7	5120
Au	Co	2.5	5900
Pb	Sb	0.77	2170
Eu	Co	0.64	5110
Cu	Fe	3.0	8520
Ag	Ni	−1.1	4530
Pb	Ni	1.8	5480
Pb	Cd	0.81	2160

[a] From J. F. Freedman and A. S. Nowick, *Acta Met.*, **6**, 176 (1958).

10.7 had to be modified. This was done by expanding $\Delta \bar{H}_B$ and $\Delta \bar{S}_v$ in a Taylor's series and keeping the second order term, so now these quantities are considered not only to be related to X_B but also to X_B^2. Thus it was found that

$$\frac{\ln X_{B(sat)}^{\alpha}}{1 - 2X_{B(sat)}^{\alpha}} = \frac{-\Delta \bar{H}_B}{kT} + \frac{\Delta \bar{S}_v}{k}$$

for the type of system being considered here. The entropy terms obtained in this manner are shown in Table 10.1 for a variety of eutectic systems. Note that all of the values of $\Delta \bar{S}_v$ except one are positive, in agreement with the statements made earlier. Note also that all values of $\Delta \bar{H}_B$ are positive and are of the order of several kilocalories per gram-atom of solute.

Case where Elements A and B Are Mutually Soluble in Each Other to a Limited Extent

The phase diagram appropriate to the situation is shown in Fig. 10.5. This situation is only slightly different from that discussed earlier. At

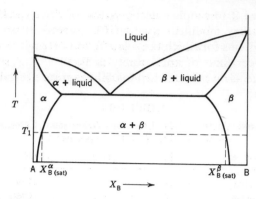

Fig. 10.5 Phase diagram showing limited mutual solubility of A and B.

temperature T_1, for composition $X^{\alpha}_{B(sat)} < X_B < X^{\beta}_{B(sat)}$, phase α is in equilibrium with phase β, which means that the chemical potential of A is the same in both saturated phases and also that the chemical potential of B is the same in both phases. Using component B for our calculations as before,

$$B(X^{\alpha}_{B(sat)}) = B(X^{\beta}_{B(sat)}) \qquad \Delta G = 0$$

Hence

$$\mu^{\beta}_{B(sat)} = \mu^{\alpha}_{B(sat)}$$

The difference between this case and the former case is that

$$\mu^{\beta}_{B(sat)} \neq \mu_B{}^{\cdot}$$

Since α and β are both dilute solutions, Henry's law is obeyed by the solutes and Raoult's law is obeyed by the solvents. In the case of the β phase, B is the solvent and hence

$$\mu_B{}^{\beta} = \mu_B{}^{\cdot} + RT \ln a_B{}^{\beta} = \mu_B{}^{\cdot} + RT \ln X_B{}^{\beta} \qquad (10.8)$$

for the solvent, since $\gamma_B = 1$. At the composition $X^{\beta}_{B(sat)}$

$$\mu^{\beta}_{B(sat)} = \mu_B{}^{\cdot} + RT \ln X^{\beta}_{B(sat)}$$

In saturated phase α, component B is the solute and follows Henry's law. Thus

$$\mu_B{}^{\alpha} = \mu_B{}^{\cdot} + RT \ln X^{\alpha}_{B(sat)} + RT \ln \gamma_B{}^{\circ} \qquad (10.9)$$

Equating 10.8 to 10.9, we see that

$$\ln X^{\beta}_{B(sat)} = \ln X^{\alpha}_{B(sat)} + \ln \gamma_B{}^{\circ}$$

or

$$\gamma_B{}^\circ = \frac{X^\beta_{B(sat)}}{X^\alpha_{B(sat)}} \qquad (10.10)$$

The activities of A and B are shown schematically in Fig. 10.6 at temperature T as a function of composition.

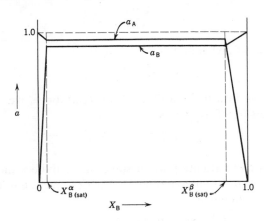

Fig. 10.6 Activities of components A and B at temperature T_1. Corresponds to the phase diagram in Fig. 10.5.

Illustration

Problem. Nickel and element A are related by a phase diagram of the type shown in Fig. 10.5. At 1000°K, element A will dissolve 4 at % nickel and nickel will dissolve 6 at % A.

Calculate the oxygen pressure at which nickel dissolved in A to the extent of 1 at % will just begin to oxidize to NiO. Element A is more stable than nickel and will oxidize only at higher oxygen pressures.

Solution. From thermodynamic data we find the standard free energy for the reaction

$$NiO(s) = \tfrac{1}{2}O_2(g, 1 \text{ atm}) + Ni(s)$$

to be

$$\Delta G^\circ = 34{,}900 \text{ cal} = -RT \ln K$$

Thus the equilibrium constant K is

$$K = 3.7 \times 10^{-8} = \frac{a_{Ni} \times p_{O_2}^{\frac{1}{2}}}{a_{NiO}}$$

The activity of NiO is 1, since it is presumed to form as pure NiO. The problem then is to find the activity of nickel in a 1 at % solution. The activity for pure nickel is 1, and in the nickel-rich terminal solution, the nickel will follow Raoult's law. Thus the activity at the solvus line, where $X_{Ni} = 0.94$, is 0.94. This phase is in equilibrium with the A-rich solution, α containing 4 at % Ni, so the activity of nickel at $X_{Ni} = 0.04$ is 0.94. Since the nickel is assumed to follow Henry's law, the activity coefficient $\gamma_{Ni}°$ is constant and, since $a_{Ni} = \gamma_{Ni}° X_{Ni}$, we know a_{Ni} at $X_{Ni} = 0.04$.

$$\gamma_{Ni}° = \frac{0.94}{0.04} = 23.5$$

Thus the activity of nickel in a 1 at % solution is

$$a_{Ni} = 0.01(23.5) = 0.235$$

Upon substitution into the equilibrium constant above, we find that the equilibrium pressure of oxygen is

$$p_{O_2} = 2.5 \times 10^{-14} \text{ atm}$$

Let us now turn our attention to the solvus lines of the α and β solutions in order to see what thermodynamic information may be obtained. Our basic reaction is, of course,

$$B(X_{B(sat)}^\beta) = B(X_{B(sat)}^\alpha) \qquad \Delta G = 0$$

As before, however, this is not useful for this problem since $\Delta G = 0$ and no meaningful operations may be performed.

To eliminate this problem let us start with our basic reaction and transfer one gram-atom of B in β from concentration $X_{B(sat)}^\beta$ to, say, $X_B^\beta = 0.99$. Similarly let us transfer one gram-atom of B from $X_{B(sat)}^\alpha$ to, say, $X_B^\alpha = 0.01$.

(1) $\qquad B(X_{B(sat)}^\beta) = B(X_{B(sat)}^\alpha) \qquad \Delta G_1 = 0$

(2) $\qquad B(X_{B(sat)}^\alpha) = B(X_B^\alpha = 0.01) \qquad \Delta G_2 = RT \ln \dfrac{0.01}{X_{B(sat)}^\alpha}$

(3) $\qquad B(X_B^\beta = 0.99) = B(X_{B(sat)}^\beta) \qquad \Delta G_3 = RT \ln \dfrac{X_{B(sat)}^\beta}{0.99}$

$$B(X_B^\beta = 0.99) = B(X_B^\alpha = 0.01) \qquad \Delta G_1 + \Delta G_2 + \Delta G_3 = \mu_B^\alpha - \mu_B^\beta$$

Upon addition of the free energy terms,

$$\Delta G = \mu_B^\alpha - \mu_B^\beta = RT \ln \frac{(0.01)X_{B(sat)}^\beta}{(0.99)X_{B(sat)}^\alpha}$$

Thus

$$\frac{\partial(\mu_B^\alpha/T)}{\partial(1/T)} - \frac{\partial(\mu_B^\beta/T)}{\partial(1/T)} = \bar{H}_B^\alpha - \bar{H}_B^\beta = R \frac{\partial \ln X_{B(sat)}^\beta}{\partial(1/T)} - R \frac{\partial \ln X_{B(sat)}^\alpha}{\partial(1/T)}$$

Since component B follows Raoult's law in phase $\beta \; \bar{H}_B{}^\beta = H_B{}^\cdot$,

$$\frac{\partial \ln X^\alpha_{B(sat)}}{\partial(1/T)} - \frac{\partial \ln X^\beta_{B(sat)}}{\partial(1/T)} = -\frac{(\Delta \bar{H}_B{}^\alpha)}{R} \tag{10.11}$$

Repeating the same procedures for component A, we obtain

$$\frac{\partial \ln(1 - X^\beta_{B(sat)})}{\partial(1/T)} - \frac{\partial \ln(1 - X^\alpha_{B(sat)})}{\partial(1/T)} = -\frac{\Delta \bar{H}_A{}^\beta}{R} \tag{10.12}$$

The term $\Delta \bar{H}_B{}^\alpha$ corresponds to the enthalpy expended in transferring pure component B to dilute α, hence it is the relative partial molal enthalpy of B in α. Similarly $\Delta \bar{H}_A{}^\beta$ corresponds to the relative partial molal enthalpy of A in B. Solving equations 10.11 and 10.12, we find

$$\frac{X^\alpha_{B(sat)}}{X^\beta_{B(sat)}} = A \exp\left(-\Delta \bar{H}_B{}^\alpha / RT\right) \tag{10.13}$$

$$\frac{1 - X^\beta_{B(sat)}}{1 - X^\alpha_{B(sat)}} = B \exp\left(-\Delta \bar{H}_A{}^\beta / RT\right) \tag{10.14}$$

where A and B are integration constants. As a result we see that, by plotting experimental values of the ratios of $X^\alpha_{B(sat)}$ and $X^\alpha_{B(sat)}$ in the manner of equations 10.13 and 10.14, both $\Delta \bar{H}_B{}^\alpha$ and $\Delta \bar{H}_A{}^\beta$ may be obtained. Furthermore, if the logarithms of these ratios are plotted as reciprocals of absolute temperature, two straight lines should be obtained. In fact, from equation 10.11, it is seen that $X^\alpha_{B(sat)}$ and $X^\beta_{B(sat)}$ should vary exponentially with temperature. If this is not found for dilute solutions, the validity of the experimental data should be questioned.

The constants A and B may be found by use of methods of statistical mechanics as in the previous case with the result

$$A = \exp\left(\Delta \bar{S}_v{}^\alpha / k\right) \tag{10.15}$$

$$B = \exp\left(\Delta \bar{S}_v{}^\beta / k\right) \tag{10.16}$$

$\Delta \bar{S}_v{}^\alpha$ refers to the vibrational entropy change corresponding to the transfer of a B atom from the pure state to the α phase, and $\Delta \bar{S}_v{}^\beta$ corresponds to the vibrational entropy change corresponding to the transfer of an A atom from the pure state to the β phase.

10.3 THOMSON-FREUNDLICH EQUATION

In the first case of section 10.2, the solubility of component B in α solid solution is treated as a function of temperature alone, assuming that the pressure is constant. For very fine particles of B, however, interface effects may be important and in fact can markedly influence the solubility. To investigate this problem, consider the case of spherical particles of B immersed in an α matrix as shown in Fig. 10.7. The interfacial free energy between the particle and the α matrix will be designated σ. Let us approach the solution of the problem through calculation of the vapor pressure of B as a function of the radius of curvature. The vapor pressure data

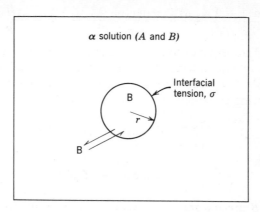

Fig. 10.7 Small particles of B in equilibrium with α solid solution.

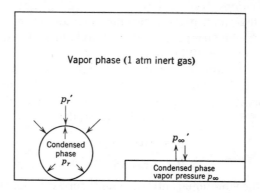

Fig. 10.8 Pressure of B in the vapor phase and gas phase of spherical particle and particle with an infinite radius of curvature.

generally available pertain to large particles of B, for which the radius of curvature is large and is essentially infinite. Therefore we will compare two cases; the vapor pressure of the particle of radius r, p_r, and the vapor pressure of B over a flat surface, p_∞. The pressure inside the particles will be p_r and p_∞ respectively, and the pressure of B outside the particle in the vapor phase immediately adjacent to the particles will be p_r' and p_∞' respectively, as shown in Fig. 10.8. Since at a constant external pressure and constant temperature a pressure gradient in the gas phase is not stable,

$$p_r' = p_\infty' = p' \tag{10.17}$$

The question of the pressure inside the particles is more difficult. Consider a curved surface of radius r_1 as shown in Fig. 10.9. Let the phase B be enclosed by the surface and surrounded by the vapor phase. Consider a

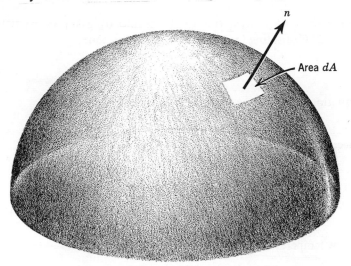

n

Area dA

Fig. 10.9 Element of the surface of a spherical particle.

segment of the surface s with a normal n, and let us move an element of surface dA an amount dn keeping the volume constant. At equilibrium under the constraint of total constant volume, the Helmholtz free energy F will be a minimum, and hence at constant temperature

$$dF = -dW = 0 \tag{10.18}$$

After the process is complete the vapor phase will have undergone a volume change dV_g and the particle at pressure p_r will have undergone a volume change dV_B. In addition the element of area dA has changed by $d(dA)$. The volume change of vapor and particle result in work, dW, of $p_r' \, dV_g$ and $p_r \, dV_B$ respectively. The area change of the particle results in work, dW, equal to $-\sigma \, d(dA)$. The total work will be the sum of these terms. Substitution in equation 10.18 gives

$$-p_r' \, dV_g - p_r \, dV_B + \sigma \, d(dA) = 0 \tag{10.19}$$

From considerations of solid geometry, we find the relation between the area change and dn to be

$$d(dA) = \frac{2}{r} dA \cdot dn$$

However, $dA \cdot dn = dV_B$, hence

$$d(dA) = dV_B \frac{2}{r} \tag{10.20}$$

Also $-dA \cdot dn = dV_g$, since the total volume of gas plus particle is constant, and substituting into equation 10.19 we find

$$p_r - p_r' = \frac{2\sigma}{r} \tag{10.21}$$

From equation 10.21 we see that, when $r = \infty$,

$$p_\infty' = p_\infty$$

and hence

$$p_r' = p_\infty$$

Insertion into equation 10.21 yields

$$p_r - p_\infty = \frac{2\sigma}{r} \tag{10.22}$$

At constant temperature the chemical potential change is

$$d\mu = V_B^{\cdot} dp$$

We find

$$\mu_r - \mu_\infty = V_B^{\cdot}(p_r - p_\infty) = \frac{2\sigma V_B^{\cdot}}{r} \tag{10.23}$$

Also $\mu_\infty = \mu_B$, and hence $a_\infty = 1$. The solubility of B in α is considered to be small, so Henry's law is followed by the solute, and thus

$$a_\infty = 1 = \gamma_B^{\circ} X_{B(sat)}^{\alpha}$$

The chemical potential of atoms in a particle of radius r is given by

$$\mu_r = \mu_B^{\cdot} + RT \ln a_r$$

and upon substitution of equation 10.23 we find

$$RT \ln a_r = \frac{2\sigma V_B^{\cdot}}{r}$$

Since Henry's law is followed by the solute,

$$a_r = \gamma_B^{\circ}(X_{B(sat)}^{\alpha})_r$$

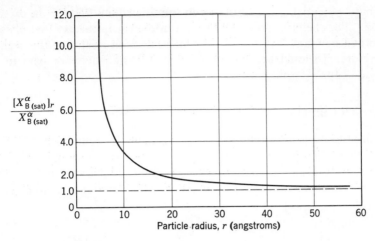

$\dfrac{[X^{\alpha}_{B\,(sat)}]_r}{X^{\alpha}_{B\,(sat)}}$

Particle radius, r (angstroms)

Fig. 10.10 Solubility of small particles of B in α solid solution compared to the solubility of very large particles.

and thus

$$\ln \frac{(X^{\alpha}_{B(sat)})_r}{X^{\alpha}_{B(sat)}} = \frac{2\sigma V_B^{\bullet}}{TRr} \tag{10.24}$$

The quantity $V_B^{\bullet} = M/\rho$, and thus

$$\ln \frac{[X^{\alpha}_{B(sat)}]_r}{[X^{\alpha}_{B(sat)}]} = \frac{2M\sigma}{rRT\rho} \tag{10.25}$$

Equation 10.25 is known as the *Thomson-Freundlich* equation. It shows that the solubility of B in α at a given temperature depends exponentially upon the particle radius r. The smaller the radius of the particle, the higher the chemical potential of atoms in the particle will be, and hence the higher the solubility will be. Physical reasoning would suggest that this effect due to the interfacial free energy would only be important for particles having a large area to volume ratio, which corresponds, of course, to very small particles. To illustrate, let us consider the ratio $(X^{\alpha}_{B(sat)})_r$ for a typical material with an atomic weight of 50, a density, ρ, of 10 gm/cm³, and an interfacial free energy of 500 ergs/cm² at 500°K. The solubility ratio is plotted versus radius r in Fig. 10.10. From this figure it is observed that the effect of particle size on solubility is pronounced only for particles less than about 50 A in radius.

This discussion is intended to illustrate an important point, namely, that there is no such parameter as a maximum solubility by itself. The maximum solubility of one substance in another occurs only when the chemical potential of the substance in solution equals that for the external phase. The chemical potential of the component in the external phase is governed by many factors, one of which has been treated in this section. Therefore, it should be emphasized that attention must be paid to the nature of the external phase.

10.4 SOLUBILITY OF A METASTABLE PHASE

Consider the problem of the saturated β phase in contact with saturated α. Suppose that β does not have its equilibrium structure but rather is in a metastable form. In particular suppose that solid β is superheated above the eutectic temperature. The question then arises as to what is the

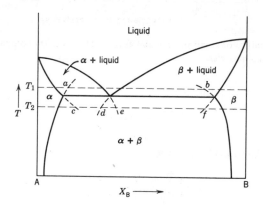

Fig. 10.11 Phase diagram showing extensions of phase boundaries into metastable regions.

composition of α in equilibrium with this metastable β above the eutectic temperature. The relative partial molal enthalpy of component A in the β phase, $\Delta \bar{H}_A{}^\beta$, for example, is the same above the eutectic as below. Similarly $\Delta \bar{H}_B{}^\alpha$ is the same above the eutectic temperature. Thus the quantity

$$\frac{\partial \ln X_{B(sat)}^\alpha}{\partial (1/T)} - \frac{\partial \ln X_{B(sat)}^\beta}{\partial (1/T)} = \frac{\Delta \bar{H}_B{}^\alpha}{R}$$

remains unchanged above the eutectic. This means that the solvus lines above the eutectic temperature are extensions of those below. As a generalization, therefore, the lines on the phase diagram are continued as shown in Fig. 10.11. At temperature T_1, β of composition b is in metastable equilibrium with α of composition a. At temperature

T_2, α of composition c is in metastable equilibrium with liquid of composition e, and liquid of composition d is in metastable equilibrium with β of composition f. It is seen from Fig. 10.11 that the solubility of a metastable phase (for example superheated β in α at T_1) is higher than the equilibrium phase at this temperature (eutectic liquid). That this should be so is apparent since the chemical potential of B for example in superheated β is higher than the chemical potential of B in the stable phase of eutectic liquid. (If it were not, β would be stable at T_1.) Hence according to equations 10.8 through 10.10, $X_{B(sat)}^{\alpha}$ will be larger in this case than in the case of the stable phase.

As another example suppose that β at temperature T_2 is present in the form of a metastable crystal structure. Since the stable structure has the lowest free energy, and thus the individual components have the lowest chemical potentials, the value of $X_{B(sat)}^{\alpha}$ will again be larger for the metastable structure.

It is clear from this brief discussion that a phase has no fundamental solubility for another element. The solubility must be expressed in terms of the nature of the phase dissolved. The generalization may be made, however, that the solubility of a metastable phase is always higher than the solubility of a stable phase.

10.5 RETROGRADE SOLUBILITY

An important phenomenon, which has recently received attention because of its occurrence in phase diagrams of germanium and silicon with many solutes, is shown in Figs. 10.12 and 10.13, for the germanium-copper and silicon-copper systems respectively. Instead of the maximum solubility of a solute in a given phase occurring at the eutectic temperature as in Fig. 10.5, in a system showing retrograde solubility, it occurs at a considerably higher temperature. The effect may be very pronounced, as seen in Figs. 10.12 and 10.13. The solubility of copper in germanium, for example, is about 15 times higher at 850°C than it is at the eutectic temperature.

In order to examine the thermodynamic causes of this effect, known as *retrograde solubility*, let us consider that the α phase behaves as a regular solution and the liquid phase in equilibrium with α above the eutectic temperature behaves as an ideal solution.[1] These assumptions are not necessary, but the treatment is simplified if they are made. The chemical potential difference between pure solute B and solute dissolved in

---

[1] For further treatment of the problem, the reader is referred to articles by J. L. Meijering, *Philips Research Repts.*, **3**, 281 (1948), and C. S. Thurmond and J. S. Struthers, *J. Electrochem. Soc.*, **57**, (1953).

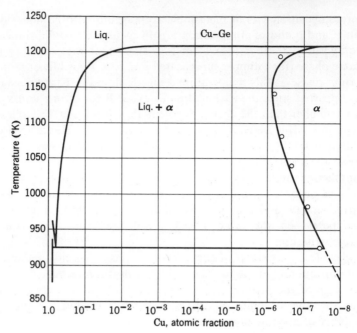

Fig. 10.12 Phase diagram for the Ge-Cu system showing retrograde solubility. From C. D. Thurmond and J. D. Struthers, *J. Phys. Chem.*, **57**, 831 (1953).

saturated α (α phase is considered to be a dilute solution) is given by

$$\mu^{\alpha}_{B(sat)} - \mu_{B}^{\bullet} = RT \ln \gamma_{B}^{\circ} X^{\alpha}_{B(sat)} \qquad (10.26)$$

which in turn is equal to

$$\mu^{\alpha}_{B(sat)} - \mu_{B}^{\bullet} = \Delta \bar{H}_{B}{}^{\alpha} - T \Delta \bar{S}_{B}{}^{\alpha} \qquad (10.27)$$

Equating 10.26 to 10.27, we find

$$RT \ln \gamma_{B}^{\circ} X^{\alpha}_{B(sat)} = \Delta \bar{H}_{B}{}^{\alpha} - T \Delta \bar{S}_{B}{}^{\alpha} \qquad (10.28)$$

Since the solution is considered to be regular we know

$$\Delta \bar{S}_{B}{}^{\alpha} = -R \ln X^{\alpha}_{B(sat)} \qquad (10.29)$$

and also $\Delta \bar{H}_{B}{}^{\alpha}$ is a constant.

Substituting into equation 10.28, we find

$$RT \ln \gamma_{B}^{\circ} = \Delta H_{B}{}^{\alpha} \qquad (10.30)$$

The next step is to consider the chemical potential of B in the liquid phase. For the liquid in equilibrium with α, the fact that the solute is often stable as a solid at the retrograde temperatures must be taken into account.

This is clear because in the formation of an ideal solution, no heat is evolved. For the case of our liquid phase, this means that if pure liquid A is mixed with pure liquid B no heat is evolved. This of course means that the atoms have no affinity for one another. Suppose now that one of the components is stable as a solid at the solution temperature. It is impossible, of course, to form a liquid solution now without converting

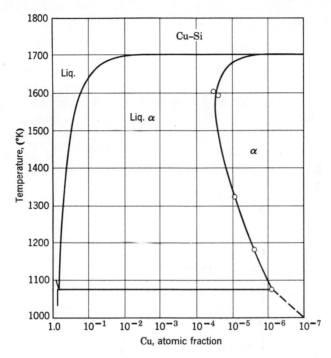

Fig. 10.13 Phase diagram for the Si-Cu system showing retrograde solubility. From C. D. Thurmond and J. D. Struthers, *J. Phys. Chem.*, **57**, 831 (1953).

this component to the liquid state. This involves the heat of fusion. The liquids may now mix ideally. If both components are in the solid state, in order to form the liquid solution, both must be converted to pure liquids and then mixing may occur. Addressing ourselves to the case where B is normally solid, let the step of forming the solution be carried out by the following reversible steps.

(1)   Solute (solid, retrograde T) = Solute (solid, $T_{m.p.}$)

$$\Delta H_1 = \int_{T}^{T_{m.p.}} C_P{}^s \, dT$$

(2)   Solute (solid, $T_{m.p.}$) = Solute (liquid, $T_{m.p.}$) $\Delta H_2 = \Delta H_{f_B}$.

(3)   Solute (liquid, $T_{m.p.}$) = Solute (liquid A, retrograde T)

$$\Delta H_3 = - \int_T^{T_{m.p.}} C_P{}^l \, dT$$

(4)   Solute (liquid, retrograde T) = Solute (liquid, X_B, retrograde T)

$$\Delta H_4 = \Delta \bar{H}_B{}^l = 0$$

---

(5)   Solute (s, retrograde T) = Solute ($X_B{}^l$, retrograde T)

$$\Delta H_5 \cong \Delta H_{f_B}$$

The enthalpy changes for reactions 1 and 3 will be corrections due to heat capacity and will partially cancel out. For our purpose they may be neglected. Since the liquid solution is considered to be ideal, ΔH_4 is zero. Thus ΔH for the overall process, reaction 5, is equal to that for reaction 2, namely ΔH_{f_B}. Similarly the entropy changes for reactions 1 and 3 will be disregarded since they are small. ΔS for reaction 2 is ΔS_{f_B} and $\Delta \bar{S}_B{}^l$ for reaction 4 is $-R \ln X_B$. Thus ΔS for the overall reaction is given by

$$\Delta S_5 = \Delta S_{f_B} - R \ln X_B{}^l$$

The chemical potential difference between solute in liquid solution and pure solid solute then is

$$\mu_B{}^l - \mu_B{}^\bullet = \Delta H_5 - T \, \Delta S_5 = \Delta H_{f_B} - T \, \Delta S_{f_B} + RT \ln X_B{}^l \quad (10.31)$$

At equilibrium $\mu_B{}^l = \mu_B{}^\alpha$, and therefore, equating $\mu_B{}^l$ from 10.31 with $\mu_B{}^\alpha$ from 10.26 and making the substitution for $\gamma_B{}^\circ$ given by equation 10.30, we find that

$$\ln \frac{X_{B(sat)}^\alpha}{X_B{}^l} = \frac{\Delta H_{f_B} - \Delta \bar{H}_B{}^\alpha}{RT} - \frac{\Delta S_{f_B}}{R} \quad (10.32)$$

The relation $X_{B(sat)}^\alpha / X_B{}^l$ is known as the distribution coefficient and is often designated by the symbol k. Since $X_{B(sat)}^\alpha$ and $X_B{}^l$ both vary with temperature, and since we are really interested in the equation for $X_{B(sat)}^\alpha$ and not $X_B{}^l$ as a function of temperature, it is necessary to eliminate the latter quantity. This may be done by consideration of the thermodynamic properties of component A in the α and the liquid phases. Since, generally $X_B \ll 1$, $X_A \sim 1$ and the chemical potential of component A is nearly identical with that for the pure component. Thus

$$\mu_{A(sat)}^\alpha - \mu_A{}^\bullet = RT \ln X_A \cong 0$$

since

$$X_A \sim 1$$

Furthermore, the liquid solution is considered here to behave ideally, so for the reaction

$$A \text{ (pure liquid, } T) = A \text{ (in liquid solution, } T)$$

$$\mu_A{}^l - (\mu_A{}^\cdot)_l = RT \ln X_A{}^l \qquad (10.33)$$

The standard state for component A is not pure liquid, however, but pure solid, since the temperature is below the melting point of component A. Thus we must consider the reaction

$$\text{Component } A(s, T) = \text{Component } A(l, T)$$

and

$$\Delta G = (\mu_A{}^\cdot)_l - \mu_A{}^\cdot = \Delta H_{f_A} - T \Delta S_{f_A} \qquad (10.34)$$

Inserting 10.34 into 10.33, we find

$$\mu_A{}^l - \mu_A{}^\cdot = RT \ln X_A{}^l + \Delta H_{l_A} - T \Delta S_{f_A}$$

At equilibrium

$$\mu_A{}^l = \mu_A{}^\cdot$$

and therefore

$$\ln X_A{}^l = \ln (1 - X_B{}^l) = - \frac{\Delta H_{f_A}}{RT} + \frac{\Delta S_{f_A}}{R} \qquad (10.35)$$

ΔS_{f_A} may be eliminated from equation 10.35 since at the melting point

$$\Delta G_{f_A} = 0 = \Delta H_{f_A} - T_{\text{m.p.}} \Delta S_{f_A}$$

and

$$\Delta S_{f_A} = \frac{\Delta H_{f_A}}{T_{\text{m.p.}_A}} \qquad (10.36)$$

Since ΔS_{f_A} and ΔH_{f_A} are not strongly dependent upon temperature, equation 10.36 may be substituted into 10.35 and

$$\ln (1 - X_B{}^l) = \frac{\Delta H_{f_A}}{R} \left(\frac{1}{T_{\text{m.p.}_A}} - \frac{1}{T} \right) \qquad (10.37)$$

Equation 10.37 is the equation for the liquidus line in equilibrium with α. If $X_B{}^l$ from equation 10.37 is substituted into equation 10.32, $X_{B(\text{sat})}^\alpha$ is obtained explicitly as a function of temperature, if the thermodynamic terms, $\Delta \bar{H}_B{}^\alpha$ and ΔH_{f_A} are known. In order to facilitate calculations let us assume that ΔH_{f_A} and ΔS_{f_B} are 8000 cal/gm-atom and 3 e.u. respectively. Thus, using equation 10.32, $X_{B(\text{sat})}^\alpha$ may be plotted versus T for various values of $\Delta \bar{H}_B{}^\alpha$. Several solvus lines obtained in this manner are shown in Fig. 10.14 for germanium as the solvent. Curve (e) in Fig. 10.14 is the liquidus line calculated from equation 10.37. The solidus curves labeled (a), (b), (c), and (d) were calculated from equation 10.32 using values of $\Delta H_B{}^\alpha$ equal to 22,000, 16,600, 11,000, and 5500 cal/gm-atom respectively. It is observed that the tendency toward retrograde solubility is directly related to the relative partial molar enthalpy of

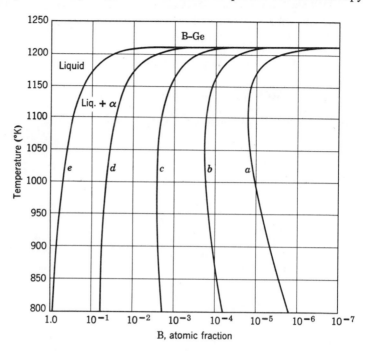

Fig. 10.14 Solvus lines calculated from equation 10.32 for various values of $\Delta \bar{H}_B{}^\alpha$. Curve a, $\Delta \bar{H}_B{}^\alpha = +22$ kcal/mole; b, $+16.6$ kcal/mole; c, $+11$ kcal/mole; d, $+5.5$ kcal/mole; e, liquidus. From C. D. Thurmond and J. D. Struthers, *J. Phys. Chem.*, **57**, 831 (1953).

solute in solid solvent. Curve (d) for example, for which $\Delta \bar{H}_B{}^\alpha$ is relatively low, shows no tendency toward retrograde solubility, but, as $\Delta \bar{H}_B{}^\alpha$ is increased, the tendency toward retrograde solubility is also increased. If the solute has a low melting point, ΔH_{f_B} will not appear in equation 10.32, and thus retrograde solubility will occur for much lower values of $\Delta \bar{H}_B{}^\alpha$. The reason why retrograde solubility is not observed in most metallic systems is that $\Delta \bar{H}_B{}^\alpha$ is too low. Actually the values of $\Delta \bar{H}_B{}^\alpha$ needed for this appearance of this phenomenon are quite large. From our earlier discussions, it may be seen that a large value of $\Delta \bar{H}_B{}^\alpha$ is associated with a low solubility of B in the α phase. As a result this retrograde solubility phenomenon will generally only be observed in systems exhibiting low solubility. Most systems involving germanium and silicon as solvents are of this type.

For the above example, it was not necessary to assume that the solid and liquid solutions behave regularly and ideally, respectively, but the simplicity achieved warranted the assumptions. These restrictions do not invalidate the general conclusion that retrograde solubility is associated directly with a large value of $\Delta \bar{H}_\mathrm{B}^{\alpha}$.

chapter 11

Free Energy of Binary Systems

11.1 INTRODUCTION

In the last chapter some special cases were considered for which quantitative thermodynamic data could be obtained strictly from phase diagrams. It is the purpose of this chapter to examine the problem of equilibrium of coexisting phases from a more general point of view. Generally speaking, this point of view does not yield quantitative results but important semiquantitative deductions often result.

First, let us examine the general shape of a free energy versus composition curve for a general solution, in the vicinity of either end of the binary. The free energy of mixing at some particular composition will be given by the equation

$$\Delta G_m = X_A \Delta \bar{H}_A + X_B \Delta \bar{H}_B + RT[X_A \ln X_A + X_B \ln X_B] \\ - TX_A \Delta \bar{S}_{v_A} - TX_B \Delta \bar{S}_{v_B} \quad (11.1)$$

if short range order is not important. Differentiating ΔG_m with respect to X_B at constant temperature and pressure, we find

$$\frac{\partial \Delta G_m}{\partial X_B} = -\Delta \bar{H}_A + \Delta \bar{H}_B + RT \ln \left(\frac{X_B}{1 - X_B} \right) - T\Delta \bar{S}_{v_A} - T\Delta \bar{S}_{v_B}$$

$$(11.2)$$

Considering a dilute solution of component B in A, we may say that $\Delta \bar{H}_A$ and $\Delta \bar{S}_A = 0$ and $(1 - X_B) \cong 1$. Thus

$$\frac{\partial \Delta G_m}{\partial X_B} \cong \Delta \bar{H}_B + RT \ln X_B - T\Delta \bar{S}_{v_B} \quad (11.3)$$

In equation 11.3, $\Delta \bar{H}_B$ and $\Delta \bar{S}_{v_B}$ will not depend on composition in the dilute range and hence the value of $(\partial \Delta G_m/\partial X_B)$ will depend on composition only, through the second term on the right hand side of the equation. Regardless of the sign of $\Delta \bar{H}_B$ and $\Delta \bar{S}_{v_B}$ terms, $(\partial \Delta G_m/\partial X_B)$ will always be negative at sufficiently small values of X_B, since $\ln X_B \to -\infty$ as $X_B \to 0$. Thus the introduction of a solute into a crystal will always result in a decrease in free energy of the system, hence a pure phase is always thermodynamically unstable. This conclusion has important ramifications in connection with the important process of manufacturing hyper-pure materials, since it says that the pure material will always tend to become impure by the process of absorbing impurities from its environment. Thus, if a pure material is being contained in a crucible, the crucible material will tend to dissolve in the pure material, at least to a limited extent.

11.2 FREE ENERGY VERSUS COMPOSITION FOR CASE WHEN A AND B HAVE THE SAME CRYSTAL STRUCTURE

In this situation it is theoretically possible for A and B to form a continuous solid solution since both components have the same crystal structure. A little reflection will show that if A and B have different structures a continuous solution is impossible. We know that

$$\Delta G_m = \Delta H_m - T \Delta S_m$$

at a given temperature. If ΔH_m is negative, ΔG_m as a function of X_B will be negative at all compositions, since $-T \Delta S_m$ is always negative. These terms are shown in Fig. 11.1. If, on the other hand, ΔH_m is positive, the situation becomes more complicated. The shape of the free energy versus composition curve may change strongly with temperature. At high temperatures, the $T \Delta S_m$ term will be more important than at low temperatures, hence it is possible at high temperatures that the curve ΔG_m versus X_B will be concave downward at all compositions, as shown in Fig. 11.1. As the temperature is lowered, however, the ΔH_m term will begin to dominate in the free energy expression, and the ΔG_m versus X_B curve will tend to be positive. As discussed in Section 11.1, near the ends of the binary ΔG_m is always negative, so the complete curve will be shown in Fig. 11.2. If the solution is regular, the minima are symmetric about $X_B = 0.5$ and are associated with the same value of ΔG_m.

Consider now an alloy of composition a. It will have a value of ΔG_m equal to ΔG_a and negative. Therefore this solution is stable relative to pure A and B. The same is true for alloy c. Consider alloy x, however.

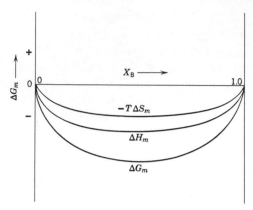

Fig. 11.1   Free energy versus composition for a solution when ΔH_m is negative.

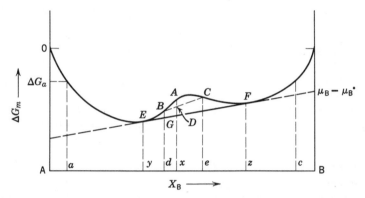

Fig. 11.2   Free energy versus composition for a solution when ΔH_m is a large positive value.   From L. S. Darken and R. W. Gurry, *Physical Chemistry of Metals*, McGraw-Hill, New York, 1953.

It might have a negative value of ΔG_m, but we have to question whether or not ΔG_m could be lower by dissociating the solution.   Suppose it dissociates into two solutions having compositions d and e respectively. The free energy of the system now will be the free energy of solution of composition d given by B times the amount of solution of this composition, plus the free energy of solution of composition e given by C times the amount of the solution.   The fraction of the system which is solution of composition d is obtained from the lever rule, and is equal to $(e - x)/(e - d)$. Similarly the fraction of solution of composition e is $(x - d)/(e - d)$. Thus the value of ΔG_m of the whole system is

$$\Delta G_m = \frac{(e - x)}{(e - d)}B + \frac{(x - d)}{(e - d)}C = D$$

The value of D is lower than A, the initial value of ΔG_m before dissociation, but ΔG_m will be lowered still further by making the solution of composition d richer in component A and the solution of composition e richer in component B. The lowest stable value of ΔG_m which can be attained by the decomposition is G at compositions y and z respectively. These solutions are in equilibrium with one another since component B would have the same chemical potential in both. It is important to note that compositions y and z are not necessarily associated with the minima of the ΔG_m versus X_B curve. The free energies E and F may be considerably different from the minimum values, since the important criterion

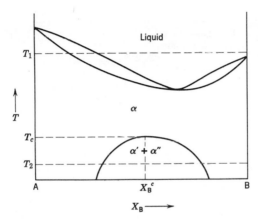

Fig. 11.3 Phase diagram showing a miscibility gap. At T_2, free energy diagram is given by Fig. 11.2.

for equilibrium is that the chemical potential of a given component is the same in both phases, not that the free energy of each phase be a minimum. This criterion obviously cannot be met by drawing tangents at the minimum values of the ΔG_m versus X_B curve unless they happen to coincide at the same ΔG_m values. Thus, solutions to the left and the right of y and z respectively are stable, whereas solutions of composition y and z are unstable and will dissociate into two coexisting phases. Such a free energy curve is associated with a miscibility gap on a phase diagram. At higher temperatures the minima move closer together in composition and finally disappear completely at a critical temperature, T_c. The type of phase diagram associated with Fig. 11.2 is shown in Fig. 11.3. At temperature T_2, the free energy versus composition diagram would be similar to that shown in Fig. 11.2. In connection to Fig. 11.2 it will be observed that two inflection points exist between y and z. Such an inflection point is called a *spinode* and plays an important role in the kinetics of phase decomposition.

Let us now consider the activity of components A and B associated with the free energy curve shown in Fig. 11.2. Considering component B as an example we may find ($\mu_B - \mu_B^\cdot$) at any composition by extrapolating the slope of the curve at that composition to $X_B = 1$. The value of a_B may readily be obtained since

$$\mu_B - \mu_B^\cdot = RT \ln a_B$$

As derived from Fig. 11.2, the curve of a_B versus X_B is shown in Fig. 11.4. At the compositions y and z, component B will have the same activity

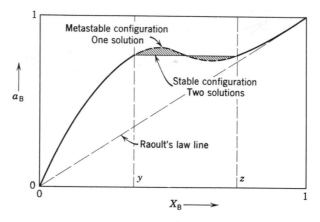

Fig. 11.4   Activity of component B at temperature T_2 for solution of Fig. 11.3. From L. S. Darken and R. W. Gurry, *Physical Chemistry of Metals*, McGraw-Hill, New York, 1953.

according to the requirement for equilibrium. The maximum and minimum in a_B correspond to the spinodal points of the ΔG_m versus X_B diagram. It may be shown that the areas of the shaded portions are equal.

Let us now consider the phase diagram shown in Fig. 11.3 at temperature T_1. The situation is somewhat more complicated, since T_1 is above the melting point of component B, and therefore the standard state of component B has changed from solid B to liquid B. It is impossible to have a continuous free energy curve between solid and liquid solutions and therefore two curves will be needed; one for the solid solution and one for the liquid solution, as shown schematically in Fig. 11.5. At pure component B, the solid curve intersects the free energy axis at a point equal to the negative of the free energy of fusion for component B. This point represents the free energy of formation of solid B from liquid B. ΔG_m for liquid B is equal to zero since this is the standard state. Similarly, the liquid curve intersects the free energy axis at a point higher than zero for pure A since ΔG_m for solid A is zero at T_1. It is apparent from free energy considerations that when $X_B < X_B{}^s$ on Fig. 11.5, the solid solution is stable and when $X_B{}^s < X_B < X_B{}^l$, two phases will coexist, α solid phase of composition $X_B{}^s$, and liquid phase of $X_B{}^l$. When $X_B > X_B{}^l$, liquid solution is stable.

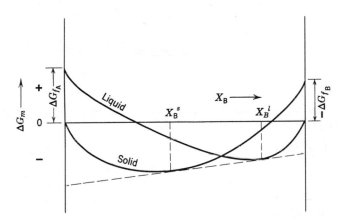

Fig. 11.5   Free energy of solid and liquid solutions corresponding to temperature T_1 on the phase diagram of Fig. 11.3.

The value of $(\mu_B{}^s - \mu_B{}^\cdot)$ and $(\mu_A{}^l - \mu_A{}^\cdot)$ may be readily estimated at any temperature.   For component B at the melting point

$$\Delta G_f = \Delta H_f - T_{\text{m.p.}} \, \Delta S_f = 0$$

At a temperature different from $T_{\text{m.p.}}$

$$\Delta G_f = \Delta H_f - T \, \Delta S_f \neq 0$$

Neglecting the small temperature dependence of ΔH_f and ΔS_f, we find on substitution for ΔS_f

$$\Delta G_f = \Delta H_f(1 - T/T_{\text{m.p.}_B}) \tag{11.4}$$

In the case of component B at T_1 we are interested in the reaction

$$B(l) = B(s) \qquad \Delta G = -\Delta G_f = -(\mu_B{}^s - \mu_B{}^\cdot) = -\Delta H_f(1 - T_1/T_{\text{m.p.}_B})$$

At a temperature above the melting point of component A, both liquid A and B are stable and the ΔG_m versus X_B diagrams for liquid and solid solutions are shown in Fig. 11.6.

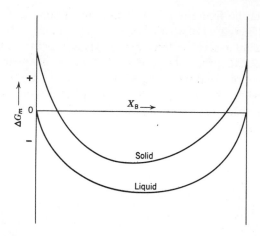

Fig. 11.6 Free energy of solid and liquid solutions corresponding to a temperature above $T_{m.p.}$ of component A of Fig. 11.3.

The critical temperature, T_c, associated with the miscibility gas of the phase diagram of Fig. 11.3, is determined by the magnitude of the heat of mixing. For purpose of illustration, let us consider a miscibility gap for a regular solution, because of ease of calculation for this type of system. For such a system

$$\Delta H_m = X_A X_B \Omega$$

$$\Delta S_m = -R(X_A \ln X_A + X_B \ln X_B)$$

and   (11.5)

$$\Delta G_m = \Omega X_A X_B + RT(X_A \ln X_A + X_B \ln X_B)$$

Let us calculate the maximum critical temperature, T_c, where decomposition will occur and the composition of the solution $X_B{}^c$, at this temperature. These points are shown on Fig. 11.3. Above the temperature T_c, the curve of ΔG_m versus X_B is everywhere concave downward. Below this temperature, two minima will occur as already discussed and there will be two inflection points where

$$\left(\frac{\partial^2 \Delta G_m}{\partial X_B{}^2}\right) = 0$$

As the temperature is raised toward T_c, the minima will move closer together in composition and as a result so will the inflection points. At T_c, both minima and the inflection points will coincide at the same temperature. Thus T_c is the temperature where both $\partial \Delta G_m / \partial X_B$ and

$\partial^2 \Delta G_m / \partial X_B^2$ equal zero at the critical composition X_B^c. Performing these operations upon equation 11.2 we find

$$\frac{\partial \Delta G_m}{\partial X_B} = \Omega(1 - 2X_B^c) + RT_c \ln \frac{X_B^c}{1 - X_B^c} = 0$$

$$\frac{\partial^2 \Delta G_m}{\partial X_B^2} = -2\Omega + \frac{RT_c}{X_B^c(1 - X_B^c)} = 0$$

Solving for T_c we find

$$T_c = \frac{2X_B^c(1 - X_B^c)\Omega}{R} \tag{11.6}$$

From equation 11.6 we see that Ω must be positive in order for T_c to be positive. Further, X_B^c is such that T_c is the maximum decomposition temperature associated with the miscibility gap. The value of X_B^c that makes T_c a maximum in equation 11.6 is $X_B^c = 0.5$. Thus

$$T_c = \frac{\Omega}{2R} \tag{11.7}$$

According to quasichemical theory, a positive value of Ω indicates a repulsive interaction between unlike components. Thus, from equation 11.7, the larger this repulsive interaction, the higher the temperature will be where decomposition begins. As a generalization, we might say that virtually all systems with a positive ΔH_m should show a miscibility gap. This is not found experimentally. The reason for this lack of agreement with theory is related to the fact that unless ΔH_m is sufficiently large, T_c will be so low that the kinetics of the decomposition in the solid state will be infinitesimally fast, and thus a solid solution will be generally found which is actually metastable. Because of the slow rate of diffusion at low temperatures, most phase diagrams are probably not accurate in their low temperature region.

11.3 FREE ENERGY VERSUS COMPOSITION FOR CASE WHERE COMPONENTS A AND B HAVE DIFFERENT CRYSTAL STRUCTURES

A typical ΔG_m versus composition diagram is shown in Fig. 11.7. On this diagram the ΔG_m versus composition curves are shown for the two terminal solid solutions. In addition a curve is shown for a hypothetical intermediate phase. The question arises as to what the phase diagram looks like for this situation. Does β exist as a stable phase at this temperature? It might be noted that ΔG_m for the β phase of composition c is negative, so clearly β is more stable than pure A and B.

It must be asked, however, whether or not some other combination of phases might not be more stable. From examination of the diagram, it is clear than when $a < X_B < b$, the situation yielding the most negative value of ΔG_m is a coexistence of α and γ phases. For β to be present in this range, the ΔG_m curve for the intermediate phase must be lower than the dashed line representing the equilibrium composition of α in

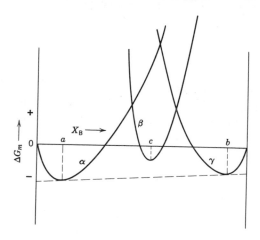

Fig. 11.7 Free energy of solid phases having different crystal structures.

equilibrium with the equilibrium composition of γ. Such a situation is shown in Fig. 11.8. From examination of the diagram it can be seen that when

(a) $X_B < X_{B(sat)}^{\alpha}$, α phase is stable

(b) $X_{B(sat)}^{\alpha} < X_B < b$, $\alpha + \beta$ coexist

(c) $b < X_B < c$, β phase is stable

(d) $c < X_B < X_{B(sat)}^{\gamma}$, $\beta + \gamma$ coexist

(e) $X_B > X_{B(sat)}^{\gamma}$, γ phase is stable

It should be noted that even though the composition limits of β may be small, a very large variation in $\mu_B - \mu_B^{\cdot}$, and hence a_B may occur across the composition range. As shown in Fig. 11.8, the value of $(\mu_B - \mu_B^{\cdot})$ in β at the composition where α and β are in equilibrium is considerably different from the value when β is in equilibrium with γ. In fact an order of magnitude change in a_B may result across a narrow composition range. In Fig. 11.9 is shown the diagram for a_A and a_B versus composition derived from Fig. 11.8.

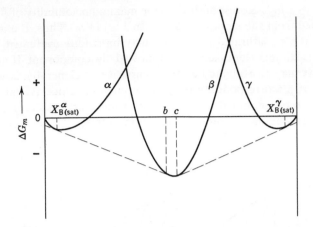

Fig. 11.8 Free energy versus composition diagram showing intermediate phase.

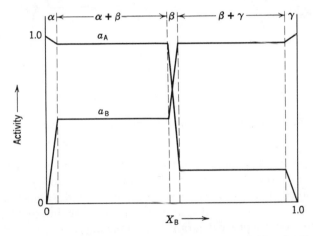

Fig. 11.9 Activity of components A and B versus composition for Fig. 11.8.

The phase diagram corresponding to Fig. 11.8 is shown in Fig. 11.10.

From Fig. 11.8 we see that the more negative the value of the free energy of formation of the intermediate phase the more restricted the terminal solutions α and γ will be. In other words, the intermediate phase might be said to form at the expense of the terminal solid solutions.

It is often desirable to know the activity of solute in a terminal solid solution for systems which involve one or more intermediate phases. If the curve of ΔG_m versus X_B for the intermediate phase shown in Fig. 11.8 is known, no problem is presented, since from the shape of the curve, $(\mu_B - \mu_B^\cdot)$ corresponding to the maximum solubility of β in α may be obtained from the slopes as shown in Fig. 11.8. Thus, the activity of component β in saturated α solution may be readily evaluated. If the α solution is dilute, Henry's law is followed by component B and hence the activity may be evaluated at any composition. Generally, however, the curve of ΔG_m (corresponding to ΔG_f°) versus X_B is not available for the intermediate phase, but for some phases a more or less average value of ΔG_f° corresponding to some composition between b and c is available.

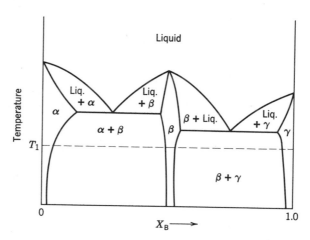

Fig. 11.10 Phase diagram corresponding to free energy versus composition diagram of Fig. 11.8.

If this datum is available, a close approximation of a_B in α may be made through the method described below. Let both α and γ be restricted solutions so Henry's law is followed by the solute and Raoult's law by the solvent. Since we supposedly know ΔG_f° for the intermediate phase adjacent to α on the phase diagram, this is the logical reaction to consider first, since this phase is in equilibrium with saturated α. Since we are going to need $(\mu_B - \mu_B^\cdot)$ in saturated α in order to obtain a_B and hence γ_B° in α, let us assume that ΔG_f° for the intermediate phase of composition b is the same as the average value which has been measured. ΔG_m^α for the saturated α solution is given by

$$\Delta G_m^\alpha = RT[(1 - X_{B(sat)}^\alpha) \ln (1 - X_{B(sat)}^\alpha) + a_B \ln a_B] \quad (11.8)$$

Therefore the slope of ΔG_m versus X_B for the α phase at composition a in equilibrium with the intermediate phase is

$$\frac{\partial \Delta G_m}{\partial X_B} = \left[\frac{(\Delta G_f^\circ - \Delta G_m^\alpha)}{b - X_{B(sat)}^\alpha} \right] \quad (11.9)$$

We have shown that

$$\mu_B - \mu_B^{\cdot} = \Delta G_m + (1 - X_B)\left[\frac{\partial \Delta G_m{}^{\alpha}}{\partial X_B}\right] \tag{11.10}$$

Upon substitution we find

$$\mu_B - \mu_B^{\cdot} + \Delta G_f{}^{\circ} + (1 - b)\left[\frac{\Delta G_f{}^{\circ} - \Delta G_m{}^{\alpha}}{b - X_{B(sat)}^{\alpha}}\right] = RT \ln a_B \tag{11.11}$$

For a restricted solution, $|\Delta G_m{}^{\alpha}| \ll |\Delta G_f{}^{\circ}|$, and so will be neglected. Thus, since a_B in the intermediate phase at b is the same as a_B in saturated α, we find upon equating 11.11 with 11.10 with substitution of 11.9:

$$RT \ln a_B = RT \ln \gamma_B{}^{\circ} + RT \ln X_{B(sat)}^{\alpha} \cong \left[\frac{1 - X_{B(sat)}^{\alpha}}{b - X_{B(sat)}^{\alpha}}\right] \Delta G_f{}^{\circ}$$

or

$$\gamma_B{}^{\circ} = \frac{1}{X_{B(sat)}^{\alpha}} \exp\left[\frac{(1 - X_{B(sat)}^{\alpha}) \Delta G_f{}^{\circ}}{(b - X_{B(sat)}^{\alpha}) RT}\right] \tag{11.12}$$

Thus, by knowing the composition of the saturated α phase and the intermediate phase as well as $\Delta G_f{}^{\circ}$ for formation of this phase, the activity coefficient $\gamma_B{}^{\circ}$ in α may be evaluated. Very often, however, the free energy of formation of intermediate phases is not available. The heat of formation, however, may have been evaluated. The entropy of formation, $\Delta S_f{}^{\circ}$, is composed of a vibrational contribution and a mixing contribution. Generally the mixing term is close to zero, since the intermediate phases are usually strongly ordered and hence the mixing randomness is small. The vibrational contribution, although sometimes significant, is generally small even when multiplied by T, compared with $\Delta G_f{}^{\circ}$. Thus we may say that $\Delta G_f{}^{\circ} \cong \Delta H_f{}^{\circ}$. As an approximation therefore, $\Delta H_f{}^{\circ}$ may be substituted for $\Delta G_f{}^{\circ}$ in equation 11.12, particularly for very stable intermediate phases. Suppose now that the β phase exists in a metastable crystal structure. The free energy of formation of this structure will be more positive than the corresponding value for the stable structure. This is, of course, true since if $\Delta G_f{}^{\circ}$ were more negative it would be more stable. As a result the common target to the α and β phases will become more horizontal and the composition $X_{B(sat)}^{\alpha}$ will become larger indicating, as discussed in Section 10.4, that the solubility of a metastable phase is always higher than the solubility of a stable phase.

11.4 SOLIDUS AND LIQUIDUS LINES FOR AN IDEAL SOLUTION

Consider that components A and B form ideal solutions in both the liquid and the solid states. Intuitively it might be anticipated that, for such a system, the solidus and liquidus lines merge. It will be shown that this is not the case. Consider the free energy curves of liquid and solid solutions below the melting point T for component A but above the melting point for component B. Thus our reference states are pure solid component A and pure liquid component B. The ΔG_m versus X_B curves

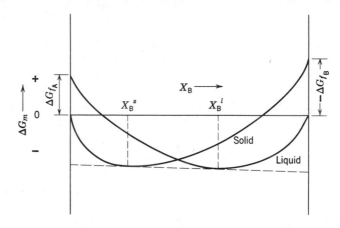

Fig. 11.11 Free energy for solid and liquid solutions below the melting point of component A but above the melting point of component B.

for the two phases are shown in Fig. 11.11. We may now derive analytically the curves for each type of solution. Since the liquid solution is ideal, we have for the reaction

$$X_A \text{ moles of A}(l) + X_B \text{ moles of B}(l) = \text{liquid solution }(X_A, X_B) \quad (11.13)$$

The free energy of mixing is

$$\Delta G_m = RT(X_A \ln X_A + X_B \ln X_B) \quad (11.14)$$

Since our standard state is solid component A, instead of liquid, we must consider the following reaction in order to obtain the equation for the curve on Fig. 11.11:

$$X_A \text{ moles of A}(s) = X_A \text{ moles of A}(l) \qquad \Delta G = X_A \, \Delta G_{f_A} \quad (11.15)$$

Adding equation 11.13, we have

$$X_A \text{ A}(s) + X_B \text{ B}(l) = \text{liquid solution }(X_A, X_B) \quad (11.16)$$

$$\Delta G_m{}^l = X_A{}^l \, \Delta G_{f_A} + RT\,(X_A{}^l \ln X_A{}^l + X_B{}^l \ln X_B{}^l) \quad (11.17)$$

Similarly for the solid solution,

$$X_A \, A(s) + X_B \, B(s) = \text{solid solution } (X_A, X_B)$$

$$\Delta G_m = RT(X_A{}^s \ln X_A{}^s + X_B{}^s \ln X_B{}^s)$$

$$X_B \, B(l) = X_B \, B(s) \qquad \Delta G = -X_B{}^s \, \Delta G_{f_B}$$

$$X_A \, A(s) + X_B \, B(l) = \text{solid solution } (X_A, X_B)$$

$$\Delta G_m{}^s = -X_B{}^s \, \Delta G_{f_B} + RT \, (X_A{}^s \ln X_A{}^s + X_B{}^s \ln X_B{}^s) \quad (11.18)$$

In a previous section we showed that if the small heat capacity corrections to ΔH_f and ΔS_f are neglected

$$\Delta G_{f_A} = \Delta H_{f_A} \left(1 - \frac{T}{T_{\text{m.p.}_A}} \right)$$

At equilibrium, the chemical potential of component B is the same in liquid and solid, and thus the slopes are equal, or

$$\frac{\partial \, \Delta G_m{}^s}{\partial X_B} = \frac{\partial \, \Delta G_m{}^l}{\partial X_B}$$

Performing the differentiation, equating, and rearranging, we find at a given temperature

$$-\ln \frac{X_B{}^s}{X_B{}^l} + \ln \frac{X_A{}^s}{X_A{}^l} = \frac{\Delta H_{f_A}}{R} \left(\frac{1}{T} - \frac{1}{T_{\text{m.p.}_A}} \right) - \frac{\Delta H_{f_B}}{R} \left(\frac{1}{T} - \frac{1}{T_{\text{m.p.}_B}} \right) \quad (11.19)$$

The equation above contains two unknowns, so appeal must be made to other considerations in order to solve. As we approach $T_{\text{m.p.}_A}$, $X_A{}^s$ and $X_A{}^l \to 1$ and hence $\ln X_A{}^s/X_A{}^l \to 0$. The second term on the left hand side of equation 11.19 $\to 0$ and, since $1/T \to 1/T_{\text{m.p.}_A}$, we have the relation

$$\ln \frac{X_B{}^s}{X_B{}^l} = \frac{\Delta H_{f_B}}{R} \left(\frac{1}{T} - \frac{1}{T_{\text{m.p.}_B}} \right) \quad (11.20)$$

Doing the same thing at the other end of the diagram, we have

$$\ln \frac{X_A{}^s}{X_A{}^l} = \frac{\Delta H_{f_A}}{R} \left(\frac{1}{T} - \frac{1}{T_{\text{m.p.}_A}} \right) \quad (11.21)$$

Solving equations 11.20 and 11.21 as a function of T, we find the phase diagram shown in Fig. 11.12. Thurmond,[1] using such an approach, has

[1] C. D. Thurmond, *J. Electrochem Soc.*, **57**, 827 (1953).

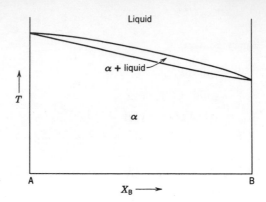

Fig. 11.12 Phase diagram for case where A and B form ideal solutions in both liquid and solid states.

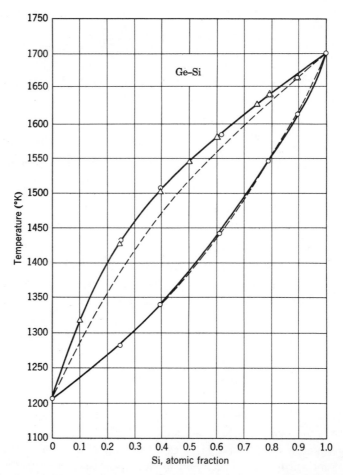

Fig. 11.13 Phase diagram for the nearly ideal Ge-Si system. Solid line, experimental; dashed line, calculated. From C. D. Thurmond, *J. Phys. Chem.*, **57,** 827 (1953).

calculated the liquidus and solidus curves for the germanium-silicon binary system and finds very close agreement with experimental curves. As a result, from the phase diagram data, one is able to conclude that germanium and silicon form nearly ideal solutions. This diagram is shown in Fig. 11.13.

11.5 RELATIONS BETWEEN PHASE DIAGRAMS OF DIFFERENT TYPES

Superficially there does not seem to be much similarity between, say, a phase diagram for which both elements are miscible in all proportions such as shown in Fig. 11.12 and a eutectic phase diagram. Thermodynamically, however, these diagrams represent only differences in degree

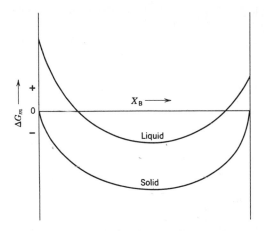

Fig. 11.14   Free energy diagrams of liquid and solid solutions at temperature T_1 below melting points of A and B; $\Delta H_m{}^s$ more negative than $\Delta H_m{}^l$.

and not necessarily fundamental differences in the nature of the components. We have just considered the phase diagram resulting for components forming an ideal solution in the liquid and solid states. Let us remove this restriction and consider a general case for which ΔH_m is negative. Consider further that ΔH_m is more negative for the solid than for the liquid solution. At a temperature T_1 well below the melting points of either component, the free energy versus composition curves would appear schematically as shown in Fig. 11.14. Above the melting point of both components at temperature T_2, the curves would appear as shown in Fig. 11.15. The curve for the solid reaches a lower value than does that for the solid since $\Delta H_m{}^s$ is more negative in this case than $\Delta H_m{}^l$.

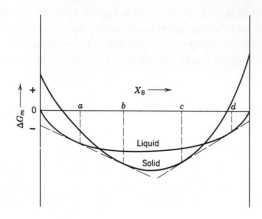

Fig. 11.15 Free energy diagrams of liquid and solid solutions at temperature T_2 above the melting points of both components.

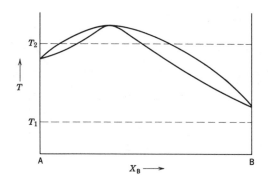

Fig. 11.16 Phase diagram corresponding to free energy curves of Figs. 11.14 and 11.15.

The lowest free energy of the system is attained if when

(a) $X_B < a$, liquid solution is stable

(b) $a < X_B < b$, liquid and solid solutions coexist

(c) $b < X_B < c$, solid solution is stable

(d) $c < X_B < d$, liquid and solid coexist

(e) $X_B > d$, liquid solution is stable

This gives rise to a melting point maximum and a phase diagram as shown in Fig. 11.16.

In a qualitative sense this diagram is readily understood in quasi-chemical terms. A negative value of ΔH_m reflects an attractive interaction between unlike neighbors. Since ΔH_m is more negative for the solid solution than for the liquid, this attraction would be more pronounced in the solid, and because of the strong bonding resulting from this attraction, the melting point would be increased of the solid solution relative to both components.

Let us now consider the case of a positive value of the heat of mixing with ΔH_m for the solid solution being more positive than that for the liquid. Above the melting point of either component the ΔG_m versus X_B

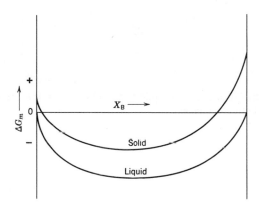

Fig. 11.17 Free energy diagrams of liquid and solid solutions at temperature T_1 above the melting points of both components; $\Delta H_m{}^s > \Delta H_m{}^l > 0$.

diagram may appear as shown in Fig. 11.17. At some temperature T_2 below the melting point of the components, the curves would appear as shown in Fig. 11.18. The free energy curve for the solid solution would exhibit minima at a higher temperature than the curve for the liquid solution, since $\Delta H_m{}^s > \Delta H_m{}^l > 0$.

The most stable situation at various compositions is

(a) $X_B < a$, solid solution is stable
(b) $a < X_B < b$, solid and liquid coexist
(c) $b < X_B < c$, liquid solution is stable
(d) $c < X_B < d$, solid and liquid coexist
(e) $X_B > d$, solid solution is stable

This gives rise to a melting point minimum, and in quasichemical terms results from a repulsive interaction between unlike nearest neighbors and hence a weakening of the crystal structure. At a lower temperature, T_3, the situation may be as shown in Fig. 11.19.

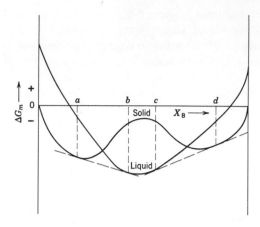

Fig. 11.18 Free energy diagrams of liquid and solid solutions at temperature T_2 below melting points of both components.

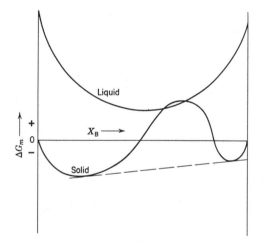

Fig. 11.19 Free energy diagrams of liquid and solid solutions at temperature T_3 below T_2.

At this temperature a miscibility gap will result. The phase diagram associated with this type of system is shown in Fig. 11.20, with Figs. 11.17, 11.18, and 11.19 being associated with T_1, T_2, and T_3 respectively. If a case is considered for which the heat of mixing is more positive than in the former case, the melting point minimum is reduced in temperature and the critical temperature for the miscibility gap is raised until finally they overlap. When this occurs a simple eutectic will result.

This gradation between various types of phase diagrams is shown in Fig. 11.21. Fig. 11.21a shows a phase diagram for an ideal solution. If the heat of mixing in the solid and liquid solutions is positive but $\Delta H_m^s >$ ΔH_m^l, the critical temperature for the miscibility gap is raised and the melting point minimum is lowered until finally they overlap, with the

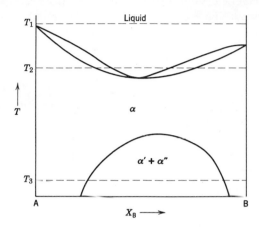

Fig. 11.20 Phase diagram corresponding to Figs. 11.17, 11.18, and 11.19.

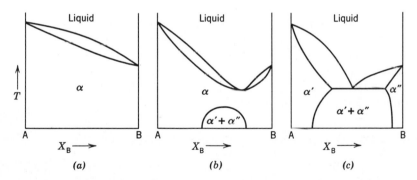

Fig. 11.21 (a) Phase diagram for an ideal solution. (b) Phase diagram for case where $\Delta H_m^s > \Delta H_m^l > 0$. (c) Same as (b) except that ΔH_m is more positive.

resultant eutectic phase diagram shown in Fig. 11.21c. A further increase in ΔH_m will result in a larger two-phase region ($\alpha + \alpha'$) and thus more narrow terminal solution regions.

The opposite situation, for which the heat of mixing is negative, is shown in Fig. 11.22. If the heat of mixing for liquid and solid solutions is negative but ΔH_m^s is more negative than ΔH_m^l, a melting point maximum will result. Further, at low temperatures, the solid solution will tend to order so as to maximize the number of unlike pairs in solution. This was discussed in Chapter 9. The resultant phase diagram is shown in Fig. 11.22b. As $\Delta H_m{}^s$ becomes more negative, the tendency for ordering in the solid solution in order to maximize the number of unlike pairs will be increased. Ultimately an intermediate phase would result which would have a crystal structure different from the parent phases. This structure would be such as to maximize the number of unlike pairs

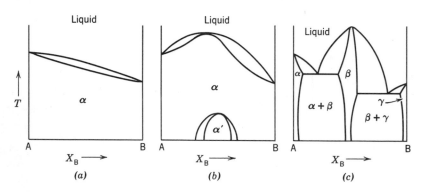

Fig. 11.22 (*a*) Phase diagram for an ideal solution. (*b*) Phase diagram for case where $\Delta H_m{}^s < \Delta H_m{}^l < 0$. (*c*) Same as (*b*) except that ΔH_m is more negative.

and minimize their distance of separation. Such a phase would tend to be stable and hence would have a high melting point. In a sense, this would be similar to the critical temperature for ordering being increased. If this phase were sufficiently stable, its melting point would be higher than the maximum of the liquidus and solidus resulting in a phase diagram of the type shown in Fig. 11.22c.

11.6   COMPOSITION FLUCTUATIONS IN SOLUTIONS

In the chapter concerning quasichemical theory, ordering in solid solutions was discussed from the point of view of the energetics of inter-action of the atoms in solution. We are at the point now in the presenta-tion of thermodynamic principles where more general considerations may be invoked. The principles to be discussed in this section are of paramount importance to the theory of phase transformations. At an elevated temperature, the atoms in a solution are in continual motion and as a result various metastable configurations will occur. We are concerned here, in particular, with the probability that a region containing n atoms in a homogeneous solution will deviate in composition an amount ΔX_B from the average composition $\bar{X}_B$. It can be seen that this phenomenon has considerable importance in understanding phase transformations, since in a decomposition or precipitation reaction, a phase considerably different in composition from the parent solution must form. Obviously then a small region rich in solute must be present in the parent solution. One way in which such regions may form is through random composition fluctuations of the type discussed here. Consider the free energy versus composition diagram shown in Fig. 11.23, where the average composition

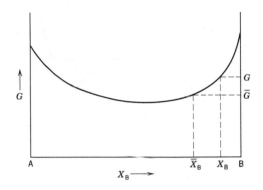

Fig. 11.23   Free energy versus composition diagram.

$\bar{X}_{\mathrm{B}}$ and average free energy per atom $\bar{G}$ are shown. Consider now that a region containing n atoms forms in which the composition is X_{B}. The free energy per atom in this region is G. From Boltzmann statistics, the probability that an atom will have a free energy G different from the average free energy per atom in solution, $\bar{G}$, is

$$p_{\Delta G} = A \exp\left[-(G - \bar{G})/kT\right] = \exp\left[-\Delta G/kT\right] \qquad (11.22)$$

The probability that n atoms will have this same free energy G simultaneous will be

$$p_{\Delta G}{}^{n} = A \exp\left[-n\,\Delta G/kT\right] \qquad (11.23)$$

Let us consider for ease of calculation, the situation for which ΔX_{B} is small and hence ΔG is small. We expand G in a Taylor's series about $\bar{X}_{\mathrm{B}}$. Thus

$$G = \bar{G} + \frac{1}{2}\left(\frac{d^{2}G}{dX_{\mathrm{B}}{}^{2}}\right)(X_{\mathrm{B}} - \bar{X}_{\mathrm{B}})^{2} + \cdots \qquad (11.24)$$

If $|X_{\mathrm{B}} - \bar{X}_{\mathrm{B}}| \ll 1$, terms which are of higher order than the second are

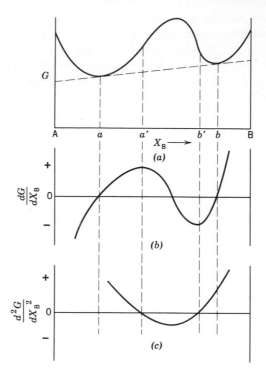

Fig. 11.24 (a) Free energy versus composition diagram for case where $\Delta H_m > 0$. (b) First derivative of (a) as a function of composition. (c) Second derivative of (a) as a function of composition.

neglected. Substituting equation 11.24, we find that the probability of a small composition fluctuation involving n atoms is

$$p_{\Delta G}{}^n = A' \exp \left(\frac{-n(X_B - \bar{X}_B)^2 (d^2 G_2 / d \bar{X}_B{}^2)_{\bar{x}_B}}{2kT} \right) \qquad (11.25)$$

From equation 11.25 we see that a high probability of a composition fluctuation is associated with a small value of $(d^2 G / d X_B{}^2)_{\bar{X}_B}$. For ease of calculation let us examine this term for a regular solution.

$$G = X_A G_A{}^{\cdot} + X_B G_B{}^{\cdot} + X_A X_B \Omega + RT [X_A \ln X_A + X_B \ln X_B]$$

and

$$\left(\frac{d^2 G}{d X_B{}^2} \right)_{\bar{x}_B} = -2\Omega + \frac{RT}{X_B (1 - X_B)} \qquad (11.26)$$

For a given initial composition and temperature, the second term on the right hand side of equation 11.26 is a constant and thus

$$\left(\frac{d^2G}{dX_2^2}\right)_{\bar{X}_2} = \text{constant} - 2\Omega \qquad (11.27)$$

For an exothermic solution in which Ω is a large negative quantity, the second derivative is large and hence composition fluctuations will not readily occur. When Ω is positive (corresponding to a positive heat of mixing), however, the situation is different. Consider that the solution has a free energy versus composition curve such as shown in Fig. 11.24a. Thermodynamically, of course, solutions of composition in the region $a < \bar{X}_B < b$ are unstable at this temperature, and decomposition will be favored. Hence it is of interest to investigate the value of d^2G/dX_B^2 as a function of initial solution composition. From Fig. 11.24c, it is seen that, if the initial solution has a composition in the region $a' < X_B < b'$, d^2G/dX_B^2 is negative, whereas, if $X_B < a$ or if $X_B > b$, d^2G/dX_B^2 is positive and in fact increases as the value of X_B approaches a and b. Compositions a' and b' correspond to the spinodal points. When $a' < X_B < b'$, the exponent in equation 11.25 is positive and hence $p_{\Delta G}{}^n$ may be greater than 1. A probability larger than unity has no significance, since a value of one indicates that the event will occur. As a result, segregation should occur readily for a solution initially in this composition range. Outside this range the exponent is negative and a fluctuation in composition is increasingly less probable as X_B approaches composition a or c.

chapter 12

Thermodynamics of Interfaces

For purposes of discussion it is convenient to classify interfaces or surfaces into two general categories: (a) external surfaces, and (b) internal surfaces. Specifically, the former category pertains to the interface between the solid phase and the vapor phase, or between the solid phase and a liquid phase. The latter category is conveniently subdivided into: (1) interfaces between crystals of the same phase, called crystal boundaries or grain boundaries, and (2) interfaces between phases of different structure and composition. Before proceeding to a discussion of these specific types of interfaces, it will be worthwhile to discuss some general aspects of the thermodynamic properties of interfaces.

12.1 THE GENERAL THEORY OF INTERFACES

Consider a planar interface between pure phases α and β as shown in Fig. 12.1. This interface is characterized by a surface tension σ expressed in terms of force per unit length. The interface is always a site of disturbance on an atomic scale, since the environment of atoms at the interface is not regular as it is in the interior of the phase. As a result, to increase the area of an interface, work must be expended by the system. In Section 2.2 this work was found to be given by

$$dW = -\sigma \, dA \qquad (12.1)$$

From the first law,

$$dE = DQ - dW$$

and for a reversible process $DQ = T \, dS$. If the only work done by the system is to increase the area of interface, dW is given by equation 12.1.

Thus

$$dE = T\,dS + \sigma\,dA \tag{12.2}$$

Since $H = E + PV$,

$$dH = dE + P\,dV + V\,dP$$

At constant volume and pressure

$$dH = dE \tag{12.3}$$

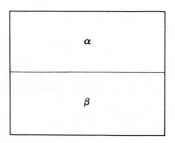

Fig. 12.1 Interface between phases α and β.

The Gibbs free energy is given by

$$G = H - TS$$

and hence

$$dG = dH - T\,dS - S\,dT \tag{12.4}$$

Substitution of equations 12.2 and 12.3 into 12.4 at constant temperature yields

$$dG = \sigma\,dA \tag{12.5}$$

and upon integration we obtain

$$G = \sigma A \tag{12.6}$$

or

$$\sigma = \frac{G}{A} \tag{12.6}$$

if σ is independent of interfacial area A.

We have shown, therefore, that the surface tension or interfacial tension is identical numerically to the surface free energy if expressed in the same type of units. In other words, an interface with a tension of 500 dynes/cm has a surface free energy of 500 ergs/cm^2 from equation 12.6. This numerical identity is very important, since the vector quantity of interfacial tension is the interface term generally measured experimentally. For thermodynamic calculations, however, the free energy term is the most important term. Since the Gibbs free energy is a function of temperature, pressure, and composition, the surface tension is also a function of these quantities. Since the most stable system is one with the lowest value of G, any process that will lower σ, such as selective adsorption of impurities, shortening of interface, etc., will occur spontaneously. It will be recalled that the free energy may be conveniently expressed as the following function of temperature, if ΔH and ΔS are considered to be constants for a given reaction,

$$G = a - bT$$

Hence from 12.6 we find

$$\sigma = \sigma^\circ - b'T \tag{12.7}$$

where a, b, σ°, and b' are constants. In fact from equations 12.6 and 12.7 we see that σ° is the surface tension extrapolated to absolute zero in temperature.

In applying the previous general deductions to solid phases considerable caution must be exerted. For example, let us consider the equilibrium shape of a phase. The geometric form of a body possessing the smallest area per unit volume is, of course, a sphere. As a result, one would expect that objects would tend to assume a spherical shape in order to lower the total free energy of the phase, since $G = \sigma A$. Familiar examples of this are the formation of spherical droplets of mercury, oil, etc. This does not necessarily occur with a crystalline solid, however. Suppose that a single crystal is cut in the form of a sphere and then heated to an elevated temperature or immersed in an acid. Instead of maintaining a spherical shape, crystalline faces begin to develop as shown in Fig. 12.2 for germanium. The reason for this is that σ is not independent of crystal orientation but is strongly dependent upon the types of crystallographic planes forming the interface. This difference between the behavior of liquid and solid is understandable since, for a liquid, the packing of atoms is identical on any arbitrary plane cut through the phase. For a solid however, the arrangement of atoms is a function of the plane. Several arrangements are shown in Fig. 12.3 for a face-centered cubic crystal. It is seen that the arrangement of atoms is considerably different in these faces. One would expect that the energy of the atoms at the interface would depend strongly upon the efficiency of packing and hence of bonding to neighbors. Normally the more close-packed planes would be expected to have the lowest values of σ and hence these would be the planes most likely to develop as interfaces. On the basis of this discussion we may state an important difference between solids and liquids in the following manner: *The value of the interfacial tension between a solid phase and another phase is a function of the plane of the solid forming the interface.*

There is another important distinction between solids and liquids which relates to the derivation of equation 12.6. In order to obtain equation 12.6, equation 12.5 was integrated at constant volume, pressure, and temperature. In the derivation, it was assumed that σ, equal to the free energy per unit area, is not a function of area. This seems to be a very

Fig. 12.2 Etched sphere of germanium. Note crystal faces which have appeared. From B. W. Batterman, *J. Appl. Phys.*, **28**, 1236 (1957).

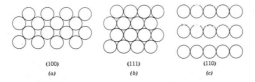

Fig. 12.3 Atomic arrangement on (*a*) (100) face, (*b*) (111) face, and (*c*) (110) face for a face-centered cubic structure.

good approximation, but let us examine it more closely for a solid. Suppose that an interface between a solid and another phase is extended by an amount dA. The question then arises whether the change in free energy is proportional to dA as given by equation 12.5, as would be the case if σ is constant. Since σ is closely related to the arrangement of atoms at the interface, the question then arises whether the geometry of the interface changes. It is clear that upon expansion of the area by an amount dA the geometry of a crystalline interface will change significantly at low temperatures, since the atoms are not mobile, and hence the interface will be expanded by creation of vacancies and the increased equilibrium separation of atoms, thereby changing σ. If the temperature is sufficiently high, atomic diffusion is sufficiently rapid, so that the geometry may be essentially preserved. If the geometry of the interface were originally

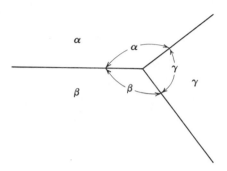

Fig. 12.4 Interfacial boundaries between phases.

disordered this would not be a problem. Some interfaces, such as high-angle crystal boundaries, appear to be disordered and in many respects similar to a liquid and this reservation is thus not important for this case. This discussion, therefore, leads to the second important difference between solids and liquids: *The value of the interfacial free energy for an interface involving a solid is generally not numerically equal to the interfacial tension of the interface. This reservation is not important if the interface is atomically disordered or if the temperature is sufficiently elevated.*

Let us now consider the intersection of boundaries between various phases coexisting as shown in Fig. 12.4.

The angles α, β, and γ will tend to adjust themselves into the lowest energy configuration possible. The question then arises as to what are the factors governing the magnitude of these respective angles. Consider the problem in terms of interfacial tension. There is a boundary between the α and β phases with a surface tension $\sigma_{\alpha\beta}$. This tension is acting in such a way as to reduce the length of the boundary between the α and β phases. This force may therefore be represented as a vector acting along the α–β boundary, in such a direction as to shorten the boundary (from the origin of the three boundaries outward). Similarly there are α–γ and β–γ boundaries with tensions $\sigma_{\alpha\gamma}$ and $\sigma_{\beta\gamma}$ respectively acting in such a way as to shorten the respective boundaries. These forces are shown in Fig.

12.4. The angles α, β, and γ will correspond to the equilibrium between these forces. At equilibrium we have from trigonometry

$$\frac{\sigma_{\alpha\beta}}{\sin \gamma} = \frac{\sigma_{\alpha\gamma}}{\sin \beta} = \frac{\sigma_{\beta\gamma}}{\sin \alpha} \qquad (12.8)$$

or

$$\sigma_{\alpha\beta} - \sigma_{\alpha\gamma} \cos \phi - \sigma_{\beta\gamma} \cos \theta = 0 \qquad (12.9)$$

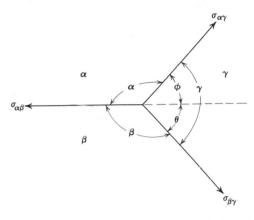

Fig. 12.5 Forces along boundaries which govern the boundary angles.

For the special case where $\sigma_{\alpha\beta} = \sigma_{\alpha\gamma} = \sigma_{\beta\gamma}$,

$$\alpha = \beta = \gamma = 120^\circ$$

These equations are well known and are valid for liquid phases. For interfaces in solid bodies they are not complete, however, since there is an additional factor pointed out by Herring[1] which has not been included in the above treatment. This consideration comes from the fact that σ is a function of crystallographic orientation of the boundary in the case of solids. As a result there will exist the forces previously discussed trying to shorten the boundaries; in addition there may be angular forces attempting to cause the boundary to turn into a crystallographic orientation having lower energy. Herring treated this problem along the following general lines. Consider a balance of forces similar to that shown in Fig. 12.5; let us now displace the boundaries as shown in Fig. 12.6. The displacements $\overline{AP}$, $\overline{BP}$, and $\overline{OP}$ are chosen to be infinitesimal and we shall place the further condition that $\overline{OP} \ll \overline{AP}$ and $\overline{OP} \ll \overline{BP}$. Let us consider

[1] C. Herring, in *Physics of Powder Metallurgy*, W. E. Kingston, ed., McGraw-Hill, New York, 1951.

that the free energy change is related to σ by equation 12.5 and that the specimen has dimension L perpendicular to the plane of the page. The boundary α–β therefore increased by an area $\overline{OP} \times L$. The force opposing this is

$$(\sigma_{\alpha\beta} - \sigma_{\alpha\gamma} \cos \phi - \sigma_{\beta\gamma} \cos \theta)$$

and hence the free energy change from this contribution is

$$dG_1 = (\sigma_{\alpha\beta} - \sigma_{\alpha\gamma} \cos \phi - \sigma_{\beta\gamma} \cos \theta)(\overline{OP} \times L) \qquad (12.10)$$

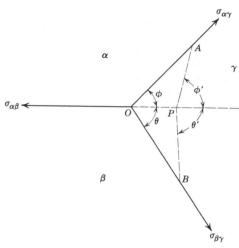

Fig. 12.6 Force diagram for angular displacement of boundaries between phases.

In addition there will be free energy contributions resulting from the orientation change of the α–γ and β–γ boundaries. These will be

$$dG_2 = \left(\frac{\partial \sigma_{\alpha\gamma}}{\partial \phi} \delta\phi\right) \overline{AP} \times L \qquad (12.11)$$

and

$$dG_3 = \left(\frac{\partial \sigma_{\beta\gamma}}{\partial \phi} \delta\phi\right) \overline{BP} \times L \qquad (12.12)$$

The angle changes $\delta\phi$ and $\delta\theta$ are, from Fig. 12.6, the differences $(\phi' - \phi)$ and $(\theta' - \theta)$ respectively. These expressions may be simplified by expressing $\overline{AP}$ and $\overline{BP}$ in terms of $\overline{OP}$. To do this let us consider Fig. 12.6 in more detail. The angle OPA is equal to $180 - \phi'$ and thus the angle OAP is equal to $\delta\phi$. As a result, from trigonometric consideration,

$$\frac{\sin (\delta\phi)}{\overline{OP}} = \frac{\sin \phi}{\overline{AP}} \qquad (12.13)$$

Since $\delta\phi$ is infinitesimal, $\sin(\delta\phi) \cong \delta\phi$, and rearranging equation 12.13 we find

$$\delta\phi = \overline{OP}\,\frac{\sin\phi}{\overline{AP}} \qquad (12.14)$$

Similarly angle OBP is equal to θ and

$$\delta\theta = \overline{OP}\,\frac{\sin\theta}{\overline{AP}} \qquad (12.15)$$

Substituting equations 12.14 and 12.15 into 12.11 and 12.12 respectively yields

$$dG_2 = \frac{\partial\sigma_{\alpha\gamma}}{\partial\phi}\sin\phi \cdot \overline{OP} \times L \qquad (12.16)$$

$$dG_3 = \frac{\partial\sigma_{\beta\gamma}}{\partial\theta}\sin\theta \cdot \overline{OP} \times L \qquad (12.17)$$

The total free energy change is the sum of equations 12.10, 12.16, and 12.17 and

$$\frac{dG}{L} = (\sigma_{\alpha\beta} - \sigma_{\alpha\gamma}\cos\phi - \sigma_{\beta\gamma}\cos\theta)\overline{OP}$$

$$+ \frac{\partial\sigma_{\alpha\gamma}}{\partial\phi}\sin\phi \cdot \overline{OP} + \frac{\partial\sigma_{\beta\gamma}}{\partial\theta}\sin\theta \cdot \overline{OP} \qquad (12.18)$$

At equilibrium, $dG = 0$ and thus

$$\sigma_{\alpha\beta} - \sigma_{\alpha\gamma}\cos\phi - \sigma_{\beta\gamma}\cos\theta + \frac{\partial\sigma_{\alpha\gamma}}{\partial\phi}\sin\phi + \frac{\partial\sigma_{\beta\gamma}}{\partial\theta}\sin\theta = 0 \quad (12.19)$$

In the special case of a liquid, the boundary is not a function of orientation; thus $\partial\sigma/\partial\theta$ is zero and equation 12.19 becomes identical to 12.9.

For most internal boundaries in solids the change of interfacial tension with angle ($\partial\sigma/\partial\alpha$) is small, so 12.9 is also a good approximation in these cases. When the boundary between two phases is of a special type the situation may be different. As an example consider a very low energy boundary such as represented by a coherent twin boundary. For this case σ may change very rapidly with orientation since coherency at the boundary is lost very rapidly with misorientation.

12.2 NATURE OF SOLID INTERFACES AND IMPURITY SEGREGATION

Suppose that two phases of different composition meet to form an interface. Two types of discontinuities may appear. If the phases are of different structure or different lattice parameter for the same structure, a *geometrical* discontinuity will occur. If the phases are of different composition a *chemical* discontinuity will occur. Discussion of geometrical discontinuities will be deferred to a later section. Let us consider the problem of the chemical discontinuity here. It is tempting in this case, but not accurate, to represent the composition of, say, component B as a function of distance normal to the plane of the boundary as shown in Fig. 12.7. In other words the interface would appear as an abrupt chemical

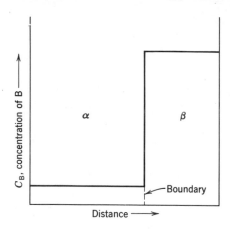

Fig. 12.7   Idealized composition of phases α and β normal to the plane of the boundary.

discontinuity. Cahn and Hilliard[1] have examined the problem of interface thickness anew. (Gibbs performed the initial analysis.) The boundary thickness and composition in the boundary will not be independent variables, but will be governed by the thermodynamic necessity of minimizing the ~~boundary~~ *total* free energy. Hence the boundary thickness and composition will be governed by the configuration having the lowest free energy. Applying thermodynamic reasoning to a regular solution, Cahn and Hilliard obtained the result shown in Fig. 12.8 for the composition as a function of distance away from the boundary. In Fig. 12.8 the effective width of the interface, *l*, depends on temperature and the value of the heat of mixing.

In the case of crystals having the same structure and composition a boundary of substantial width may also result, as illustrated in Fig. 12.9 for a high angle grain boundary by use of a soap bubble model.

Let us now consider the problem of impurity segregation in interfacial boundaries from a thermodynamic point of view. (In a later chapter we shall examine grain boundary segregation from an atomic point of view.)

[1] J. W. Cahn and J. E. Hilliard, *J. Chem. Phys.*, **28**, 258 (1958).

For simplicity, consider α and β to be the same pure phase and consider also that both contain a single impurity, component B. The only difference between the crystals is considered to be their orientation. As we have just seen, the interface must be considered to be a rather diffuse region and hence it is logical to visualize the boundary as being enclosed by two parallel surfaces U and V. Imagine now a third parallel surface Y lying between U and V. Consider this arbitrary surface to be the boundary

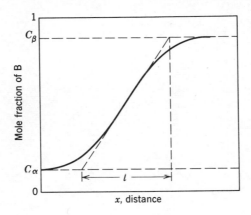

Fig. 12.8 Composition of α and β in the vicinity of the interfacial boundary. From J. W. Cahn and J. E. Hilliard, *J. Chem. Phys.*, **28**, 258 (1958).

separating the α and β phases. The α phase consists of n_α gram-atoms and contains uniform mole fractions X_A^α and X_B^α of solvent and impurity respectively in the interior of α. Similarly the β phase consists of n_β gram-atoms and contains mole fractions X_A^β and X_B^β of solvent and solute in interior. The total number of moles of component B, n_B, in the entire system is given by

$$n_B = X_B^\alpha n_\alpha + X_B^\beta n_\beta + n_B^Y \qquad (12.20)$$

where n_B^Y refers to the number of moles of solute at surface Y. This surface Y has an area A, and the concentration of solute at Y is defined as

$$\Gamma_B^Y = \frac{n_B^Y}{A} \qquad (12.21)$$

Similarly for component A

$$n_A = X_A^\alpha n_\alpha + X_A^\beta n_\beta + n_A^Y \qquad (12.22)$$

and

$$\Gamma_A^Y = \frac{n_A^Y}{A} \qquad (12.23)$$

If segregation of impurities occurs at the boundary Y resulting in an enrichment of solute, $n_B{}^Y$ will be positive and $n_A{}^Y$ will be negative. Conversely if solute is excluded from the boundary, $n_B{}^Y$ will be negative and $n_A{}^Y$ will be positive. The values of $n_A{}^Y$ and $n_B{}^Y$ depend, of course,

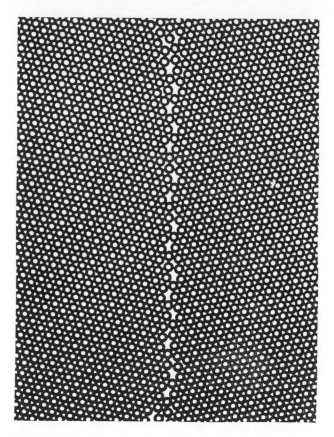

Fig. 12.9 Soap bubble model of a high angle grain boundary. From W. M. Lomer and J. F. Nye, *Proc. Roy. Soc.* (*London*), **A212**, 576 (1952).

on the location of the plane Y. For the sake of ease in future calculations it is convenient to locate this arbitrary surface Y in the position where $n_A{}^Y = 0$. This can be done by moving it to the appropriate point between surfaces U and V, hence at Y

$$n_A = X_A{}^\alpha n_\alpha + X_A{}^\beta n_\beta \qquad (12.24)$$

and

$$\Gamma_A{}^Y = 0 \qquad (12.25)$$

For a one-component system the free energy of an interface (if σ is not a function of A) is given by

$$G^Y = \sigma A \tag{12.6}$$

For a two-component system at constant temperatures we know that

$$G^Y = \sigma A + n_A{}^Y \mu_A{}^Y + n_B{}^Y \mu_B{}^Y \tag{12.26}$$

Upon differentiation

$$dG^Y = \sigma\, dA + A\, d\sigma + n_A{}^Y d\mu_A{}^Y + \mu_A{}^Y dn_A{}^Y + n_B{}^Y d\mu_B{}^Y + \mu_B{}^Y dn_B{}^Y$$

but, as shown in Chapter 8,

$$\sum \mu_i\, dn_i = 0$$

Therefore

$$dG^Y = \sigma\, dA + n_A{}^Y d\mu_A{}^Y + n_B{}^Y d\mu_B{}^Y$$

At equilibrium $dG^Y = 0$ and thus

$$A\, d\sigma + n_A{}^Y d\mu_A{}^Y + n_B{}^Y d\mu_B{}^Y = 0$$

or

$$d\sigma = -\Gamma_A{}^Y d\mu_A{}^Y - \Gamma_B{}^Y d\mu_B{}^Y \tag{12.27}$$

Choosing Y so that $\Gamma_A{}^Y = 0$ yields

$$d\sigma = -\Gamma_B{}^Y d\mu_B{}^Y \tag{12.28}$$

At equilibrium the chemical potential of B in all phases is the same, so

$$\mu_B{}^\alpha = \mu_B{}^\beta = \mu_B{}^Y = \mu_B$$

and thus

$$d\mu_B{}^Y = d\mu_B$$

Therefore from equation 12.28 we find that

$$\Gamma_B{}^Y = -\left(\frac{\partial \sigma}{\partial \mu_B}\right)_T \tag{12.29}$$

Now

$$\mu_B = \mu_B{}^\cdot + RT \ln a_B = \mu_B{}^\cdot + RT \ln X_B + RT \ln \gamma_B$$

and for a dilute solution of B in A, $\gamma_B = \gamma_B{}^\circ$, the Henry's law constant, and thus

$$d\mu_B = RT\, d \ln X_B \tag{12.30}$$

Substitution of equation 12.30 into equation 12.29 yields

$$\Gamma_B{}^Y = -\frac{1}{RT}\left(\frac{\partial \sigma}{\partial \ln X_B}\right)_T \tag{12.31}$$

From equation 12.31, we see that if addition of X_B to the boundary lowers the surface tension, solute will be adsorbed, whereas if the solute raises the surface tension, solute will be rejected from the boundary. This equation, a special form of Gibbs' adsorption equation, is fundamental to much of the work in surface chemistry.[1] For most interfaces in solids $(\partial\sigma/\partial \ln X_B)$ is negative, because the strain energy contribution of the heat of solution of the solute is reduced if the solute migrates to the disordered boundary. Also the energy of disorders of the boundary itself is reduced and hence segregation occurs. Very few quantitative data are available concerning the effect for solid interfaces.

12.3 SURFACE ENERGIES OF METALS AND COMPOUNDS

If the temperature is high enough, so that σ is not a function of A, the surface tension may be identified numerically with the surface free energy ΔG^{SV} (the solid-vapor interface) as discussed previously. Since

$$\Delta G^{SV} = \Delta H^{SV} - T\,\Delta S^{SV}$$

for a solid where ΔH^{SV} and ΔS^{SV} are virtually independent of temperature it is possible to obtain ΔH^{SV} and ΔS^{SV} by measuring σ as a function of temperature. At absolute zero in temperature, $\sigma = \Delta H^{SV}$, since $T\,\Delta S^{SV} = 0$. The surface tension has been evaluated at several temperatures for

TABLE 12.1

Values of Free Energy, Enthalpy, and Entropy of Solid-Gas Interfaces

Metal	ΔG^{SV} (ergs/cm²)	ΔH^{SV} (ergs/cm²)	ΔS^{SV} (ergs/cm² °K)	T (°C)
Ag[a]	1140	1678	0.47	903
Au[b]	1400	2006	0.43	1204
Cu[c]	1650	2350	0.55	1000

[a] E. R. Funk, H. Udin, and J. Wulff, *J. Metals*, **3**, 1206 (1951).
[b] F. H. Buttner, H. Udin, and J. Wulff, *J. Metals*, **3**, 1209 (1951).
[c] H. Udin, A. J. Shaler, and J. Wulff, *J. Metals*, **1**, 1936 (1949).

copper, gold, and silver, and thus ΔH^{SV} and ΔS^{SV} may be obtained from the slope and intercept at $T = 0°K$. These data are shown in Table 12.1, where the thermodynamic values are average values without the variation of σ with crystallographic direction being considered.

It is tempting to calculate ΔH^{SV} by use of quasichemical theory. This approach seems reasonable since the forces between atoms are short range, and one might think of the interfacial energy as resulting from the

[1] The reader is referred to N. K. Adams, *Physics and Chemistry of Surfaces*, Second Edition, Oxford, London, 1938.

fact that the atoms on the surface are not bonded to as many neighbors as in the interior. Following Herring,[1] let us consider a crystal with a coordination number Z. The number of bonds in a crystal containing N_0 atoms is $\frac{1}{2}ZN_0$. The bond energy ϵ is equal to the heat of sublimation ΔH_s divided by the total number of bonds or

$$\epsilon = \frac{\Delta H_s}{\frac{1}{2}ZN_0} \tag{12.32}$$

Let us consider a face-centered cubic crystal where a surface is created by cleaving the crystal, and consider that the surface is formed along a (111) plane. Each atom in the (111) plane is bonded to 6 neighbors in the plane, 3 below the plane and 3 above the plane. Upon formation of the surface, therefore, 3 bonds are broken per atom. By the process, however, two surfaces are formed, so the number of bonds broken per atom on one surface is $\frac{3}{2}$. Thus the enthalpy of surface formation per atom is

$$\frac{\Delta H}{\text{surface atom}} = \frac{3}{2}\epsilon = \frac{\Delta H_s}{4N_0} \tag{12.33}$$

If there are N atoms per square centimeter in the (111) phase, the surface enthalpy per unit area

$$\Delta H^{SV} = \frac{N \Delta H_s}{4N_0} \tag{12.34}$$

For typical atoms with diameters of about 3 A, N is equal to about $10^{15}/\text{cm}^2$. This leads to values for ΔH^{SV} of 1140, 1550, and 1380 ergs/cm² for silver, gold, and copper respectively. These values are surprisingly close to the experimental values listed in Table 12.1. For a (100) surface the surface enthalpy is found to be

$$\Delta H^{SV} = \frac{N \Delta H_s}{3N_0} \tag{12.35}$$

From these considerations it is seen that the value of the surface enthalpy for a substance should be proportional to the heat of sublimation.

Values of ΔG^{SV} have been determined for silicon [(111) face], zinc [(0001) face], and iron containing 3% silicon [(100) face], and were found to be 1240, 105, and 1360 ergs/cm² respectively.[2] The experiments from which the values were obtained were performed at a low temperature and, since the $T \Delta S^{SV}$ correction will be small at low temperatures, these ΔG^{SV} values will be close to ΔH^{SV}. From the quasichemical theory discussed

[1] C. Herring in *Metal Interfaces*, ASM, Cleveland, 1952.
[2] J. J. Gilman, *J. Appl. Phys.*, **31**, 2208 (1960).

above, one bond will be broken for silicon, three for zinc, and four for iron. This leads to calculated values for ΔH^{SV} of 1310 and 510 ergs/cm² for silicon and zinc respectively. Calculations for body-centered cubic iron on this basis are not valid since bonding between second nearest neighbors is important and thus nearest neighbor considerations are not sufficient.

Values of surface free energies are available for a wide variety of compounds. Some representative values are shown in Table 12.2. The values in Table 12.2 were obtained at low temperatures, so are virtually equal to ΔH^{SV} because of the small $T \Delta S^{SV}$ contribution.

TABLE 12.2
Values of Surface Free Energies for Compounds

Compound	ΔG^{SV} (ergs/cm²)	Compound	ΔG^{SV} (ergs/cm²)
NaCl[a] (100)	300	CaF$_2$[a] (111)	450
LiF[b] (100)	340	BaF$_2$[b] (111)	280
MgO[b] (100)	1200	CaCO$_3$[b] (1010)	230

[a] From U. D. Kusnetsov and P. P. Feterim in *Surface Energy of Solids*, Her Majesty's Stationery Office, London, 1957.

[b] From J. J. Gilman, *J. Appl. Phys.*, **31**, 2208 (1960).

In the case of ionic crystals, it is not as useful to speak of chemical bonds between atoms, since the forces holding the atoms together are more coulombic in nature. As a result it is useful to take a more general view which, however, may also be applied to metallic and covalent crystals. Consider a plane in a crystal which is cleaved in order to form two surfaces. Prior to cleavage, the energy between atoms across the plane as a function of interatomic distance will be represented as shown in Fig. 12.10a. At equilibrium the spacing will be x_0. The surface energy may be thought of, in terms of Fig. 12.10b, as the work needed to separate the atoms across the plane to a distance of infinity. In Fig. 12.10b the force is plotted as derived from Fig. 12.10a by taking the derivation dE/dx. The work (and hence surface energy) needed to separate the atoms from their equilibrium distance x_0 to $x \to \infty$ is the area under curve or

$$\text{Work} = \int_{x_0}^{\infty} f \, dx \qquad (12.36)$$

To perform the integration analytically the equation for f as a function of x must be known. To a good approximation the major part of the curve must be approximated by a sine function (dashed line in Fig. 12.10b).

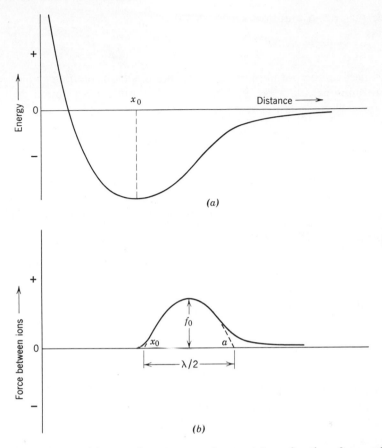

Fig. 12.10 (a) Potential energy between atoms in a crystal as a function of separation. (b) Force between atoms in crystal as function of separation.

The departure from the actual curve may be seen schematically in Fig. 12.10b. If a sine function is assumed the integration is considerably simplified and only a small part of the area (from $x = a$ to $x = \infty$) is neglected. Thus the function $f = f(x)$ is given approximately by

$$f = f_0 \sin \left[\frac{2\pi(x - x_0)}{\lambda} \right] \tag{12.37}$$

The work per unit area in separating the crystal is given by

$$W = \int_{x_0}^{\lambda/2} f_0 \sin \left[\frac{2\pi(x - x_0)}{\lambda} \right] dx = \frac{\lambda f_0}{\pi} \tag{12.38}$$

Two surfaces of unit area are formed thus

$$\Delta E^{SV} = \tfrac{1}{2}W \quad \text{or} \quad \Delta E^{SV} = \frac{\lambda f_0}{2\pi} \tag{12.39}$$

This needs to be put in more meaningful terms from the point of view of performing calculations, since the force f_0 is difficult to obtain directly. Near x_0, Hooke's law is obeyed, and hence

$$f = Y\left(\frac{Y - Y_0}{Y_0}\right) \tag{12.40}$$

where Y is Young's modulus. Thus at small strains

$$\frac{df}{dx} = Y \tag{12.41}$$

Differentiating 12.37 yields

$$\frac{df}{dx} = f_0 \cos\left[\frac{2\pi(x - x_0)}{\lambda}\right] \times \frac{2\pi}{\lambda} \tag{12.42}$$

Equating 12.42 to 12.41 gives

$$f_0 = \frac{Y\lambda}{2\pi} \cdot \frac{1}{\cos\left[\dfrac{2\pi(x - x_0)}{\lambda}\right]} \tag{12.43}$$

Under the conditions of the derivation of f_0, namely that the strains are small, $(x - x_0) \ll 1$, and thus

$$\cos\left[\frac{2\pi(x - x_0)}{\lambda}\right] \cong 1$$

Therefore

$$f_0 \cong \frac{Y\lambda}{2\pi} \tag{12.44}$$

Substitution of equation 12.44 into 12.39 yields

$$\Delta E^{SV} = \frac{Y\lambda^2}{4\pi^2} \tag{12.45}$$

Young's modulus is available for most substances and hence, if λ can be obtained, ΔE^{SV} may be calculated. Furthermore since the PV term is small for solids, $\Delta E^{SV} \cong \Delta H^{SV}$, and if the temperature is relatively low, $\Delta H^{SV} \cong \Delta G^{SV}$. Because of the short-range exponential nature of atomic attractive forces, λ will be a small quantity and for the sake of calculation we will approximate λ by x_0. The forces are small when the ions are

TABLE 12.3

Comparison of Calculated and Experimental Values of Surface Energies[a]

Crystal	Experimental ΔG^{SV} (ergs/cm²)	Calculated ΔG^{SV} (ergs/cm²)
NaCl	300	310
LiF	340	370
MgO	1200	1300
CaF$_2$	450	540
BaF$_2$	280	350
CaCO$_3$	230	380
Si	1240	890
Zn	105	185
Fe (3% Si)	1360 (?)	1400

[a] From J. J. Gilman, *J. Appl. Phys.*, **31**, 2208 (1960).

separated by this distance. The values of surface energies obtained in this manner are compared with experimental values of ΔG^{SV} in Table 12.3. The agreement between theory and experiment is generally excellent.

12.4 INTERNAL BOUNDARIES

As discussed previously, an interfacial energy is always a positive quantity and hence, thermodynamically speaking, internal boundaries are unstable and tend to adjust themselves geometrically in order to minimize their total free energy. It might be expected from this that a single crystal of a single phase would be more stable than a polycrystalline array of the same phase. This is generally true but Fullman[1] has shown that there could be exceptions to this generalization. The total interfacial energy is the sum of the surface energies and the energies of the internal boundaries. For a crystal with anisotropic surface energies, Fullman has shown that it is possible for a polycrystalline array to be arranged in such a way with regard to internal and external surfaces that the total interfacial energy is less than for a single crystal of the same total volume. Quantitative verification of this theory has not been performed because of the lack of experimental information concerning interfacial energies as a function of orientation for real materials.

It is convenient for purposes of discussion to divide internal boundaries into two classes; (1) internal boundaries between crystals of the same phase, resulting therefore from orientation differences (hereafter referred to as grain boundaries), and (2) internal boundaries separating phases of different structure or compositions or both.

[1] R. L. Fullman, *Acta Met.*, **5**, 638 (1957).

Grain Boundaries

In order to assist our understanding of grain boundaries it will be worthwhile to examine some special idealized boundaries first. These are low angle boundaries of the pure tilt type and the pure twist type. These boundaries may be considered to consist of regions of perfect fit and

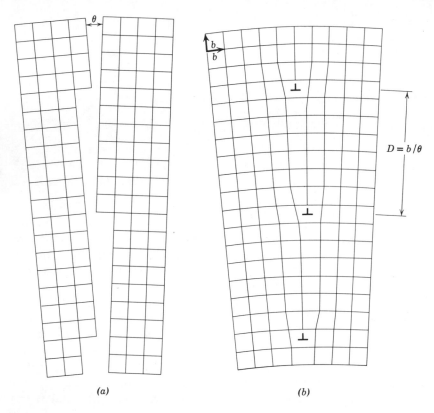

(a)   (b)

Fig. 12.11 Low angle tilt boundary. From W. T. Read, *Dislocations in Crystals*, McGraw-Hill, New York, 1953.

regions of misfit, resulting in the formation of dislocations at the boundaries. The tilt and twist boundaries are shown in Figs. 12.11 and 12.12 and may be considered to consist of pure edge and screw dislocations respectively. Examination of the figures shows that the dislocation count should be simply related to the misorientation angle θ. Since the only disturbance in the boundaries is due to the presence of dislocation, the energy of those boundaries should therefore be simply related to θ.

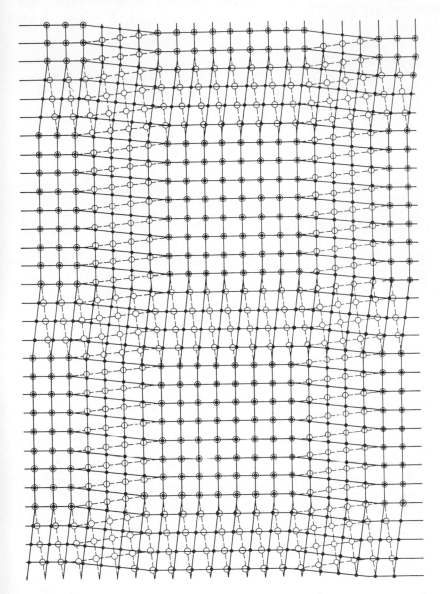

Fig. 12.12 Low angle twist boundary. From W. T. Read, *Dislocations in Crystals*, McGraw-Hill, New York, 1953.

Geometrically it is seen from Figs. 12.11 and 12.12 that the dislocation spacing D is given by

$$D = \frac{b}{\sin \theta} \cong \frac{b}{\theta} \text{ for small } \theta \tag{12.46}$$

for tilt boundaries, and

$$D = \frac{b}{2 \sin \theta} \cong \frac{b}{2\theta} \text{ for small } \theta \tag{12.47}$$

for twist boundaries, where b is Burger's vector. The energy per unit length of a single edge dislocation has been derived to be

$$E_\perp = \frac{Gb^2}{4\pi(1-\nu)} \ln \frac{R}{b} + B \tag{12.48}$$

where G is the shear modulus, ν is Poisson's ratio, B is a constant (a measure of the core energy of the dislocation), and R is the distance the elastic stress field extends away from the core. The extent of the stress field of an edge dislocation R has been shown by Read and Shockley[1] to be equal to the dislocation spacing D. Therefore, upon substitution of equation 12.46 into 12.48, we find

$$E_\perp = \frac{Gb^2}{4\pi(1-\nu)} \ln \left(\frac{1}{\theta}\right) + B \tag{12.49}$$

as the energy per unit length of dislocation. The number of dislocations per unit length of boundary is $1/D$ and hence the energy E per unit area of boundary is $E_\perp/D$ or

$$E = \frac{Gb\theta}{4\pi(1-\nu)} \ln \left(\frac{1}{\theta}\right) + \frac{B\theta}{b} \tag{12.50}$$

Equation 12.50 may be put into the form

$$E = E_0\theta[A - \ln \theta] \tag{12.51}$$

where E_0 and A are constants given by

$$E_0 = \frac{Gb}{4\pi(1-\nu)}$$

$$A = \frac{4\pi(1-\nu)B}{Gb^2}$$

[1] See W. T. Read, *Dislocations in Crystals*, McGraw-Hill, New York, 1953.

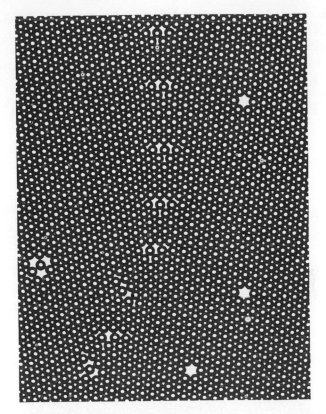

Fig. 12.13 Bubble raft model of a low angle grain boundary. From W. M. Lomer and J. F. Nye, *Proc. Roy. Soc.* (*London*), **A212**, 576 (1952).

An equation identical in form to 12.51 is obtained for twist boundaries with E_0 and A given by

$$E_0 = \frac{Gb}{2\pi}$$

$$A = \frac{2\pi B}{Gb^2}$$

These derivations, it must be emphasized, are only applicable to low angle boundaries. In the case of high angle boundaries, the dislocation spacing is decreased to such a small value that the concept of the boundary as being composed of separate dislocations becomes meaningless. This is illustrated quite lucidly by the bubble-raft models shown in Figs. 12.13 and 12.14, showing the comparison between a low angle boundary and a high angle boundary. In addition to this important factor, the equality between R and D in equation 12.49 is only valid when the dislocation spacing is large. This assumed equality between R and D is in error to the extent of about 10% for a 20° boundary, for example. The general theory has been improved by van der Merwe[1] by consideration of the forces

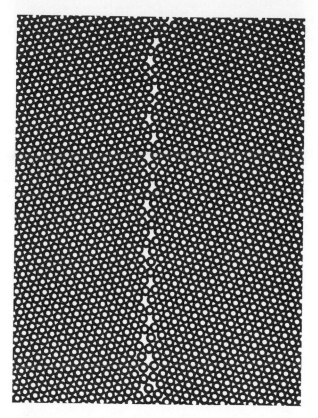

Fig. 12.14 Bubble raft model of a high angle grain boundary. From W. M. Lomer and J. F. Nye, *Proc. Roy. Soc.* (*London*), **A212**, 576 (1952).

between atoms adjacent to the boundary in a more rigorous fashion than discussed here. The predictions of the two theories are shown in Figs. 12.15 and 12.16 for tilt and twist boundaries as a function of misorientation. From these figures, it is observed that the gram boundary energy is zero at $\theta = 90°$. This is physically reasonable since as θ increases from 0 to 45°, the disregistry between the crystals increases. Between a misorientation θ of 45° and 90°, the disregistry decreases for a simple tilt or

[1] J. H. van der Merwe, *Proc. Phys. Soc.* (*London*), **A63**, 613 (1950).

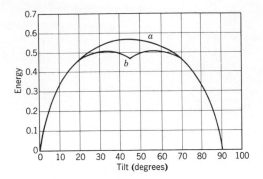

Fig. 12.15 Calculated values of grain boundary energy versus misorientation for tilt boundary. (*a*) van der Merwe's calculation; (*b*) Read and Shockley's calculation. From D. McLean, *Grain Boundaries in Metals*, Oxford, London, 1957.

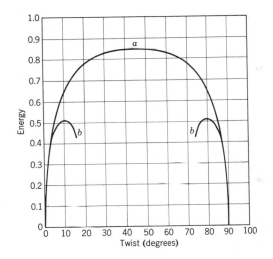

Fig. 12.16 Calculated values of grain boundary energy versus misorientation for twist boundary. (*a*) van der Merwe's calculation; (*b*) Read and Shockley's calculation. From D. McLean, *Grain Boundaries in Metals*, Oxford, London, 1957.

twist boundary in a cubic crystal and in fact at $\theta = 90°$, the boundary disappears since the registry is again perfect.

Gjostein and Rhines[1] have made an experimental study of boundary energies for simple tilt and twist boundaries in copper as a function of θ. The results are shown in Figs. 12.17 and 12.18. From these figures, it is observed that the experimental points follow curves of the general type

[1] N. A. Gjostein and F. N. Rhines, *Acta Met.*, **7**, 319 (1959).

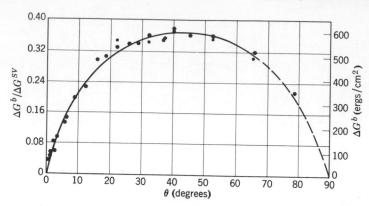

Fig. 12.17 Experimental value of the grain boundary energy as a function of mis-orientation for a simple tilt boundary in copper at 1065°C. From N. A. Gjostein and F. N. Rhines, *Acta Met.*, **7**, 319 (1959).

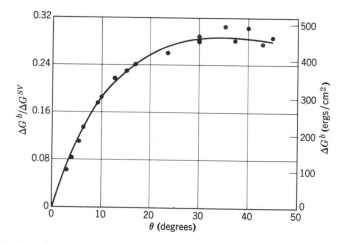

Fig. 12.18 Experimental value of the grain boundary energy as a function of misorientation for a simple twist boundary in copper at 1065°C. From N. A. Gjostein and F. N. Rhines, *Acta Met.*, **7**, 319 (1959).

shown in Figs. 12.15 and 12.16 as derived by van der Merwe. The values of ΔG^b for high angle tilt and twist boundaries ($\theta \sim 45°$) are about 600 and 500 ergs/cm² respectively. Comparison between these values and ΔG^{SV} for the surface energy of copper of 1650 ergs/cm² lead to the generalization that for a high angle boundary

$$\frac{\Delta G^b}{\Delta G^{SV}} = \frac{\sigma_b}{\sigma_{SV}} \cong \frac{1}{3} \qquad (12.52)$$

The figures also indicate that ΔG^b does not vary much for misorientations $20° < \theta < 70°$, and so for practical purposes ΔG^b and σ_b may be considered to be independent of orientation angle for a high angle boundary. As a result, our earlier statement that $\partial\sigma/\partial\alpha$ is small for most boundaries is verified. Some typical values of ΔG^b are listed in Table 12.4 for representative metals. There are certain special orientation relationships for

TABLE 12.4

Interfacial Energies for High Angle Grain Boundaries and Relation to Surface Energy

Crystal	ΔG^b (ergs/cm^2)	$\Delta G^b/\Delta G^{SV}$	Reference
Copper	600	0.36	N. A. Gjostein and F. N. Rhines, *Acta Met.*, **7**, 319 (1959)
γ-Iron	850	—	L. H. Van Vlack, *J. Metals*, **3**, 25 (1951)
α-Iron (4% Si)	760	0.55	L. H. Van Vlack, *ibid.*
Lead	200	—	K. T. Aust and B. Chalmers, *Proc. Roy. Soc.* (*London*), **A204**, 359 (1951)
Tin	100	—	K. T. Aust and B. Chalmers, *Proc. Roy. Soc.* (*London*), **A201**, 210 (1950)
Silver	400	0.35	A. P. Greenough and R. King, *J. Inst. Met.*, **79**, 415 (1951)

which the atom spacing on one side of the boundary is very similar to the spacing on the other side. As a result we would expect the boundary energy corresponding to these orientations to be low. These special low energy boundaries will lead to the occurrence of cusps in the grain boundary energy versus θ curve. Such a special boundary is called a *coherent* boundary. An example of such a coherent boundary is a twin boundary when the boundary coincides with the twinning plane. A twin boundary will be *noncoherent* if the boundary does not coincide with the twinning plane. In Table 12.5 are listed some representative values of twin boundary energies of both the coherent and noncoherent type. From Table 12.5 it is seen that a coherent twin boundary has a much lower energy than an ordinary boundary, whereas the energy for a noncoherent twin boundary is approximately the same as for an ordinary boundary. The consideration previously discussed concerning the torque on a boundary due to the anisotropic nature of interfacial energies become of particular importance in this case. Consider the situation shown in Fig. 12.19, where the dashed

TABLE 12.5
Interfacial Energies for Crystals in Twin Relationship[a]

Crystal	ΔG^b (ergs/cm²)	Reference
Cu (coherent)	25	R. L. Fullman, *J. Appl. Phys.*, **22**, 448 (1951)
Cu (noncoherent)	440	R. L. Fullman, *ibid.*, **22**, 456 (1951)
Fe (coherent)	187	C. G. Dunn, F. W. Daniels, and M. J. Bolton, *J. Metals*, **2**, 368 (1950)
Fe (noncoherent)	705	*Ibid.*
Al (coherent)	120	R. L. Fullman, Table III in article by H. Brooks in *Metal Interface*, ASM, 1952

[a] From D. McLean, *Grain Boundaries in Metals*, Oxford, London, 1957.

line represents a twinning plane and the solid line represents the actual position of the boundary between the two crystals situated at an angle of ϕ for the twin plane. The boundary energy versus the angle ϕ is shown schematically in Fig. 12.20. At $\phi = 0$, the boundary becomes coherent with the low energy shown in Table 12.5. At $\phi = 0$ the misorientation

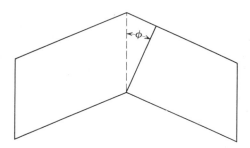

Fig. 12.19 Noncoherent twin boundary. Dashed line represents twinning, plane and solid line represents actual boundary.

between atoms on either side of the boundary is small but this increases rapidly as ϕ increases. As a result, the boundary energy increases rapidly and there will be a large value of $\partial\sigma/\partial\phi$, which would lead to a large force tending to pull the boundary into a low energy position of the type discussed in Section 12.1.

Let us now consider briefly a method used for measuring boundary energies. This is due to an interesting phenomenon which occurs when a crystal containing a grain boundary, such as shown in Fig. 12.21a, is heated to an elevated temperature in an inert atmosphere. After a period of time, a groove will appear on the surface as shown schematically in

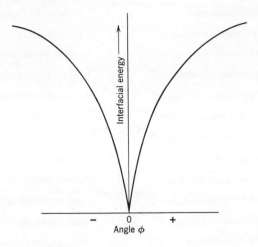

Fig. 12.20 Boundary energy versus angle ϕ for noncoherent boundary of Fig. 12.19.

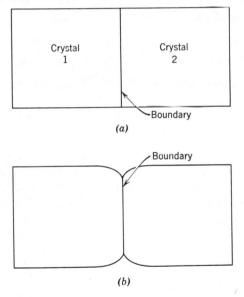

Fig. 12.21 (a) Grain boundary in a crystal. (b) Same boundary after heating to an elevated temperature.

Fig. 12.22 Interferogram for a grain boundary groove in copper at the surface of a crystal. From N. A. Gjostein and F. N. Rhines, *Acta Met.*, **7**, 319 (1959).

Fig. 12.21*b* (scale exaggerated). Experimentally this grooving may be observed quantitatively by the study of interference fringes. An interferogram for such a boundary is shown in Fig. 12.22. This grooving results from the grain boundary attempting to minimize its energy by diminishing its area. Equilibrium will be reached when the force relationships of equation 12.9 are satisfied. The particular relationships for this situation are shown in Fig. 12.23. At equilibrium

$$\sigma_b - \sigma_{SV} \cos \phi - \sigma_{SV} \cos \phi = 0$$

or

$$\frac{\sigma_b}{\sigma_{SV}} = 2 \cos \phi$$

This particular relation is widely used for obtaining boundary energies. The angle ϕ is measured by use of the interferogram and if σ_{SV} is known, σ_b may be evaluated.

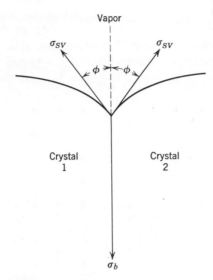

Fig. 12.23 Force diagram applicable to Fig. 12.21*b* at equilibrium.

Boundaries between Different Solid Phases

The situation with regard to this more general case of an interface is similar to the considerations advanced in the previous section, with the additional factor of chemical interaction being important. In fact it is useful to consider two separate contributions to interfacial energy (after Turnbull):[1]

   (a) *Chemical energy*—due to mismatch of bonds across the boundary.
   (b) *Geometrical energy*—due to dislocation structure of boundary.

The interfacial energy between two solid phases, α and β, will be the sum of these contributions. Let us consider first the chemical energy contribution. For simplicity, consider that pure α and β have perfect matching across the phase boundary as shown[2] in Fig. 12.24. The bonding in the α phase is exclusively of the A–A type, the bonding in the β phase is exclusively of the B–B type, and at the boundary A–B bonds are formed. Each A atom at the interface will be bonded to a certain number of B atoms in the β phase, which depends upon the crystal structure of A and B and the plane of the interface. Let this number be called z_b. For a (111) boundary in face-centered cubic structure, $z_b = 3$, and for a (100) interface $z_b = 4$. There are n_b atoms per unit area of interface and hence

---

[1] D. Turnbull in *Impurities and Imperfections*, ASM, Cleveland, 1955.
[2] The original calculation was performed by R. Becker, *Ann. der Physik*, **32**, 128 (1938).

the number of A–B bonds per unit area of interface will be $n_b z_b$. If, in Fig. 12.24, only α phase were present on both sides of the boundary, the total bonding enthalpy across the boundary would be $n_b z_b H_{AA}$, and if only β phase were present on both sides of the boundary, the bonding enthalpy would be $n_b z_b H_{BB}$, where H_{AA} and H_{BB} are the A–A and B–B

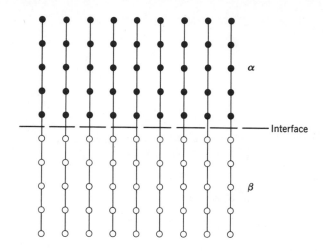

Fig. 12.24 Illustration of chemical term in connection with the interfacial energy between two different solid phases.

bonding enthalpies respectively. When the α–β interface is formed, however, the interface enthalpy will be $n_b z_b H_{AB}$. The chemical contribution to the interfacial enthalpy $\Delta H_c{}^b$ will be, therefore,

$$\Delta H_c{}^b = n_b z_b [H_{AB} - \tfrac{1}{2}(H_{AA} + H_{BB})] \tag{12.53}$$

It is convenient to put equation 12.53 into a form somewhat more useful for actual calculations. In Section 9.2 we found that the heat of mixing ΔH_m for a solution of A and B is equal to

$$\Delta H_m = N_0 (1 - X_B) X_B Z [H_{AB} - \tfrac{1}{2}(H_{AA} + H_{BB})] \tag{12.54}$$

if the solution is regular.

The relative partial molar enthalpy for component B is

$$\Delta \bar{H}_B = \Delta H_m + (1 - X_B)\frac{\partial \Delta H_m}{\partial X_B}$$

or

$$\Delta \bar{H}_B = N_0 Z[(1 - X_B)X_B + (1 - X_B)(1 - 2X_B)][H_{AB} - \tfrac{1}{2}(H_{AA} + H_{AB})] \tag{12.55}$$

If B is very dilute in A, Henry's law is followed by the solute and $\Delta \bar{H}_B$ is a constant given by equation 12.55 for $X_B \rightarrow 0$ or

$$\Delta \bar{H}_B = N_0 Z[H_{AB} - \tfrac{1}{2}(H_{AA} + H_{BB})] \tag{12.56}$$

This relative partial molal enthalpy term is available for many binary systems. Substituting equation 12.56 into equation 12.53, the chemical contribution to the interfacial enthalpy may be expressed as

$$\Delta H_c{}^b = \frac{n_b z_b \, \Delta \bar{H}_B}{N_0 Z} \tag{12.57}$$

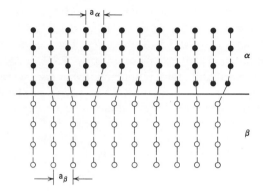

Fig. 12.25 Interfacial boundary between two crystals of same orientation but having different lattice parameters. From D. Turnbull in *Impurities and Imperfections*, ASM, Cleveland, 1955.

To illustrate the magnitude of this term, consider a (111) interface between copper and silver. The relative partial molal enthalpy of copper in silver is $\Delta \bar{H}_{Cu} = 8500$ cal/mole. Substitution into equation 12.57 yields a chemical interface term of about 200 ergs/cm².

Let us now consider the geometric term $\Delta H_g{}^b$ for two crystals α and β having the same crystal structure and orientation but different lattice parameters, where the difference or disregistry δ is defined as

$$\delta \equiv \left| \frac{a_\alpha - a_\beta}{a_\alpha} \right| \tag{12.58}$$

where the a terms refer to the planar spacing normal to the boundary between crystals. Consider as an illustration a case for which $\delta = \tfrac{1}{6}$. This boundary is shown in Fig. 12.25. It is observed from this figure that perfect registry occurs every seven spacings for α and every six spacings for β. As a result there is an extra half plane in α every six β spacings. Consequently the above interface may be pictured as a coherent interface with a dislocation existing every six β spacings. This may be put in the form of an equation with the dislocation spacing D given by

$$D = \frac{a_\beta}{\delta} \tag{12.59}$$

The problem of calculating $\Delta H_g{}^b$ is the same, to a first approximation, as that of calculating the energy of a low angle grain boundary of dislocation spacing D. For the case of the copper-silver system with a (111) interface, $a_{Ag} = 2.88$ A and $a_{Cu} = 2.55$ A. Thus $\delta = 0.12$. This corresponds to a dislocation every 24 A or about 8 atomic spacings. From equation 12.46 we see that this match corresponds to a low angle boundary with an angle θ of 0.12 radians or $7°$. From Fig. 12.17 we see that this corresponds to a value of $\Delta G_g{}^b$ of about 250 ergs/cm^2 at 1065°C. From Table 12.1 we found that the surface entropy ΔS^{SV} is equal to 0.55 e.u., and since the ratio of the grain boundary free energy to the surface free energy is about $\frac{1}{3}$, we may estimate $\Delta S_g{}^b = \frac{1}{3}\Delta S^{SV}$ or about 0.20 erg/cm^2 degree for a high angle boundary. Assuming a proportionality between $\Delta G_g{}^b$ and $\Delta S_g{}^b$ for a low angle boundary, we find, for a 7° boundary, from Fig. 12.17 that $\Delta S_g{}^b = 0.1$ erg/cm^2 degree. Thus the value of $\Delta G_g{}^b$ corresponds to a value of $\Delta H_g{}^b$ of about 380 ergs/cm^2. The total interfacial energy may now be estimated by assuming that the strain at the boundary does not change H_{AB}.[1] The total boundary energy will thus be the sum of the chemical and geometric contributions.

$$\Delta H^b \cong \Delta H_c{}^b + \Delta H_g{}^b \tag{12.60}$$

For the case of copper-silver the sum is $\Delta H^b \cong 580$ ergs/cm^2. This value is very close to the enthalpy of formation of a grain boundary.

It is not obvious, *a priori*, however, that the interface has the dislocation structure shown. The energy associated with a dislocation is very large and very often the total energy of the system may be reduced if, instead of forming dislocations as shown in Fig. 12.25 and according to equation 12.59, the planar spacing is changed in the vicinity of the boundary so as to increase the dislocation spacing. This process, of course, results in the storage of elastic energy in the matrix of the crystal and the actual situation will represent an optimum value of the two.

For phases of radically different structures or cases where δ is large, the situation is not quantitatively as simple as that just described. It is still useful to consider the energy as consisting of a chemical contribution and a structural contribution, however. The dislocations in this case are too close together for the low angle boundary analogy to be valid. Rather,

---

[1] D. Turnbull in *Impurities and Imperfections*, ASM, Cleveland, 1955.

TABLE 12.6

Relative Interface Free Energies[a]

System	Interface between Phase A	Interface between Phase B	Grain Boundary Used as a Comparison Interface, D	$\dfrac{\Delta G_{AB}{}^{b}}{\Delta G_{D}{}^{b}}$	T (°C)
Cu-Zn[b]	α F.C.C.	β B.C.C.	α/α	0.78	700
Cu-Zn[b]	α F.C.C.	β B.C.C.	β/β	1.00	700
Cu-Al[b]	α F.C.C.	β B.C.C.	α/α	0.71	600
Cu-Al[b]	β B.C.C.	γ C.C.[e]	γ/γ	0.78	600
Cu-Sn[b]	α F.C.C.	β B.C.C.	α/α	0.76	750
Cu-Sb[c]	α F.C.C.	β B.C.T.	α/α	0.71	600
Cu-Ag[c]	α (Cu) F.C.C.	β (Ag) F.C.C.	β/β	0.74	750
Cu-Si[c]	α F.C.C.	β B.C.C.	α/α	0.53	845
Cu-Si[c]	α F.C.C.	β B.C.C.	β/β	1.18	845
Fe-C[a]	α B.C.C.	Fe_3 C.o.r.[e]	α/α	0.93	690
Fe-C[a]	α B.C.C.	γ F.C.C.	α/α	0.71	750
Fe-C[d]	α B.C.C.	γ F.C.C.	α/α	0.74	950
Fe-Cu[d]	α B.C.C.	F.C.C.	α/α	0.74	825
Zn-Sn[c]	β (Sn) B.C.T.	α (Zn) H.C.P.	α/α	0.74	160

[a] From C. S. Smith in *Imperfections in Nearly Perfect Crystals*, W. Shockley, ed., John Wiley and Sons, New York, 1952.

[b] C. S. Smith, *Trans. AIME*, **175**, 15 (1948).

[c] C. S. Smith, unpublished.

[d] J. Van Vlack, *J. Metals*, **3**, 251 (1951).

[e] C.C. = complex cubic; o.r. = orthorhombic.

the situation is similar to a high angle boundary. As a result we would expect the structural contribution for this type of interface to be about equal to the energy of a high angle grain boundary. The chemical contribution will generally be considerably smaller than 250 ergs/cm² calculated for the copper-silver system, since $\Delta \bar{H}_B$ is generally much smaller for this particular case.

In Table 12.6 are listed interfacial free energies for various systems relative to the free energy of high angle grain boundaries on these systems. The energies for the interfacial energies are found to be very close to the grain boundary values in agreement with the general statements above.

chapter 13

Introduction to Defects in Crystals

A great many of the important properties of crystals are strongly dependent upon the types and concentrations of various defects which are present in the crystal. As examples of some of these properties we may list mechanical strength, kinetics of phase transformations, electrical conductivity of semiconductors and ionic crystals, luminescence phenomena, photoconductivity, and color. As a result of the importance of defects in determining many of the technologically important properties of crystals, an increasing amount of attention is being devoted to their study. Investigations to date indicate that the detailed behavior of defects is very complex. It is often found that not only are the primary defects important but that association of various types of defects often occur, particularly at low temperatures where entropy considerations are not so important.

One of the prime interests of scientists working with defect crystals is concerned with the control of the concentrations of various defects in crystals, and hence the control of the crystal properties related to these defects. An important contribution to the understanding and control of defects comes from the *statistical-thermodynamic* study of defects. This approach was pioneered by Wagner and Schottky in many papers. This general approach will be discussed in later chapters. By use of this approach we shall be able to obtain the interrelations between defects of various kinds and to judge the important types of defects present in a crystal of a given material.

13.1 TYPES OF POINT DEFECTS

It is convenient to divide crystalline point defects into two groups: (1) primary defects, and (2) secondary defects. The types of primary defects which will be discussed in this treatment can be divided in turn into two types: (a) atomic defects, and (b) electronic defects.

As atomic primary defects in elements we will consider the following types in a later chapter:

(1) Vacant lattice sites.
(2) Interstitials.
(3) Foreign atoms.

The first two types are shown schematically in Fig. 13.1. The foreign atoms may be present substitutionally or interstitially depending on their atomic size in relation to the size of the various sites.

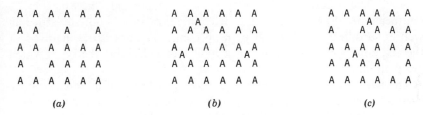

Fig. 13.1 Types of primary point defects. (*a*) Vacancies; (*b*) interstitials; (*c*) equal numbers of interstitials and vacancies, Frenkel disorder.

For stoichiometric compounds the same basic defects are present, but various relations exist between their concentrations, because of the need to maintain a simple relationship between the concentration of the atomic species in the crystal. For this special case of stoichiometry consideration we shall need to consider five basic types of disorder. Any one of these types of disorder may exist in a crystal M_aX_b, and the ratio a/b will still be a small integer.

1. Equal numbers of vacancies on X sublattice and the formation of X interstitial atoms; the M sublattice remains unperturbed, called *Frenkel disorder*.

2. Equal numbers of vacancies on M sublattice and the formation of M interstitial atoms; X sublattice unperturbed; *Frenkel disorder*.

3. Equal number of vacant sites on M sublattice and X sublattice. This discussion is restricted for simplicity to the case where the absolute valences of M and X are equal; called *Schottky disorder*.

4. Equal numbers of M and X interstitials.

5. Substitutional disorder in which M atoms occupy X sites and X atoms occupy M sites.

The basic types of Frenkel, Schottky and substitutional disorder are shown

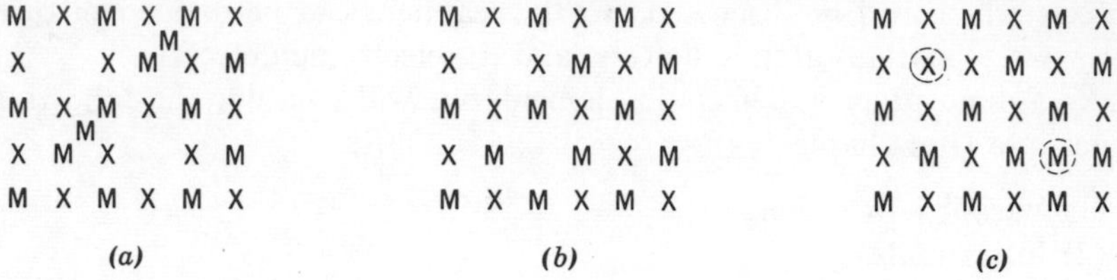

```
M  X  M  X  M  X          M  X  M  X  M  X          M  X  M  X  M  X
          M
X     X  M  X  M          X     X  M  X  M          X (X) X  M  X  M
M  X  M  X  M  X          M  X  M  X  M  X          M  X  M  X  M  X
   M
X  M  X     X  M          X  M     M  X             X  M  X  M (M) M
M  X  M  X  M  X          M  X  M  X  M  X          M  X  M  X  M  X
```

(a)   (b)   (c)

Fig. 13.2 Point defects in a stoichiometric compound. (a) Frenkel disorder; (b) Schottky disorder; (c) substitutional disorder.

in Fig. 13.2. These five types of disorder are the basic types to be considered. In an actual crystal several of these types of disorder may coexist. The occurrence of one type does not preclude the existence of another type. For example, vacancies might exist on both sublattice as well as substitutional disorder being present. The energetics involved in the creation of disorder is the important factor deciding the types which are predominant.

The five types of disorder were discussed in terms of a stoichiometric crystal in which it was necessary to keep the concentration components M and X related by a small integer. In actuality, however, most compounds are stable over a range of composition. Thus, in the crystal M_aX_b, a and b will cover a range of values. Quite obviously in a case of this type, the five types of defect pairs described above do not need to be present. For this case, vacancies may occur on either sublattice, interstitials may form for either component, etc. without the necessity of forming specific pairs as described above. The important criterion which must be fulfilled at all times is that pertaining to charge neutrality. The crystal must be electrically neutral at all times so the formation of a charged defect of one sign must be balanced by defects of the opposite sign. This involves the discussion of primary electronic defects.

With regard to primary electronic defects, we shall be concerned with excess electrons in the conduction bond and holes in the valence band. This consideration will be important only for nonmetals (insulators and semiconductors) in which case the *valence band* can be clearly separated energetically from the conduction band by an *energy gap*, as shown in Fig. 13.3.[1] At absolute zero of temperature a pure perfect semiconductor or an insulator crystal will have its valence bond filled with electrons and

---

[1] Much discussion in later chapters will involve the concept of energy bands. It is suggested that the reader obtain an elementary text concerning solid state physics for review if needed. Typical books are: L. V. Azaroff, *Introduction to Solids*, McGraw-Hill, New York, 1960; A. J. Dekker, *Solid State Physics*, Prentice-Hall, Englewood Cliffs, N.J., 1957; W. Hume-Rothery, *Atomic Theory for Students of Metallurgy*, Institute of Metals, London, 1955.

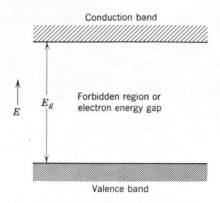

Fig. 13.3 Energy gap of an insulator or semiconductor.

its conduction bond empty. No electron may have an energy in the energy gap. Addition of atomic defects, however, or an increase in temperature, will move electrons to the conduction bond, thus creating *excess electrons*. Since the valence band is filled at absolute zero, removal of electrons will leave *holes* in the valence band. These electronic defects in turn may have a pronounced influence on the concentration of atomic defects through the law of mass action.

13.2 OTHER TYPES OF DEFECTS

Besides point defects, we may classify line defects and planar defects. The line defect is classified as the dislocation and will not be discussed at length here, since thermodynamics has contributed little to the understanding of dislocation. The planar defects were discussed in Chapter 12 and were classified as

1. Internal surfaces in crystals.
2. External surfaces in crystals.

A great number of defect complexes may also exist by various combinations of the types discussed in Section 13.1. Some examples of defect complexes for which experimental evidence exists are listed below.

1. Foreign atom—vacancy pairs.
2. Vacancy clusters of *n* vacancies.
3. Dislocation—vacancy interactions.
4. Dislocation—foreign atom complexes.
5. Foreign atom—foreign atom complexes.
6. Foreign atom—surface interactions.
7. Electronic defect—atomic defect interactions.

As can be seen, a wide variety of defects and defect complexes may be considered. Generally speaking, therefore, control of defect concentrations would be a very complicated mathematical problem. Fortunately, however, certain simple defects predominate in specific crystals and thus have the major influence on the crystal properties. As a result, consideration of the minor defects is often unnecessary in the mathematical analysis. Because the predominant types of major defects in a given crystal depend on whether the crystal is a metal, insulator, or semiconductor, it is convenient to divide our future treatment according to the following material types:

1. Elements.
   (a) Metals—electronic defects not important.
   (b) Elemental semiconductors—electronic defects important.
2. Compounds.

13.3 STABILITY OF CRYSTAL DISORDER

For purposes of illustration let us consider an elemental crystal containing vacancies. Let us start with N atoms arranged on N lattice sites in the crystal. The free energy of the perfect crystal will be G^*. Let us now remove n atoms from the crystal and place them on the surface. We have, therefore, formed n vacant sites. Each of these vacancies will be associated with an enthalpy of formation ΔH_V and a vibrational entropy resulting from the disturbance of the nearest neighbors ΔS_V. There will be a configurational or mixing entropy change associated with the formation of n vacancies given by

$$\Delta S_c = k \ln \frac{\mathscr{W}'}{\mathscr{W}}$$

since for the perfect crystal $\mathscr{W} = 1$. We may readily find $\mathscr{W}'$ since we now have n vacancies and N atoms distributed among $(N + n)$ sites. Thus from Section 4.2 we find

$$\Delta S_c = k \ln \mathscr{W}' = k \ln \frac{(N + n)!}{N! \, n!}$$

Using Stirling's approximation we find

$$\Delta S_c = -k \left[N \ln \frac{N}{(N + n)} + n \ln \frac{n}{(N + n)} \right] \tag{13.1}$$

and therefore

$$\Delta G = G - G^* = n \, \Delta H - T \left(\Delta S_c + n \, \Delta S_V \right)$$

or

$$G - G^* = n \, \Delta H_V + kT \left(N \ln \frac{N}{(N+n)} + n \ln \frac{n}{(N+n)} \right) - nT \, \Delta S_V$$

(13.2)

In Fig. 13.4 is shown a plot of $n(\Delta H_V - T \, \Delta S_V)$, ΔS_c, and G as a function of n. The entropy contribution, ΔS_c, is always negative, and in fact has a slope equal to $-\infty$ at $n = 0$. From Fig. 13.4, therefore, it is observed

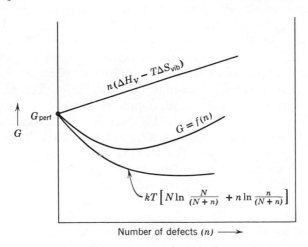

Fig. 13.4 Free energy of a crystal as a function of defect concentration.

that introduction of vacancies lowers the free energy of the crystal until an equilibrium concentration is reached, after which G increases again. This equilibrium concentration may be readily calculated in principle since at this concentration, $\partial G / \partial n = 0$. Thus, using equation 13.2, we find

$$\frac{\partial G}{\partial n} = \Delta H_V - T \, \Delta S_V + kT \ln \frac{n}{(N+n)} = 0$$

Upon rearrangement,

$$\frac{n}{N+n} = \exp \left(\frac{\Delta S_V}{k} \right) \exp \left(- \frac{\Delta H_V}{kT} \right)$$

The fraction of total sites vacant may be expressed as X_V and

$$X_V = \exp \left(\frac{\Delta S_V}{k} \right) \exp \left(- \frac{\Delta H_V}{kT} \right) = \exp \left(- \frac{\Delta G_V}{kT} \right)$$

(13.3)

From equation 13.3 we find that vacancies are indeed stable in the crystal at any temperature greater than absolute zero, and that the mole fraction varies exponentially with temperature. Equation 13.3 is identical in form with equations derived previously for the solubility of a solute in a given solvent as a function of temperature. In these terms ΔH_V may be thought of as the relative partial molar enthalpy of a vacancy in a solvent, and ΔS_V reflects the vibrational changes of the atoms surrounding the vacancy in the crystal. Using the reasoning expressed in Section 4.5 concerning the vibrational frequencies of neighbors surrounding an impurity atom, we would expect the vibrational frequencies of neighbors surrounding a vacancy to be lower than before the vacancy was formed. This will lead to a positive vibrational entropy change, ΔS_V, associated with formation of the vacancy. If X_V can be measured as a function of temperature for a particular system, therefore, quantitative information concerning the enthalpy of vacancy formation and vibrational entropy associated with a vacancy may be obtained. Physically speaking, in forming a vacancy, an atom from the interior of the crystal is removed and deposited on the surface of the crystal, thus ΔH_V refers to this process.

Calculations similar to the one above may be performed for other point defects, and it will be seen that these defects are also thermodynamically stable, since the entropy of mixing term predominates over ΔH_V and ΔS_V for small values of n. A different situation exists for dislocations, however. The enthalpy associated with the formation of a dislocation is extremely large and the entropy is very small. The result for a crystal of ordinary size is that the equilibrium dislocation content is less than one per crystal. As a result dislocations are *thermodynamically unstable*. From a practical point of view, these deductions have great significance. They show that it is possible to prepare crystals without dislocations, but impossible to do the same with regard to point defects. In the latter case we may control the concentration of a given type of defect by varying the concentration of another type of defect through the *law of mass action*. Furthermore the deductions also indicate that for the case of a compound MX, a certain fraction of M atoms will always be found on the X sublattice and vice versa since the entropy of mixing term will be positive for this situation. For the same reason a pure crystal placed in contact with an impurity will always tend to dissolve some of the impurity. The only way to keep a crystal pure is to isolate it in a perfect vacuum or, if it is in contact with an impurity (crucible, etc.), to keep the temperature so low as to inhibit the mixing process through retardation of the kinetics. In this sense then, it may be said that entropy works against people concerned with purification processes.

chapter 14

Defects in Elemental Crystals

14.1 METALS

Electronic defects are not nearly so important for metals as for semi-conductors and insulators. For these materials for which the free electron concentration is small, a small change in electronic structure may have a pronounced influence on the concentration of other defects. Metallic crystals, on the other hand, contain a concentration of free electrons about equal in concentration to the number of atoms in the crystal. In addition, the interaction of defects themselves is not as important in metallic crystals as in semiconductors and insulators, since the mobile electrons in metallic crystals may group themselves around a defect and hence screen, electrically, one defect from another. In many respects our knowledge of defects in metallic lattices is less perfect than our knowledge of defects in other types of materials. As an example of this may be cited the effective valence of an impurity atom or other point defect. Very few situations exist for which a positive statement may be made concerning the valence of a given solute in a metallic solvent crystal. In addition, because of the screening of defects as mentioned above, from one another, coulombic interactions are not very important.

The primary atomic defects which are important in metals are vacancies and interstitials. Various interactions as well have been shown to be important theoretically and experimentally, such as the coalescence of vacancies into vacancy voids and disks, segregation of impurities to dislocations, segregation of impurities at stacking faults.

In addition, defect complexes must be considered such as impurity vacancy pairs, etc. Some of the important defects are shown schematically in Fig. 14.1. In this figure the reader will see an inclusion, substitutional

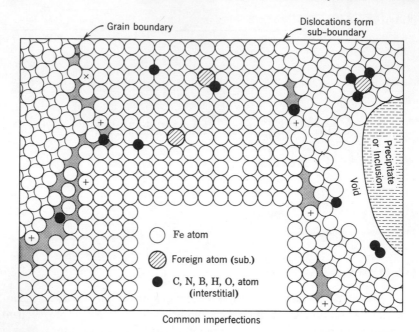

Common imperfections

Fig. 14.1 Some important defects and defect complexes in metals. From L. S. Darken in *The Physical Chemistry of Metallic Solutions and Intermetallic Compounds*, Her Majesty's Stationery Office, London, 1958.

impurities, interstitial impurities, grain boundaries, vacancies, and complexes such as those between grain boundary and impurities, impurities and other impurities, and between vacancies themselves. These will be considered in turn.

Vacancies and Interstitials

In an elemental pure crystal, it is not necessary to have a relation between the relative equilibrium concentrations of vacancies and interstitials. In the past, investigators have sometimes considered an interstitial atom as having been produced by the transfer of an atom from a normal site to an interstitial site, thus resulting in a one-to-one correspondence between the concentrations of vacancies and interstitials. This relationship is unnecessary, however, and the vacancy concentration need bear no relation to the concentration of interstitials since the surface may act as a source or sink for vacancies. For example if the vacancy concentration is thermodynamically too large in comparison with the number of interstitials produced, they may be annihilated by diffusion to the surface. Similarly, if the vacancy concentration corresponding to the

interstitial concentration is too low, vacancies may be created at the
surface as shown in Fig. 14.2. In a similar manner interstitial atoms may
be generated.

As a result there is no need to consider the concentrations to be related,
and thus the equilibrium concentration of interstitials and vacancies may
be considered to be independent.

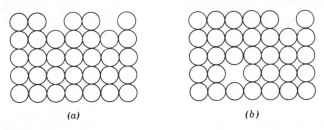

(a)   (b)

Fig. 14.2 Vacancy generation in a crystal. (a) Crystal without vacancies; (b) generation of vacancy by diffusion.

In the last chapter we showed that

$$\frac{n}{N_L} = X_V = \exp\left(\frac{\Delta S_V}{k}\right) \exp\left(\frac{-\Delta H_V}{kT}\right) \tag{14.1}$$

where n and N_L are the number of vacancies and normal lattice sites
respectively. Similarly for the case of interstitials we may find that

$$X_i = \frac{n_i}{N_i} = \exp\left(\frac{\Delta S_i}{k}\right) \exp\left(\frac{-\Delta H_i}{kT}\right) \tag{14.2}$$

where n_i, N_i, ΔS_i, and ΔH_i are the number of interstitials, total number
of interstitial sites, vibrational entropy change associated with interstitial
formation, and enthalpy of interstitial formation respectively. The
quantity N_i is, of course, related geometrically to N_L through a constant β
which is characteristic of the particular crystal structure. Thus

$$X_i = \frac{n_i}{N_L} = \frac{\beta n_i}{N_i} \tag{14.3}$$

In equations 14.1 and 14.2 the ΔS terms are not expected to be very
important compared with the ΔH terms. As a result the concentration
of a particular type of defect in a crystal is determined primarily through
the magnitude of the ΔH term. A large positive value of ΔH will result
in a small value of concentration. Approximate quantum mechanical
calculations have been made for metals of ΔH_V and ΔH_i by Huntington,
and later refined by others. It will be illuminating to consider these

calculations briefly. For vacancy formation the basic reaction to consider is

$$\text{Atom(interior of crystal)} = \text{Atom(surface)} \quad \Delta H_V$$

This reaction may be broken into several steps and the enthalpies (or energies) associated with these steps may be calculated. Consider copper as an example. The basic reaction may be conveniently divided into the following six steps. Some of these steps are obvious choices since the energies involved may be obtained experimentally. Such is the case for steps 2, 3, and 4. The energies associated with steps 1, 5, and 6 were calculated by Huntington and the appropriate values are listed for each step. Actually the energy and not the enthalpy associated with each step is calculated, but, because of the relative unimportance of the PV term, the energy will be identified with an enthalpy.

(1) $Cu^+(\text{interior } s) = Cu^+(g, \infty)$, $\Delta E_1 = \quad 370 \text{ kcal/mole}$

(2) electron, $e^-(s) = e^-(g, \infty)$, $\left.\Delta E_2\right\}$

(3) $Cu^+(g, \infty) + e^-(g, \infty) = Cu(g, \infty)$ $\left.\Delta E_3\right\} = -170 \text{ kcal/mole}$

(4) $Cu(g, \infty) = Cu(\text{surface } s)$ $\left.\Delta E_4\right\}$

(5) Electronic rearrangement around vacancy $\Delta E_5 = -160 \text{ kcal/mole}$

(6) Relaxation of atoms around vacancy $\Delta E_6 = -10 \text{ kcal/mole}$

$Cu(\text{interior } s) = Cu(\text{surface } s)$, $\Delta E_V = \quad 30 \text{ kcal/mole}$

Vacancy(surface s) = Vacancy(interior s)

The term ΔE_2 corresponds to the *work function*, $-\Delta E_3$ to the ionization potential, and $-\Delta E_4$ to the heat of sublimation. Since a metal is considered to be a collection of positive ions which repel each other and are held together by the negative electrons, an inward relaxation will occur around the vacancy upon removal of one of the ions because of the removal of a positive ion. Hence the repulsion between second and third nearest neighbors to the vacancy will cause an inward relaxation.

For the enthalpy of interstitial formation in copper we have the following basic process.

$$Cu(\text{surface}) = Cu(\text{interstitial}), \quad \Delta H_i$$

This reaction can be broken into the following convenient steps:

(1) $Cu(\text{surface}) = Cu(g, \infty)$, ΔE_1

(2) $Cu(g, \infty) = Cu^+(g, \infty) + e^-(g, \infty)$, $\Delta E_2 = \quad 170 \text{ kcal/mole}$

     $e^-(g, \infty) = e^-(s)$, ΔE_3

     $Cu(g, \infty) = Cu^+(\text{interstitial } s)$, $\Delta E_4 = \quad 100 \text{ kcal/mole}$

     Electronic rearrangement $\Delta E_5 = -60 \text{ kcal/mole}$

$Cu(\text{surface}) = Cu(\text{interstitial})$, $\Delta E_i = 210 \text{ kcal/mole}$

The terms ΔE_1, ΔE_2, and ΔE_3 correspond to the heat of sublimation, the ionization energy, and the negative of the work function, respectively; the other terms were calculated theoretically by Huntington. The calculations, albeit crude, indicate that

$$\frac{\Delta E_i}{\Delta E_V} \simeq \frac{\Delta H_i}{\Delta H_V} \simeq 7$$

From equations 14.1 and 14.2, if the relatively small values of ΔS_V, ΔS_i, and β are neglected, we find

$$\frac{X_V}{X_i} \simeq \exp\left(\frac{\Delta H_i - \Delta H_V}{kT}\right) \qquad (14.4)$$

At 1000°K, for example, this ratio is

$$\frac{X_V}{X_i} \simeq 10^{39}$$

From this result we may make the generalization, therefore, that for a close-packed crystal such as copper, the concentration of interstitials is insignificant compared with the concentration of vacancies in the crystal. We may crudely estimate the minimum concentration of vacancies in copper from equation 14.1. The vibrational entropy of a vacancy, ΔS_V, is positive, since upon formation of a vacancy, neighboring atoms relax and thus their vibrational frequency is decreased. This results in a positive value of ΔS_V. Consequently, if this term is neglected, a minimum value of X_V is obtained. Therefore, not considering this positive term, resulting in $\exp(\Delta S_V/k) > 1$, we find for Cu at 1000°K that

$$X_V \simeq 3 \times 10^{-7}$$

Thus, for a cubic centimeter of crystal (containing about 5×10^{22} sites), there should be about 10^{16} vacancies. From equation 14.4, we find that there are *no* interstitials. At 500°K there are only 5×10^9 vacancies/cm^3 in equilibrium. Intuitively, one is not surprised at the relation that $X_i/X_V \ll 1$ because of the small size of interstitial sites in close-packed crystals. Correspondingly, one would expect interstitial sites to become more important in crystals having more open packing such as the body-centered cubic and diamond structures. However, even in these cases there is no direct evidence that interstitials are present in important concentrations, and so they will not be discussed further until the next chapter.

Even though it is difficult to study vacancies by direct methods in metals, certain physical property changes can be associated with them such as changes in density and electrical resistivity of the crystal. Since the defects are present in very low concentrations, it is reasonable to assume that they follow Henry's law. That is to say, the properties associated with the defects are additive with regard to their concentration; thus the electrical resistance effect of two vacancies in a given crystal is twice that of a single vacancy. If the electrical resistivity increment of a vacancy is ρ_V and n_V is the number of vacancies, the electrical resistivity of the system is given by

$$\rho = \rho_0 + n_V \rho_V$$

where ρ_0 is the resistivity of a crystal containing no vacancies. A similar equation would also hold for the density of the system. Thus

$$n_V = \frac{\rho - \rho_0}{\rho_V} = \frac{\Delta\rho}{\rho_V}$$

For a given material, the resistivity of a vacancy, ρ_V, is constant according to the assumption of Henry's law, and since n_V is proportional to X_V, we may write

$$aX_V = \Delta\rho$$

where a is a constant. The variation of X_V with temperature may now be readily obtained. Suppose that a sample is held at an elevated temperature until X_V reaches its equilibrium value characteristic of the particular temperature. The sample is then rapidly quenched to a temperature sufficiently low that the vacancies are immobilized (room temperature is sufficient for some materials). Since, at a given measuring temperature, $\Delta\rho$ is proportional to X_V, we may find aX_V at the quench temperature by measuring $\Delta\rho$ as a function of quench temperature.

In equation 14.1 we are given the temperature dependence of X_V. Differentiating equation 14.1 in the following fashion, we see that the enthalpy of vacancy formation, ΔH_V, may be obtained.

$$\frac{\partial \ln (aX_V)}{\partial (1/T)} = -\frac{\Delta H_V}{k} = \frac{\partial \ln (\Delta\rho)}{\partial (1/T)}$$

Thus the enthalpy of vacancy formation may be obtained from the change of electrical resistivity with quench temperature. In Fig. 14.3 are shown the results for gold plotted according to the equation above as $\ln (\Delta\rho)$ versus $1/T$. The slope of this curve is equal to $-\Delta H_V/k$, and it is found for gold that ΔH_V equals 22.1 cal/mole. This value corresponds rather closely to the calculated value for copper discussed above. Of course, they should not be identical since they pertain to different materials. The value of ΔS_V may not be calculated since the value of the constant a is not known.

Listed in Table 14.1 are experimental values of the heat of formation of vacancies ΔH_V for some representative metals. Most of these data were

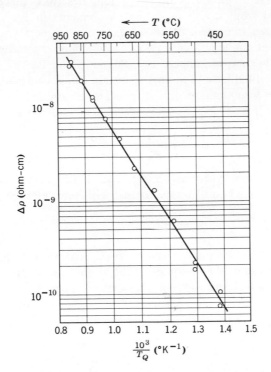

Fig. 14.3 Resistivity change of quenched gold wires as a function of quench temperature. From J. E. Bauerle and J. S. Koehler, *Phys. Rev.*, **107**, 1493 (1957).

TABLE 14.1
Heat of Formation of Vacancies in Metals

Substance	ΔH_V (kcal/mole)	Reference
Gold	22.1	*a*
Aluminum	17.3	*b, c*
Silver	25.1	*d*
Platinum	30.0	*e*
Copper	23.0	*f*

[a] J. E. Bauerle and J. S. Koehler, *Phys. Rev.*, **107**, 1493 (1957).
[b] W. Desorbo and D. Turnbull, *Acta Met.*, **7**, 83 (1959).
[c] R. O. Simmons and R. W. Balluffi, *Phys. Rev.*, **117**, 52 (1960).
[d] R. O. Simmons and R. W. Balluffi, *Phys. Rev.*, **119**, 600 (1960).
[e] Averages of several measurements.
[f] D. Airloldi *et al.*, *Phys. Rev. Letters*, **2**, 145 (1959).

obtained by use of the quenching technique described earlier, but some were obtained from length change measurements in conjunction with lattice parameter measurements as a function of temperature.

By measuring the length change in conjunction with lattice parameter change as a function of temperature, Simmons and Balluffi (references c and d in Table 14.1) have been able to obtain actual values of the vacancy concentrations for aluminum and silver. The reasoning is as follows.

The volume thermal expansion coefficient, α, of a crystal

$$\alpha = \frac{1}{V}\left(\frac{\partial V}{\partial T}\right) = \frac{3}{l}\left(\frac{\partial l}{\partial T}\right)$$

is related to 3 $\Delta a/a$, where a is a reference lattice parameter and Δa is the change as a function of temperature. This term may be expressed as

$$\frac{3\,\Delta a}{a} = p(T) + r(T) + x(T) \tag{14.5}$$

where $p(T)$ and $r(T)$ represent the thermal expansion of the crystal in terms of the vibrational amplitudes of the atoms, outside the environment of the vacancy and surrounding the vacancy respectively. $x(T)$ is the volume change due to the presence of the vacancy itself. The volume expansion may also be measured in terms of the relative length change, 3 $\Delta l/l$, and similarly

$$\frac{3\,\Delta l}{l} = q(T) + s(T) + y(T) \tag{14.6}$$

The terms $q(T)$, $s(T)$, and $y(T)$ are analogous to $p(T)$, $r(T)$, and $x(T)$ respectively. Since both the length change and lattice parameter change, measure the time average unit cell dimension:

$$p(T) + r(T) = q(T) + s(T) \tag{14.7}$$

The terms $x(T)$ and $y(T)$ are not equal, however. Suppose that a crystal of N sites contains n_V vacancies and that the volume of each atom is Ω. A certain amount of relaxation will occur around the vacancy, so its volume will be only a fraction, f, of the atomic volume. The mean lattice parameter will change therefore by an amount

$$\frac{n_V f \Omega}{N\Omega}$$

or

$$x(T) = \frac{n_V f \Omega}{N\Omega} \tag{14.8}$$

The length change due to the vacancy will not equal $x(T)$ however, since the atom originally in the vacancy has now gone to the surface and so the volume change of the crystal per vacancy is $(\Omega + f\Omega)$; hence

$$y(T) = \frac{n_V(f + 1)\Omega}{N\Omega} \tag{14.9}$$

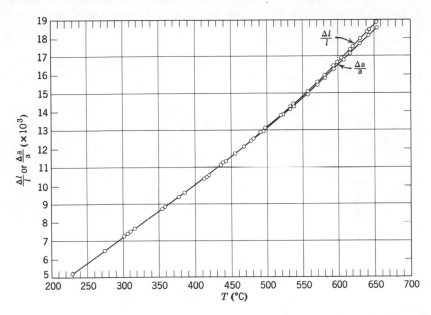

Fig. 14.4 Relative length and lattice parameter changes of aluminum as a function of temperature. From R. O. Simmons and R. W. Balluffi, *Phys. Rev.*, **117**, 52 (1960).

Substitution of equations 14.7, 14.8, and 14.9 into 14.5 and 14.6 yields

$$\frac{n_V}{N} = X_V = 3\left(\frac{\Delta l}{l} - \frac{\Delta a}{a}\right) \tag{14.10}$$

Thus, comparative measurements of $\Delta l/l$ and $\Delta a/a$ on samples should not be the same and the difference should be simply related to the mole fraction of vacancies. A comparison between $\Delta l/l$ and $\Delta a/a$ compared to room temperature values is shown in Fig. 14.4 for aluminum and it is seen indeed, that a difference exists. Using this approach absolute values of the vacancy concentration may be obtained by use of equation 14.10. For example at the melting points of aluminum and silver, X_V is equal to 9.4×10^{-4} and 1.7×10^{-4} respectively. Now since X_V is found in an absolute sense, ΔS_V may be evaluated from equation 14.1. For aluminum and silver, ΔS_V is found to be about 4.0 and 3.0 cal/mole degree respectively. It will be recalled that this is strictly a vibrational entropy resulting from the neighbors to a vacancy having a larger amplitude of vibration than those in normal sites. The experimental values of ΔS_V are positive as expected theoretically.

Since the vacancies are also associated with an increase in electrical resistivity, the resistivity per vacancy may also be calculated since X_V is known. For aluminum the vacancy resistivity is 3μ ohm-cm/% vacancies.[1]

Defect Complexes in Metals

Vacancies, similar to impurity atoms, have a strain energy associated with them. From classical elasticity theory, it may be shown that if two or more centers of strain are arranged so as to be adjacent, the total strain energy of the system is reduced. As a result one would expect that a certain fraction of vacancies would combine to form divacancies according to the reaction

$$V + V = V_2$$

where V represents a single vacancy and V_2 represents a divacancy. This reaction is shown schematically in Fig. 14.5. Because of strain energy considerations, the enthalpy of divacancy formation would be expected to be negative.

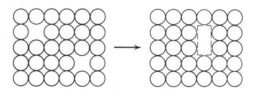

Fig. 14.5 Divacancy formation.

At equilibrium, the free energy change, ΔG, for the reaction is zero, and since

$$\Delta G = (\mu_{V_2} - 2\mu_V) = 0$$

at equilibrium,

$$\mu_{V_2} = 2\mu_V \tag{14.11}$$

The chemical potential of a vacancy is equal to

$$\mu_V = H_V - TS_V + RT \ln X_V + \mu_V{}^\circ$$

where $\mu_V{}^\circ$ is the chemical potential of a vacancy in its standard state. Similarly the chemical potential of a divacancy is given by

$$\mu_{V_2} = H_{V_2} - TS_{V_2} + RT \ln X_{V_2} + \mu_{V_2}{}^\circ$$

[1] R. O. Simmons and R. W. Balluffi, *Phys. Rev.*, **117**, 62 (1960).

where H_{V_2}, S_{V_2}, and $\mu_{V_2}{}^\circ$ are the enthalpy, entropy, and standard free energy of the divacancy. Upon substitution into equation 14.11 we find

$$\ln\left(\frac{X_{V_2}}{X_V{}^2}\right) = -\frac{(H_{V_2} - 2H_V)}{RT} + \frac{S_{V_2} - 2S_V}{R} - \frac{\mu_{V_2}{}^\circ - \mu_V{}^\circ}{RT} \quad (14.12)$$

The logical standard state for a vacancy and a divacancy is the defect at the surface. At the surface, the mole factor of vacancies and divacancies is equal to one. Thus we have

$$\mu_{V_2}{}^\circ = H_{V_2}{}^\circ - TS_{V_2}{}^\circ$$
$$\mu_V{}^\circ = H_V{}^\circ - TS_V{}^\circ$$

and substituting into equation 14.12 we find

$$\ln\left(\frac{X_{V_2}}{X_V{}^2}\right) = -\frac{\Delta H_{V_2} - 2\,\Delta H_V}{RT} + \frac{\Delta S_{V_2} - 2\,\Delta S_V}{R} \quad (14.13)$$

where the ΔH and ΔS terms refer to the enthalpy and entropy of formation of defects in the interior of the crystal, from the surface. These terms, therefore, correspond to the formation terms discussed earlier in the chapter. The term $(\Delta H_{V_2} - 2\,\Delta H_V)$ may be seen to correspond to the enthalpy of the reaction

$$V + V = V_2$$

and hence represents the binding enthalpy. On the basis of strain energy considerations, this quantity is expected to be negative. The basic reaction may be approached from a purely thermodynamic approach through the law of mass action. Since divacancies are in equilibrium with vacancies there must be an equilibrium constant, and hence

$$\Delta G^\circ = -RT \ln K$$

The equilibrium constant is given by

$$K = \frac{a_{V_2}}{a_V{}^2}$$

Since divacancies and vacancies V are both assumed to be present in small concentrations, $a_V = \gamma_V{}^\circ X_V$ and $a_{V_2} = \gamma_{V_2}{}^\circ X_{V_2}$, where $\gamma_V{}^\circ$ and $\gamma_{V_2}{}^\circ$ are the Henry's law activity coefficients. Thus

$$K = \frac{X_{V_2}}{X_V{}^2}\left[\frac{\gamma_{V_2}{}^\circ}{(\gamma_V{}^\circ)^2}\right] = \text{constant} \times \frac{X_{V_2}}{X_V{}^2}$$

and since $K = \exp(-\Delta G^\circ / RT)$

$$\frac{X_{V_2}}{X_V{}^2} = AK = A \exp\left(\frac{-\Delta G^\circ}{RT}\right)$$

Thus

$$\frac{X_{V_2}}{X_V{}^2} = \exp\left(\frac{\Delta S^\circ}{R}\right) \exp\left(\frac{-\Delta H^\circ}{RT}\right) \qquad (14.14)$$

Equation 14.14 is identical in form to 14.13, with ΔH° being identified with $(\Delta H_{V_2} - 2\,\Delta H_V)$, which represents the *binding enthalpy* of a divacancy. Actually our derivation of equation 14.13 was not complete, because there is another contribution to the configurational entropy resulting from the possible orientation of the asymmetric divacancy in the lattice. Further analysis of the problem shows that the term X_{V_2} in equation 14.12 should be multiplied by $(2/Z)$, which means that the constant A in equation 14.14 is equal to $Z/2$.

In later sections dealing with equilibrium between defects, the law of mass action will be used exclusively because of its simplicity in application.

To date no detailed evidence is available relating to the importance of divacancies and higher order complexes in metal lattices. Theoretical calculations of the binding enthalpies indicate an exothermic reaction with ΔH° being equal to about -2.0 kcal/gm-atom. Substitution into equation 14.14 indicates that the relative importance of divacancies is greater at low temperatures than it is at high temperatures.

Now let us consider complexes between impurity atoms and vacancies. Since both impurity atoms and vacancy strain the solvent structure, a reduction in strain energy will result if the impurity and vacancy reside as nearest neighbors rather than at a large separation distance. This constitutes a vacancy-impurity complex. In addition to the strain energy there may be a small coulombic interaction also resulting in a negative contribution to the binding enthalpy. The net result is that there are two types of vacancies in the structure: (a) those free vacancies whose concentration is given by equation 14.1, and (b) those bound to an impurity. These might be called *intrinsic* and *extrinsic* defects respectively. The former are intrinsic because their concentration in a given material is only a function of temperature, whereas the concentration of the latter will be a function of the type and concentration of impurity present in the lattice as well as temperature.

In order to obtain quantitative information about these complexes, let us consider the following reaction between a dissolved impurity atom B and a lattice vacancy.

$$B + V = B - V \qquad \Delta G^\circ = -RT \ln K$$

The equilibrium constant is equal to

$$K = \frac{a_{B-V}}{a_B \cdot a_V}$$

Let us assume that $X_V \ll 1$ and therefore $X_{B-V} \ll 1$. Thus these constituents follow Henry's law and their activity coefficients are, therefore, constant at a given temperature. For a given crystal, the activity of B, a_B, is constant, since the atomic composition does not change. Thus we obtain

$$\frac{X_{B-V}}{X_V} = bK = b \exp\left(-\frac{\Delta G^\circ}{RT}\right) = b \exp\left(\frac{\Delta S^\circ}{R}\right) \exp\left(-\frac{\Delta H^\circ}{RT}\right) \quad (14.15)$$

where b is a constant including a_B, γ°_{B-V}, and γ_V°. From the reaction we see that ΔH° represents the enthalpy difference between the associated and dissociated pair, and therefore is the *binding enthalpy* of the defect pair. As mentioned before, because of strain energy the sign of this term is negative. Because of the negative sign of ΔH°, we see from equation 14.15 that the ratio X_{B-V}/X_V increases as the temperature decreases. Thus pairing is of predominant importance at low temperatures. Also from the equilibrium constant we see that the number of impurity-vacancy pairs is proportional to the activity of B. Thus, if B is present in dilute concentration so that $a_B \sim \gamma_B X_B$, X_{B-V} is doubled if the impurity concentration is doubled. The total vacancy concentration $(X_V)_{total}$ will be the sum of the intrinsic plus extrinsic concentration of vacancies:

$$(X_V)_{total} = X_V + X_{B-V}$$

and we see, therefore, that the total vacancy content depends upon the amount and type of impurity B. This phenomenon is of particular importance in relation to atomic diffusion. In most crystals atoms diffuse by a vacancy mechanism. In the case of an impurity, the binding energy between vacancies and impurities indicates that an impurity atom tends to be associated with a vacancy with a higher than random probability. This will tend to facilitate a high atomic mobility of the impurity.

Let us now consider the problem of clusters forming between unlike impurity atoms as illustrated in Fig. 14.1. The enthalpy of binding of unlike impurities will generally be negative as in the previous cases discussed. The phenomenon may be more important, however, because if the appropriate impurities are concerned, ΔH° may be a large negative quantity. The reason for this comes from the fact that the strain energy is reduced upon pair or cluster formation as in the previous cases. In addition, however, there may be a strong chemical bonding interaction if one type of purity is electropositive, such as aluminum, and the other is electronegative, such as oxygen. If clustering occurs, the solubility of a constituent such as oxygen may be markedly increased over the value in a pure crystal, since there will be intrinsic oxygen and extrinsic oxygen associated with the other impurity. The total oxygen content will be the sum of the intrinsic amount plus the amount in clusters. The reaction for the cluster formation will be

$$aA + bB = cluster\,(a\text{A} + b\text{B}) \qquad \Delta G^\circ = RT \ln K$$

where a and b are the numbers of A and B atoms involved in the reaction. Because of the negative sign of ΔH°, the importance of cluster is more important at low temperatures than at high, as in the previous cases.

An interesting example illustrating this phenomenon pertains to the solubility of nitrogen in iron containing small amounts of aluminum as investigated by Darken.[1] Iron samples containing various amounts of dissolved aluminum were equilibrated with an atmosphere of ammonia and hydrogen. Nitrogen will dissolve in the crystal to the extent governed by the following reaction.

$$\text{NH}_3(g) = N(a_\text{N} \text{ in Fe}) + \tfrac{3}{2}\text{H}_2(g)$$

$$K = \frac{p_{\text{H}_2}^{3/2} \cdot a_\text{N}}{p_{\text{NH}_3}}$$

Clearly, the concentration of dissolved nitrogen depends upon the partial pressure of NH_3 gas. The solubility of nitrogen in pure iron at 600°C is low (of the order of 0.01% for an atmosphere of 1% NH_3–99% H_2). Furthermore the reaction between aluminum and nitrogen is very exothermic so it would be expected that as nitrogen diffuses into the crystal, crystals of AlN would tend to form. Thus if a chemical analysis were performed after saturation with an atmosphere containing 1% NH_3, one would expect the total nitrogen content to be the intrinsic amount (0.01%) plus the amount in AlN particles. Because of the exothermicity of the reaction

$$\text{Al}(s) + \tfrac{1}{2}\text{N}_2(g) = \text{AlN}(s)$$

virtually all the aluminum would be oxidized in solution, and since in AlN the concentration of nitrogen is equal to the concentration of aluminum, the total nitrogen content would be the sum of the intrinsic concentration (0.01%) plus the amount of aluminum. The curves shown in Fig. 14.6 show that this is not the case. The amount of excess nitrogen introduced in crystals containing aluminum corresponds to $\text{AlN}_{1.4}$ for our

[1] L. S. Darken in *The Physical Chemistry of Metallic Solutions and Intermetallic Compounds*, Proceedings of a Symposium Held at the National Physical Laboratory, 1958, Paper No. 4G.

atmosphere. Furthermore, if the pressure of the ammonia is increased to 6%, the excess nitrogen introduced over the intrinsic amount corresponds to $AlN_{1.7}$. The key to this apparent dilema is due to the temperature. At 600°C, the diffusion constant of aluminum is very low whereas that of the interstitially dissolved nitrogen is quite large. Consequently, nitrogen may rapidly diffuse in the crystal. When a nitrogen atom enters the

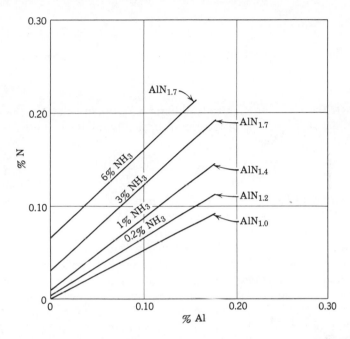

Fig. 14.6 Equilibration of Fe-Al alloys with NH_3-H_2 gas. From L. S. Darken in *The Physical Chemistry of Metallic Solutions and Intermetallic Compounds*, Her Majesty's Stationery Office, London, 1958.

proximity of an aluminum atom, binding will occur between the two because of the favorable chemical interaction. Precipitation of AlN would occur if the aluminum atoms were mobile so that discrete particles of AlN would form. Since this does not occur, complexes of nitrogen and aluminum form, with each aluminum being surrounded on the average by 1.7 atoms of nitrogen when the atmosphere consists of 6% ammonia. From the energetics of the reaction, this complexing should be more important at lower temperatures.

Let us now examine the interaction between impurities and dislocations. Consider that a crystal contains a dissolved impurity of concentration X_B. This impurity is considered here to be distributed in two ways,

(a) distributed randomly through the crystal and (b) in the environment of dislocations. Thus our reaction is

$$B(X_B, \text{ in crystal}) = B(X_B{}^d, \text{ dislocations})$$

At equilibrium, since $\Delta G = 0$

$$\mu_B{}^d(\text{dislocations}) = \mu_B(\text{in crystal})$$

or

$$\bar{H}_B{}^d - T\bar{S}_V{}^d + kT \ln X_B{}^d + (\mu^\circ)^d = \bar{H}_B - T\bar{S}_V + kT \ln X_B + \mu^\circ$$

Since the standard state of B is the same (pure B) on both sides of the reaction

$$(\mu^\circ)^d = \mu^\circ$$

Further, the vibrational entropy difference between solute in the crystal and in the vicinity of the dislocation is probably small so let it be assumed that $\bar{S}_V{}^d = \bar{S}_V$. Thus

$$\frac{X_B{}^d}{X_B} \simeq \exp\left(-\frac{\bar{H}_B{}^d - \bar{H}_B}{kT}\right) \qquad (14.16)$$

In equation 14.16 $X_B{}^d$ is the mole fraction of solute in the environment of the dislocation and X_B is the mole fraction in the bulk of the crystal. The difference in partial molal enthalpy in the vicinity of the dislocation $\bar{H}_B{}^d$ and that in the crystal $\bar{H}_B$ is equal to the binding enthalpy of the atom to dislocation. $\bar{H}_B{}^d$ is more negative than $\bar{H}_B$ because strain energy is reduced when a solute is in the vicinity of the dislocation. Equation 14.16 is only valid at high temperatures, since at a low temperature, the term $(\bar{H}_B{}^d - \bar{H}_B) \gg kT$ and hence $X_B{}^d \gg X_B$. At a sufficiently low temperature the ratio $X_B{}^d/X_B$ will be such that $X_B{}^d$ will be greater than one. In this situation, therefore, there will no longer be dissolved impurity around the dislocation but rather there will be a condensation of solute at the dislocation line forming virtually pure solute phase at the dislocation. At an elevated temperature $\bar{H}_B{}^d = f(r)$, where r represents the distance from the dislocation line, since the strain energy interaction diminishes as r increases. Thus $X_B{}^d = f(r)$ also. When r is large, the solute concentration approaches X_B.

One manner in which the solute atmosphere manifests itself is in the existence of a sharp yield point in the stress versus strain curve. It has been suggested by Cottrell[1] that the yield point results from the difficulty in pulling the dislocation away from a condensed line of impurity atoms, In the case of iron-carbon alloys the yield point is found to disappear at about 700°K. Therefore, it is suggested that condensation disappears

[1] A. Cottrell, *Dislocations and Plastic Flow in Crystals*, Oxford, London, 1953.

above this temperature. When the atmosphere is condensed, $X_B{}^d \sim 1$, Thus, the binding enthalpy at the dislocation pipes may be evaluated experimentally from equation 14.16, since 700°K is the lowest temperature for which $X_B{}^d = 1$. Upon substitution of these terms, $(\bar{H}_B{}^d - \bar{H}_B)$ is found to be about -0.5 ev.

The total number of solute atoms N_B in the crystal is given by $N_B = X_B$ (in perfect part of crystal) times the number of lattice sites in perfect part of crystal $+ X_B{}^d$ times the number of lattice sites around dislocations. The number of lattice sites in the vicinity of dislocations is far less than the number of sites in the perfect point of the crystal; therefore if N_B in the perfect part of the crystal is sufficiently large, the total concentration of solute is essentially equal to N_B (perfect part of crystal). As a result X_B is virtually equal to the average solute content of the crystal. An exception would occur when N_B in the perfect part is very small. In this situation the amount of solute located at dislocation may be an appreciable fraction of the total amount of solute in the crystal. Thus the solubility of a solute of this type is dependent upon the dislocation content of the crystal. The dislocation content may be markedly influenced by plastic deformation, hence one would expect that the solubility of a given solute would be greater in a cold-worked material than in an annealed material. Darken[1] has studied the nitrogen solubility in pure iron as a function of deformation. He finds that the nitrogen solubility may be doubled upon cold-working the iron crystals.

The principal contribution to the binding energy between impurities and dislocations is, as mentioned earlier, from strain energy reduction. In addition there may be a small coulombic interaction since the electron structure in the vicinity of the dislocation is perturbed and hence the dislocation may be thought to have an effective valence. The interaction energy between various types of defects in a variety of materials is summarized in Table 14.2. These, of course, are only approximate values.

In Chapter 12, the absorption of solute at a grain boundary was considered from a classical thermodynamic point of view. Let us now examine the interaction of impurities and dislocations from a statistical point of view. Actually the same considerations as discussed for the other interactions apply to this case. This type of interaction may be quite important. For a fine-grained material, for example, there is a significant amount of interface and as a result an appreciable amount of solute may be condensed at the grain boundaries at low temperatures. As a result, if the bulk solubility is very low, much more solute may reside in the crystal boundaries than in the bulk. This may lead to erroneous values of solute solubility unless large-grained crystals are used. As an

[1] L. S. Darken, *loc. cit.*

TABLE 14.2

Estimated Binding Energies between Dislocations and Physical and Chemical Point Defects in Various Solids[a]

Defect	Lattice Dilatation (%)	ΔE elastic (ev)	ΔE coul (ev)	ΔE total (ev)
Interstitial atoms in metals	6–20	0.2–0.5	0.02	0.2–0.5
Substitutional atoms in metals	1–4	0.05–0.10	0.02	0.05–0.10
Vacancies in metals	1	0.02	0.02	0.04
Interstitial atoms in semiconductors	5 (?)	~0.1	0.01	0.1 + chem. part (2–3 ev)
Substitutional atoms in semiconductors	1–4	0.05–0.10	0.01	0.05–0.1 + chem. part (2–3 ev)
Vacancies in semi-conductors	$\geqslant 1$	0.02?	0.01?	0.03
Interstitial and substitutional ions in polar crystals	10	0.05–0.1	0.1–1	0.1–1
Vacancies in polar crystals	5–10	0.03–0.06	0.1–1	0.1–1

[a] From H. G. Van Bueren, *Imperfections in Crystals*, North-Holland, Amsterdam, 1960.

example, consider a sample consisting of grains of 0.1 mm average diameter. The interface area per cubic centimeter of sample will be about 200 cm². An atom may be considered to have an approximate diameter of 3×10^{-8} cm and thus a cross-section area of about 10^{-15} cm². At complete saturation there would be

$$\frac{200 \text{ cm}^2}{10^{-15} \text{ cm}^2/\text{atom}}$$

or about 2×10^{17} solute atoms at the crystal boundaries if solute is concentrated only at the boundary itself. Since the number of lattice sites in a crystal is about $5 \times 10^{22}/\text{cm}^3$, a chemical analysis would show an atom fraction of $2 \times 10^{17}/5 \times 10^{22}$ or 4×10^{-6} coming from the crystal boundaries alone. If the bulk solubility were small, say only $10^{17}/\text{cm}^3$ or 2×10^{-6}, the boundaries would contribute more solute to the chemical analysis than the bulk. Many solubility studies performed in which the solubility is low are suspect because of this important problem. It has been experimentally verified by Thomas and Chalmers[1] that solute segregation at grain boundaries occurs. An example showing segregation of radioactive polonium in lead is shown in Fig. 14.7 by use of an auto-radiographic technique. A blackening of the film occurs where the film contacts a region rich in radioactive polonium. The amount of polonium

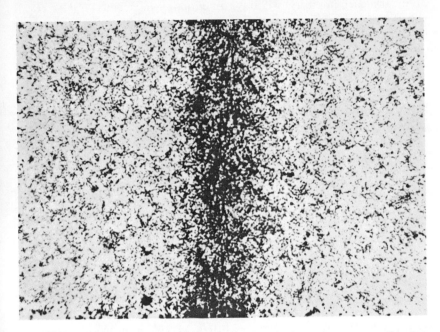

Fig. 14.7 Segregation of polonium at a grain boundary in lead; an autoradiograph. From W. R. Thomas and B. Chalmers, *Acta Met.*, **3**, 17 (1955).

segregating to the boundaries in lead was found to depend upon tempera-ture and the degree of misorientation of the crystals on either side of the boundary. The larger the misorientation, the more dislocations there are in the boundary and hence the more segregation would be expected to occur. This generalization was confirmed.

The problem of grain boundary segregation may be approached statis-tically in a rather simple fashion. This general approach may also be used to treat the problem of segregation of impurities at dislocations and is somewhat more general than the method used previously. For this case, in the limit where $(\bar{H}_\mathrm{B}{}^d - \bar{H}_\mathrm{B}) \ll 0$, the treatments are identical but differ when $(\bar{H}_\mathrm{B}{}^d - H_\mathrm{B})$ is closer to zero. In order to handle this problem, let us consider two types of sites; those outside the environment of the

[1] W. R. Thomas and B. Chalmers, *Acta Met.*, **3**, 17 (1955).

dislocations in the boundary and those in the strain field of the boundary. There will be N sites of the former type which contain N_B solute atoms, and there will be n distorted sites containing n_B atoms. For the sake of simplicity let us assume that all distorted sites are equivalent and that the solute atoms in these sites each have an enthalpy $\bar{H}_B{}^b$. Away from the boundary, each impurity[1] will have an enthalpy $\bar{H}_B$. Thus $(\bar{H}_B{}^b - \bar{H}_B)$ is the binding energy of impurities in the boundary. The number of ways of arranging N_B atoms on N sites and n_B atoms on n sites in the same system is

$$\mathscr{W} = \frac{N!}{N_B!\,(N - N_B)!} \cdot \frac{n!}{n_B!\,(n - n_B)!}$$

and the entropy of mixing for the crystal is

$$\Delta S_m = k \ln \mathscr{W}$$

Using Stirling's approximation

$$\Delta S_m = -k\left(N_B \ln \frac{N}{N - N_B} + n_B \ln \frac{n_B}{n - n_B} + N \ln \frac{N - N_B}{N} + n \ln \frac{n - n_B}{n}\right)$$

The free energy of the crystal consisting of $(N + n - N_B - n_B)$ atoms of solvent and $(N_B + n_B)$ atoms of solute is

$$G = (N + n - N_B - n_B)\bar{H}_A + N_B\bar{H}_B + n_B\bar{H}_B{}^b - T\,\Delta S_m - T\,\Delta S_{vib}$$

The free energy of $(N + n - N_B - n_B)$ atoms of pure solvent and $(N_B + n_B)$ atoms of pure solute is

$$G = (N + n - N_B - n_B)H_A{}^\circ + (N_B + n_B)H_B{}^\circ$$

If $(N_B + n_B) \ll 1$, $H_A{}^\circ = \bar{H}_A$, and ignoring the vibrational entropy ΔS_{vib}, the free energy of mixing is therefore equal to

$$\Delta G_m = N_B(\bar{H}_B - H_B{}^\circ) + n_B(\bar{H}_B{}^b - H_B{}^\circ) - T\,\Delta S_m \qquad (14.17)$$

Out of a total constant number of solute atoms $(N_B + n_B)$, the distribution is most probable which makes ΔG_m a minimum. Thus minimizing ΔG_m with respect to n_B (bearing in mind that $dN_B = -dn_B$) we find at $\partial \Delta G_m / \partial n_B = 0$

$$\frac{n_B}{n - n_B} = \frac{N_B}{N - N_B} \exp\left[\frac{-(\bar{H}_B{}^b - \bar{H}_B)}{kT}\right] \qquad (14.18)$$

The mole fraction of solute at the boundary is given by

$$X_B{}^b = \frac{n_B}{n - n_B}$$

[1] D. McLean, *Grain Boundaries in Metals*, Oxford, London, 1957.

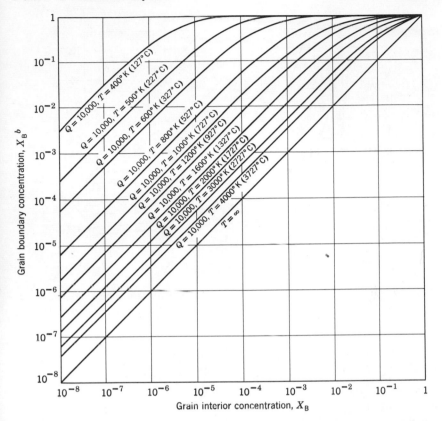

Fig. 14.8 Grain boundary concentration of solute versus concentration of solute in grain interior. From D. McLean, *Grain Boundaries in Metals*, Oxford, London, 1957.

and the mole fraction of solute in the body of the crystal is given by

$$X_B = \frac{N_B}{N - N_B}$$

The binding energy of solute to the boundary will be equal to $-Q$ where Q is defined as $(\bar{H}_B - H_B{}^b)$. Thus

$$X_B{}^b = \frac{X_B \exp (Q/kT)}{(1 - X_B) + X_B \exp (Q/kT)} \tag{14.19}$$

Generally $X_B \ll 1$ and hence may be neglected in the $(1 - X_B)$ term in the denominator; thus

$$X_B{}^b \cong \frac{X_B \exp (Q/kT)}{1 + X_B \exp (Q/kT)} \tag{14.20}$$

If, in addition, the temperature is comparatively high, $Q/kT \ll 1$. Thus,

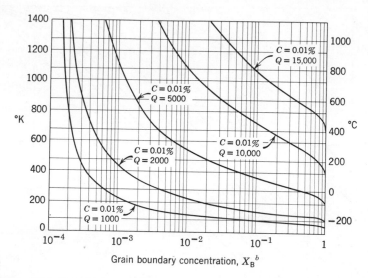

Fig. 14.9 Grain boundary segregation as a function of temperature, binding energy, and solute concentration in grain interior. From D. McLean, *Grain Boundaries in Metals*, Oxford, London, 1957.

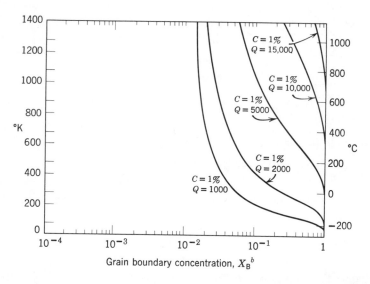

Fig. 14.10 Grain boundary segregation as a function of temperature, binding energy, and solute concentration in grain interior. From D. McLean, *Grain Boundaries in Metals*, Oxford, London, 1957.

in this case, the exponential in the denominator may be neglected compared to 1 and

$$\frac{X_B{}^b}{X_B} \cong \exp\left(\frac{Q}{kT}\right) \qquad (14.21)$$

Equation 14.21 is identical in form to equation 14.16, but is not valid unless the above conditions are true. In Fig. 14.8 are shown plots of $X_B{}^b$ versus X_B as a function of temperature based on equation 14.20. It is observed from this figure that deviation from the simple exponential relation of equation 14.21 is only found at high values of interior solute concentration. In Figs. 14.9 and 14.10 are shown the extent of grain boundary segregation as a function of temperature for various values of X_B and Q.

14.2 SEMICONDUCTORS

Both germanium and silicon have received extensive study in connection with their defect structure. In many respects, defects play a more important role in these materials than in metals. It is also found that the concentrations of defects in semiconductors may also be varied over wider

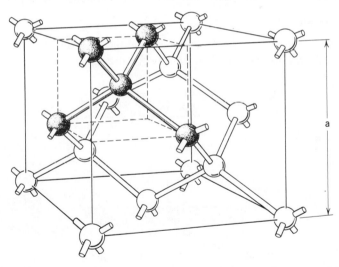

Fig. 14.11 Diamond cubic structure. From W. Shockley, *Electrons and Holes in Semiconductors*, Van Nostrand, New York, 1950.

limits than is the case for metals. Both crystals crystallize in the diamond cubic structure shown in Fig. 14.11. From Fig. 14.11, it is seen that the coordination number is 4 for this structure and hence the packing efficiency of atoms in the crystal is low. In fact, the volume of the interstitial site is identical with a regular lattice site and the environment is almost identical. An atom in the interstitial site is surrounded by four neighbors as is an atom in a regular lattice site. Therefore, the strain energy which must be expended in moving an atom from the surface into an interstitial site should be much lower than it is in the case of metals. As a result the enthalpy of formation of interstitials in a diamond structure should be considerably closer to the enthalpy of vacancy formation than in the case of metals, and hence the relative importance of interstitials should be much more important in the diamond structure than in more close packed structures. At present no information is available concerning the thermodynamic properties of interstitials, however, but this, of course, does not mean that they do not exist.

Actually, the same considerations discussed in Section 14.1 apply in the case of point defects and complexes in semiconductors. In semiconductors, however, the effects are more easily investigated since we generally know the valence of impurity atoms and the interactions between defects are more pronounced and hence more easily investigated. In addition to these types of interactions as discussed in Section 14.1, electronic defects and their interaction with atomic defects are important.

Electronic Defects

The electronic energy levels in a semiconductor group themselves into two broad regions separated in energy from each other. These regions

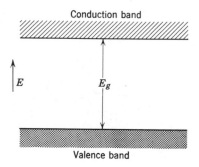

Conduction band

E

E_g

Valence band

Fig. 14.12   Energy gap for a semiconductor.

are called the valence band and conduction band, and are shown schematically in Fig. 14.12. In a pure crystal, no electron may have an energy corresponding to a state in the forbidden band. At $T = 0°K$, every state in the valence band is completely full and the conduction band is entirely empty. As a result, no electric current will flow, since there will be no available states in the valence band and there is insufficient excitation resulting from the electric field to cause an electron to move into the conduction band where it may readily respond to the field. At $T > 0°K$, the situation is different, however, and entropy considerations will dictate that some electrons will move from the valence to the conduction band. There thus exists a number of negative changes, n, in the conduction band and a number of unoccupied states or more simply, holes in the valence band. These will have an effective positive change and thus their con-centration will be designated p. The electronic band picture may be

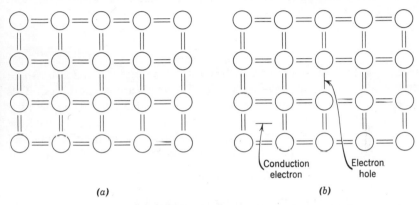

(a)   (b)

Fig. 14.13 Schematic view of covalent bonds in a semiconductor. (a) Corresponds to no electrons in conduction band or holes in the valence band; (b) corresponds to the existence of electrons in conduction band and holes in the valence band.

conveniently thought of in another way in a qualitative sense. Silicon and germanium are classed as covalent crystals which follow the $8 - N$ rule. Therefore, the atoms may be considered to be bound together by classical covalent bands as shown schematically in Fig. 14.13a. Each bond in Fig. 14.13a represents one electron. In Fig. 14.13b are shown schematically an electron in the conduction band and a hole in the valence band.

As a result of the formation of conduction electrons and holes in the valence band an electric current is capable of being maintained and may be carried by means of the electrons in the conductions band as well as those in the valence band now since empty available energy states are available. Instead of discussing the properties of the electrons in the valence band, however, it is more convenient to ascribe properties to the holes in a sense analogous to the situation for lattice vacancies and atoms in a crystal. From the standpoint of the discussion of equilibrium pro-perties of electrons, it is convenient to think of electrons and holes as being analogous to chemical constituents of the crystal and thus apply the law of mass action. At a given temperature, when equilibrium is reached, the rate of movement of electrons from the valence band to the conduction band, thus resulting in the formation of electrons and holes, is equal to the rate of *recombination* or the dropping of electrons from the conduction band to the valence band. The latter process may analogously be thought of as the formation of electron-hole pairs. Thus we have the reaction involving electrons, e^-, and holes, e^+

$$e^+ \cdot e^- = e^- + e^+$$

with concentration np respectively n, and p. Using the law of mass action, we have

$$\frac{a_{e^-} \cdot a_{e^+}}{a_{e^+} \cdot e^-}$$

Generally, at the temperatures of interest, the values of n and p are small and hence Henry's law may be applied to the electrons and holes. This means that most electrons and holes are associated (or valence band is almost full). The concentration of electron-hole pairs changes very little as n and p change, therefore, since Henry's law holds for the electrons and holes, their activity coefficients are independent of concentrations and thus

$$n \cdot p = AK' = K = A \exp\left(-\Delta F^\circ / kT\right) \tag{14.22}$$

where A is the activity coefficient term. (Instead of ΔG°, it is more convenient theoretically to use ΔF°, the Helmholtz free energy, and thus speak of a constant volume process.) For an intrinsic crystal in which there are no impurities contributing or absorbing electrons $n_i = p_i$ and thus

$$n_i^2 = K = A \exp\left(\Delta S^\circ / k\right) \exp\left(-\Delta E^\circ / kT\right) \tag{14.23}$$

In Fig. 14.14 are shown experimental values of n_i for Ge and Si as a function of temperature. From equation 14.23, we see that ΔE° may be obtained from the slope of the curves. This is equal to the width of the energy gap since this corresponds to the energy of the reaction. Equation 14.22 represents an important contribution to the study of defects and recourse will often be made to this equation.

When an atomic defect is placed in an otherwise perfect crystal, it may tend to contribute electrons to the conduction band or absorb them from the valence band, depending upon the nature of the particular defect. Many of these defects have electron energy levels which lie in the forbidden zone. Defects which contribute electrons are referred to as donors or n-type defects and those which absorb electrons to as acceptors or p-type defects. Examples are shown in Fig. 14.15. If an impurity is a donor with the donor level shown in Fig. 14.15, this means that the valence electron of the impurity, when associated with the impurity, has an energy

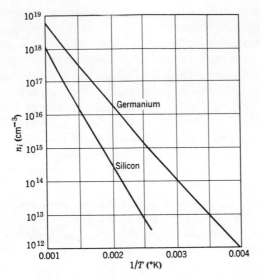

Fig. 14.14 Electron concentration in conduction band for intrinsic germanium and silicon as a function of temperature. From F. J. Morin and J. P. Maita, *Phys. Rev.*, **94**, 1525 (1954); **96**, 28 (1954).

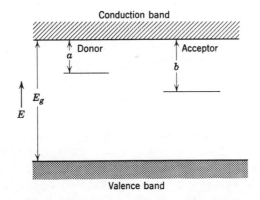

Fig. 14.15 Donor and acceptor states in the energy gap.

shown by the donor state and is a ev below the conduction band. Similarly, if the impurity is an acceptor with the acceptor level as shown in Fig. 14.15, this means that an electron, when put into association with the impurity, has the energy represented by the acceptor state and is b ev below the conduction band. Not all impurities (or defects in general) have donor or acceptor levels which lie in the forbidden region but many of them do.

It is of interest to obtain quantitative information regarding the fraction of donor impurities which have given up valence electrons and the fraction of acceptor impurities which have gained valence electrons. It might be added at this point that if a defect has given up one or more electrons, it will be a positive center, and if it has gained a valence electron, it is a negative center. To obtain this quantitative information, appeal will be made to statistical mechanics. We are interested in determining whether the available donor or acceptor energy levels corresponding to a given state of energy E_i are filled (in other words the probability that the states are occupied.) The fraction of sites occupied with a given energy E_i we will denote by the symbol $f(E_i)$. Since this is a probability, obviously $0 < f(E_i) < 1$.

Each electron in the crystal is characterized by a particular energy E_i and the number of available states at this energy is Z_i. At equilibrium, out of a total of N electrons, n_i will be situated at this energy level E_i. The total energy of the assembly of electrons is E. Thus

$$N = \sum n_i \tag{14.24}$$

$$E = \sum n_i E_i \tag{14.25}$$

Since we have a total energy of E, no level greater than E will be occupied and thus

$$Z_{\text{total}} = \sum Z_i = Z_i + Z_2 + \cdots + Z_E$$

Thus, we have Z_{total} possible states for the electrons to be distributed among. It will be assumed that a given electron has no preference for any state, therefore the probability of it being in any state p is given by

$$p = \frac{1}{Z_{\text{total}}} \tag{14.26}$$

Let us now restrict ourselves to a given energy level E_i. At this energy there are Z_i levels. Since, according to the *Pauli exclusion principle*, no two electrons may have the same quantum numbers or wave function, each state may be occupied by only one electron at most. Further, let us restrict our case to the situation where there are many more states, Z_i, than electrons occupying those states, n_i. Thus, some states will be empty. The question to be answered is the following. How many electrons, n_i, are there in the crystal with an energy E_i?

The first aspect to be answered concerns the probability of a given complexion. For example, of the Z_i levels at energy E_i, the first level Z_1 is filled, Z_2 filled, Z_3 empty, etc., until there are n_i electrons. As we stated, a given electron has a probability p of being in a particular state. Thus, the probability that n_i levels are simultaneously filled with n_i electrons for our particular complexion is p^{n_i}. There are, however, many ways in which these Z_i states may be occupied by n_i electrons besides the particular one chosen. According to Chapter 4, the number of complexions $\mathcal{W}$ is given by

$$\mathcal{W} = \frac{Z_i!}{n_i!\,(Z_i - n_i)!} \tag{14.27}$$

if the electrons are indistinguishable and if the states are indistinguishable.

Therefore the probability $P(n_i)$ of finding n_i electrons at energy E_i is the probability of a particular complexion p^{n_i} times the total number of complexions corresponding to this statistical state:

$$P(n_i) = p^{n_i}\mathcal{W}_i = p^{n_i} \cdot \frac{Z_i!}{n_i!\,(Z_i - n_i)!} \tag{14.28}$$

At a different energy E_j, the probability of finding n_j electrons among Z_j levels is, similarly,

$$P(n_j) = p^{n_j}\mathcal{W}_j = p^{n_j} \cdot \frac{Z_j!}{n_j!(Z_j - n_j)!} \tag{14.29}$$

and so on for other levels. As a result the probability of finding N electrons with n_j electrons at the level E_i, n_j electrons at E_j, etc. is $P(n_i) \cdot P(n_j) \cdot \cdots$. Thus

$$P(n_i) \cdot P(n_j) \cdot \cdots = p^{n_i} \cdot p^{n_j} \cdot \cdots \mathcal{W}_i \cdot \mathcal{W} \cdots$$

or

$$P(n_i) \cdot P(n_j) \cdot \cdots = p^N \prod \mathcal{W}_i = p^N \mathcal{W} \tag{14.30}$$

The total number of electrons, N, in the crystal is fixed, as is the total number of levels, Z_{total}. Thus p^N is a constant. The values of n_i, n_j, $\ldots$ found experimentally in a crystal will be those corresponding to the most probable state, which is represented by $P(n_i) \cdot P(n_j) \cdot \cdots$ being a maximum. This corresponds, according to equation 14.30, to $\mathcal{W}$ being a maximum. It is easier to work with $\ln \mathcal{W}$, however, and a maximum in $\mathcal{W}$ will correspond to a maximum in $\ln \mathcal{W}_i$. Thus, since

$$\mathcal{W} = \prod \mathcal{W}_i$$

we have

$$\ln \mathcal{W} = \sum \ln \mathcal{W}_i$$

Using Stirling's approximation for $\mathcal{W}_i$ we find

$$\ln \mathcal{W} = \sum \left[Z_i \ln Z_i - n_i \ln n_i - (Z_i - n_i) \ln (Z_i - n_i) \right] \tag{14.31}$$

At the maximum value of $\mathcal{W}$, a small change in the values of n_i corresponding to δn_i will result in a change in $\mathcal{W}$ of $\delta \ln \mathcal{W}$ which is equal to zero. Differentiating,

$$\delta \ln \mathcal{W} = \sum \left[-\ln n_i + \ln (Z_i - n_i) \right] \delta n_i = 0 \tag{14.32}$$

There are certain restraints placed on these values of δn_i, however, since from 14.24 and 14.25 we find that N and E are fixed.

$$\delta N = \sum \delta n_i = 0 \tag{14.33}$$

$$\delta E = \sum E_i \, \delta n_i = 0 \tag{14.34}$$

Since the maximum in $\ln \mathscr{W}$ is dependent upon several variables $(n_i, n_j, \ldots)$ and since these are connected by equations 14.33 and 14.34, our maximum is called a *constrained* maximum. A technique for handling this situation has been developed by Lagrange, using the Langrangian multiplier.[1] Applying this technique to equations 14.32, 14.33, and 14.34, we find the following set of relations.

$$\frac{\partial \ln \mathscr{W}_i}{\partial n_i} - \lambda_1 - \lambda_2 E_i = 0$$

$$\frac{\partial \ln \mathscr{W}_j}{\partial n_j} - \lambda_1 - \lambda_2 E_j = 0$$

or

$$\ln \frac{Z_i - n_i}{n_i} - \lambda_1 - \lambda_2 E_i = 0 \tag{14.35}$$

$$\ln \frac{Z_j - n_j}{n_j} - \lambda_1 - \lambda_2 E_j = 0 \tag{14.36}$$

where λ_1 and λ_2 are the Lagrangian multipliers. Solving equation 14.35 for example for n_i, the number of electrons having energy E_i yields

$$n_i = \frac{Z_i}{1 + \exp(\lambda_1) \exp(\lambda_2 E_i)} \tag{14.37}$$

which is the Fermi-Dirac distribution. Further consideration shows that

$$\lambda_2 = \frac{1}{kT}$$

and

$$\lambda_1 = -\frac{E_F}{kT}$$

Thus

$$f(E_i) = \frac{n_i}{Z_i} = \frac{1}{1 + \exp\left[(E_i - E_F)/kT\right]} \tag{14.38}$$

The term E_F is known as the *Fermi level* and represents mathematically the energy level E_i for which $f(E_i) = \frac{1}{2}$, as can be seen from equation

[1] For reference, see any text on advanced calculus, e.g., Sokolnikoff and Sokolnikoff, *Higher Mathematics for Engineers and Physicists*, McGraw-Hill, New York, 1941.

14.38. For a semiconductor this level may occur in the forbidden gap since its significance is purely mathematical. The quantity $f(E_i)$ is shown for a semiconductor at $T = 0°K$ and $T > 0°K$ in Fig. 14.16. When $E_i \gg E_F$ and hence $(E_i - E_F) \gg kT$, which is near the tail of the curve, the exponential term in equation 14.38 $\gg 1$ and equation 14.38 becomes

$$f(E_i) \cong \frac{n_i}{Z_i} \cong \exp\left[-\frac{(E_i - E_F)}{kT} \right] \qquad (14.39)$$

This is the Maxwell-Boltzmann or classical distribution factor. Classical statistics may be used without much error when $(E_i - E_F) > 4kT$. At

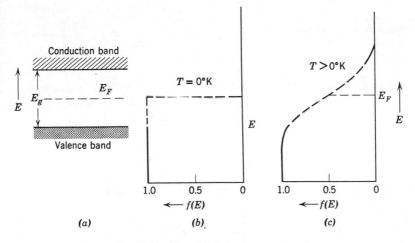

Fig. 14.16   Fermi function versus energy.

room temperature $kT \cong 0.025$ ev and hence classical statistics may be used for electronic states greater than E_F by about 0.1 ev.

When the thermodynamics of the interaction of electrons and atomic defects is discussed in later sections, it will be necessary to be concerned with the chemical potential of electrons as well as with the chemical potentials of atoms participating in the reaction. In order to obtain the chemical potential of an electron of the crystal, consider the entropy change of a crystal resulting from the introduction of one electron of zero energy into the crystal where it has an energy E_i. Thus, we shall need to find dS/dn_i. This is given by

$$\frac{dS}{dn_i} = k\left(\frac{d \ln \mathscr{W}_i}{dn_i} \right)$$

from the Boltzmann relation. Since

$$\ln \mathscr{W}_i = \frac{Z_i!}{n_i!\,(Z_i - n_i)!} = [Z_i \ln Z_i - n_i \ln n_i - (Z_i - n_i) \ln (Z_i - n_i)]$$

$$\frac{d \ln \mathscr{W}_i}{dn_i} = \ln \left(\frac{Z_i - n_i}{n_i} \right)$$

Letting $dn_i = 1$ electron, there is a change in entropy given by

$$dS = k \ln \left(\frac{Z_i - n_i}{n_i} \right)$$

and upon substitution of $f(E_i)$ for n_i/Z_i we find

$$dS = k \ln \left(\frac{f(E_i) - 1}{f(E_i)} \right)$$

Substituting equation 14.38,

$$\frac{dS}{\text{electron}} = \frac{E_F}{T} - \frac{E_i}{T} \tag{14.40}$$

We may express S thermodynamically as a function of two independent variables such as (P, T) or (E, V) etc., as well as a function of the number of electrons, N. Choosing E and V in addition to N and specifying that V is constant gives

$$dS = \left(\frac{\partial S}{\partial N} \right)_{E,V} dN + \left(\frac{\partial S}{\partial E} \right)_{N,V} dE$$

Since one electron is introduced in the crystal from zero energy to E_i, $dN = 1$ and $dE = E_i$. Thus

$$dS = \left(\frac{\partial S}{\partial N} \right)_{E,V} + \left(\frac{\partial S}{\partial E} \right)_{N,V} E_i \tag{14.41}$$

Equating 14.41 to 14.40 yields

$$\left(\frac{\partial S}{\partial N} \right)_{E,V} = \frac{E_F}{T}$$

and

$$\left(\frac{\partial S}{\partial E} \right)_{N,V} = -\frac{1}{T}$$

The chemical potential per electron is equal to

$$\mu = \left(\frac{\partial G}{\partial N} \right)_{P,T} \tag{14.42}$$

and from classical thermodynamics we find that

$$\mu = \left(\frac{\partial G}{\partial N} \right)_{P,T} = -T \left(\frac{\partial S}{\partial N} \right)_{E,V}$$

Hence we find that

$$\mu_e = E_F \qquad (14.43)$$

According to classical thermodynamics it is not possible to determine absolute thermodynamic quantities. Equation 14.43 does not violate this principle since E_F cannot be determined in an absolute sense. The

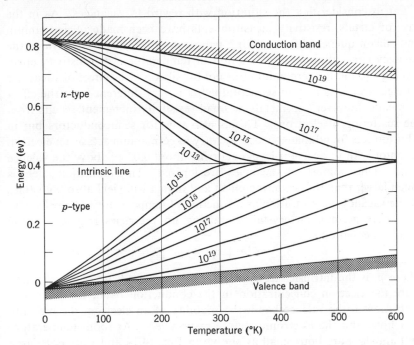

Fig. 14.17 Fermi level for germanium as a function of donor and acceptor concentration. From A. K. Jonscher, *Principles of Semiconductor Device Operation*, Wiley, New York, 1960.

position of the Fermi level is always expressed in terms of some reference level, such as the top of the valence band, etc.

The calculation of the position of the Fermi level relative to the edge of the valence band is a complicated function of the concentrations of donors or acceptor impurities, the position of their donor and acceptor levels, and also temperature. For an ideal intrinsic crystal (containing no impurities) the Fermi level is equal to $\frac{1}{2}(E_v + E_c)$ where E_v and E_c are the energies associated with the top of the valence band and bottom of the conduction band respectively. In Fig. 14.17 are shown calculated values of E_F for germanium as a function of impurity concentration and temperature, for the case where donors and acceptors are completely ionized

at all temperatures. The concentration units are given in terms of number
of impurities per cubic centimeter of crystal.

Atomic Defects and Defect Complexes

Considerable information is available concerning the nature of primary
defects and defect complexes in semiconductors.

Let us consider first the situation with regard to vacancies. As in the
case of metals, resistivity measurements have been made of germanium
and silicon quenched from a high temperature in order to determine the
vacancy concentration as a function of temperature. A resistivity effect
has been found for germanium but not for silicon. The effect of vacancies
on electrical resistivity in semiconductors is very different from the effect
in metals, however. In metals, a small resistivity increment results from
the scattering of electrons. This is also true for semiconductors but in
addition it is found that a lattice vacancy in germanium acts as an electron
acceptor with its acceptor level occurring about 0.03 ev above the valence
band. Thus, almost all vacancies are ionized. This ionization effect is
much larger than the scattering effect and in fact will yield absolute values
of the vacancy concentration as a function of temperature. The resistivity
of a pure germanium crystal containing no vacancies is given by the
standard equation

$$\rho_i^{-1} = [e^-]\mathscr{B}_e e + [e^+]\mathscr{B}_h e \tag{14.44}$$

where ρ_i is the intrinsic electrical resistivity and $[e^-]$, $[e^+]$, $\mathscr{B}_e$, $\mathscr{B}_h$, and
e are the electron concentration in the conduction band, the hole con-
centration in the valence band, the mobility of an electron, the mobility
of a hole, and the electronic charge respectively. At room temperature
$[e^-]$ and $[e^+]$ are both small as shown in Fig. 14.14 and thus ρ_i is large
(about 60 ohm-cm and 5000 ohm-cm for Ge and Si respectively).

Let us now anneal the crystal at a high temperature in order to introduce
N_V vacancies. Upon quenching to room temperature the vacancies are
frozen in. The question now arises as to how many of the N_V vacancies
have accepted electrons from the valence band. Putting this in the
language of Fermi-Dirac statistics, how many of the Z_i states (or N_V
states) at energy E_A of 0.03 ev above the valence band are occupied by
electrons? This is given by equation 14.38 as

$$n_A = \frac{N_V}{1 + \frac{1}{2}\exp\left(\dfrac{E_A - E_F}{kT}\right)} \tag{14.45}$$

The factor of $\frac{1}{2}$ in the denominator comes from the fact that each state
may hold two electrons. In this equation Z_i is equivalent to N_V since

each vacancy introduces an acceptor state. Hall effect measurements indicate that the energy difference between the acceptor level and valence is about 0.03 ev and calculations show that the difference between E_F and the valence band is about 0.30 ev. Thus $(E_A - E_F) = -0.27$ and since $kT \sim 0.025$ we find from equation 14.45 that

$$n_A \cong N_V$$

or that virtually all vacancies are ionized. These electrons have been received from the valence band, thereby leaving N_V holes. This results in a resistivity increment $\Delta\rho$ of

$$\Delta\rho = N_V \mathscr{B}_h$$

Since $\Delta\rho$ is measured experimentally and $\mathscr{B}_h$ and e are also known, N_V may be calculated in an absolute sense. The quantity $\mathscr{B}_h$ is not constant but is a function of the hole concentration or ρ so this must be evaluated experimentally.

At present two experimental values are available for the quenched-in vacancy concentration as a function of temperature for germanium. According to Logan[1]

$$X_V = 26 \exp{(-2/kT)}$$

and according to Mayburg and Rotandi[2]

$$X_V = 6 \exp{(-2.01/kT)}$$

Comparing these results with equation 14.1 we see that the enthalpy of formation of a vacancy is

$$\Delta H_V = 2 \text{ ev}$$

and

$$\exp{\left(\frac{\Delta S_V}{k}\right)} = 6 - 26 \quad \text{or} \quad \Delta S_V = 3.6 - 6.5 \text{ ev}$$

Theoretical calculations have been made by Swalin[3] of ΔS_V and ΔH_V for germanium, silicon, and diamond. In this calculation the enthalpy was assumed to consist of three terms: (1) the enthalpy needed to break four bonds as shown in Fig. 14.18b and deposit an atom on the surface, (2) the enthalpy gained upon reforming the dangling single bonds into covalent bonds, and (3) the elongation of second neighbor, third neighbor, etc., bonds as the atoms surrounding the vacancy relax inward, as shown

[1] R. A. Logan, *Phys. Rev.*, **101**, 1455 (1956).
[2] S. Mayburg and L. Rotandi, *Phys. Rev.*, **91**, 1015 (1953).
[3] R. A. Swalin, *J. Phys. Chem. Solids*, **18**, 290 (1961).

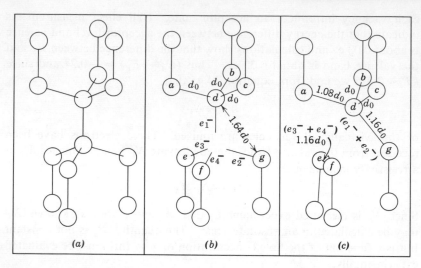

Fig. 14.18 Formation of vacancy in a diamond cubic lattice. (*a*) Normal site; (*b*) removal of atom; (*c*) relaxation of neighbors. From R. A. Swalin, *J. Phys. Chem. Solids*, **18**, 290 (1961).

in Fig. 14.18*c*. The calculated values of ΔS_V and ΔH_V are listed in Table 14.3.

Let us now turn our attention to a consideration of vacancy-impurity complexes. There are two factors which will influence the extent to which

TABLE 14.3

Calculated Values of the Entropy and Enthalpy of Vacancy Formation for Semiconductors[a]

Substance	ΔS_V (ev)	ΔH_V (ev)
Germanium	4.4	2.07
Silicon	4.4	2.32
Diamond	4.4	4.16

[a] From R. A. Swalin, *J. Phys. Chem. Solids*, **18**, 290 (1961).

pairing will occur: (1) the relief of strain energy when an impurity associates with a vacancy and (2) coulombic interaction between a charged impurity and a charged vacancy.

The equation which governs the atom fraction of complexes in semiconductors is the same as that developed for metals, namely equation 14.15.

$$\frac{X_{B-V}}{X_V} = b \exp\left(\frac{\Delta S^\circ}{R}\right) \exp\left(\frac{-\Delta H^\circ}{RT}\right) \qquad (14.15)$$

where $\Delta H°$ and $\Delta S°$ are the bonding enthalpy and vibrational entropy change associated with the complex. Rough estimation of the elastic and coulombic contributions to $\Delta H°$ may be made. The strain energy contribution to the heat of solution $\Delta \bar{H}_B$ may be crudely estimated by treating the crystal as a continuum containing a hole the size of a vacancy. A solute atom of wrong size is then placed in this hole and the elastic strain energy associated with necessary dilatation of the hole to fit the impurity is calculated. When a vacancy moves into a nearest neighbor position to the impurity, strain energy is released, since the impurity need not perform elastic works in the direction of the vacancy. Very approximately one might expect that a fraction of about $1/Z$ of the strain energy contribution to $\Delta \bar{H}_B$ is released upon pairing. This fraction is then the elastic contribution to the binding energy. Calculations by Swalin[1] indicate that this contribution for impurities in Ge and Si is about 0.3 ev. Some experimental information about this term is available. Logan[2] studied the equilibrium vacancy concentration in pure germanium and in germanium containing 6×10^{19} tin atoms per cm^3, which corresponds to an atom fraction of about 1.2×10^{-3}. Tin, like germanium and silicon, is a Group IV element and thus has the same number of valence electrons as germanium and silicon. Therefore, one expects the relative charge of a tin atom dissolved in germanium or silicon to be zero. Electrical measurements indicate this to be true. The only significant contribution to bonding, therefore, will be the elastic term. The total vacancy count in the tin-doped crystal thus will be the number of intrinsic vacancies plus the number associated with impurities or

$$X_{V \text{ total}} = X_{V_i} + X_{\text{Sn}-V} \qquad (14.46)$$

The results of Logan's studies on pure germanium and tin-doped germanium are shown in Fig. 14.19. It is clear that the number of acceptors quenched into germanium depends strongly upon the resistivity of the crystal. At 850°C a pure crystal of 35 ohm-cm resistivity contains about $10^{17}/cm^3$ acceptors, a slightly more impure crystal of 2 ohm-cm resistivity contains about $3 \times 10^{14}/cm^3$ quenched acceptors, and a heavily tin-doped crystal contains about $7 \times 10^{15}/cm^3$ acceptors. If it is assumed that a vacancy acts as an acceptor in both the free and associated state, the value of $\Delta H°$, the binding enthalpy, may be estimated. The equation for the concentration of acceptors for the tin-doped crystal as a function of T is, from Fig. 14.19, found to be

$$(X_{V \text{ total}})_{\text{tin-doped}} = a \exp(-1.3/kT) \qquad (14.47)$$

[1] R. A. Swalin, *J. Appl. Physics,* **29,** 670 (1958).
[2] R. A. Logan, *loc. cit.*

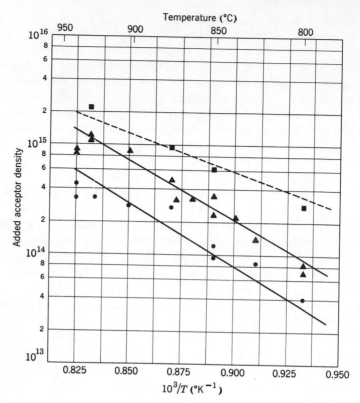

Fig. 14.19 Vacancy concentration of pure germanium and tin-doped germanium as a function of temperature. ● p-type, $\rho \sim 17$ ohm-cm; ▲ n-type, $\rho \sim 2$ ohm-cm; ■ p-type (Sn doped), $\rho \sim 35$ ohm-cm. From R. A. Logan, *Phys. Rev.*, **101**, 1455 (1956).

and X_{V_i} for the intrinsic crystal is given by

$$X_{V_i} = b \exp\left(-2.0/kT\right) \tag{14.48}$$

Substitution of equation 14.46 into 14.15 yields

$$\left[\frac{X_{V(\text{total})}}{X_{V_i}} - 1\right] = c \exp\left(\frac{\Delta S^\circ}{R}\right) \exp\left(-\frac{\Delta H^\circ}{RT}\right) \tag{14.49}$$

Plotting the data from Fig. 14.19 according to equation 14.49 yields

$$\Delta H^\circ = -1.1 \text{ ev}$$

as shown in Fig. 14.20. As mentioned previously, ΔH° represents the strain energy contribution to the binding energy. The large value of -1.1 ev is obtained since there is a large misfit in size between a tin atom and a germanium atom.

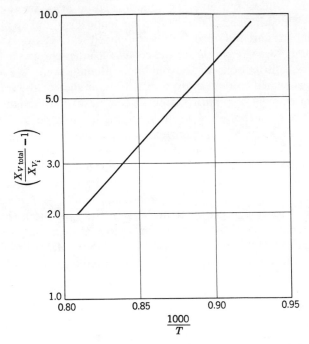

Fig. 14.20 Plot of equation 14.49 in order to obtain the binding enthalpy between tin impurity and vacancy.

The coulombic contribution may be estimated by

$$\Delta H_c^\circ = \frac{\mathscr{Z}_V \cdot \mathscr{Z}_B e^2}{\kappa x_0}$$

where $\mathscr{Z}_V$ is the vacancy valence, $\mathscr{Z}_B$ the impurity valence, e the unit of electronic charge, κ the dielectric constant, and x_0 the distance between separation of the charges. Since vacancies act as electron acceptors and thus are negative, positive impurities will be attracted to vacancies and negative impurities will be repulsed. Using the macroscopic dielectric constant for germanium (16) and the interatomic separation for germanium for x_0, we find that

$$\Delta H_c^\circ \cong \pm 0.40 \text{ ev}$$

Therefore this term should make a significant contribution to the binding energy.

It should be quite evident from this discussion that the vacancy concentration of a crystal (semiconductor, insulator, or metallic) depends very significantly upon the types and concentrations of dissolved impurities.

Let us now concern ourselves with the formation of impurity-impurity complexes. The principles which govern the tendency of unlike impurities to form complexes are the same as those discussed with regard to vacancy-impurity complexes, namely *elastic* and *coulombic* interactions. In addition to these two contributions to the binding enthalpy, there is a *chemical* term which is related to the electronegativity difference of the impurities. Theoretical treatment of impurity-impurity complexes in solids is analogous to the same phenomenon in aqueous solutions where a negative ion, for example, has an atmosphere of positive ions around it. The quantitative treatment of this phenomenon in aqueous solutions is known as the Debye-Huckel theory. Extension of these concepts to solids in both a theoretical and experimental fashion is due to the work of Reiss, Fuller, and Morin.[1]

As the first aspect of our treatment, let us restrict the discussion to the coulombic interaction of impurities. Impurities with a like charge will repel one another and hence no complexes will form. Impurities with an unlike charge will have a potential energy of interaction of

$$\frac{\mathscr{Z}_A \mathscr{Z}_B e^2}{\kappa x}$$

as mentioned previously. Aqueous solutions have a dielectric constant, κ, of about 80, whereas silicon and germanium have values of 12 and 16 respectively. This means that the interaction potential for impurities will be 5–6 times larger in Si or Ge than in aqueous solutions. Since the fraction of pairs formed is related to the exponential of ΔH, complexing will be much more important in the case of these semiconductors than for aqueous solutions. In fact, instead of a diffuse atmosphere forming as in the case of the Debye-Huckel theory, stable ion pairs will form at low temperatures because of the strong interaction. In other words, instead of there being a statistical distribution of positive charges at various distances from a negative charge and vice versa, there will tend to be distinct ion pairs in nearest neighbor sites, because of the strong potential interaction.

We therefore have the following reaction to consider:

$$A^+ + B^- = A^+ \cdot B^-$$

Let $(N_A - \mathscr{P})$, $(N_B - \mathscr{P})$, and $\mathscr{P}$ represent the concentrations of donors, acceptors, and ion pairs respectively. Through the law of mass

[1] H. Reiss, C. S. Fuller, and F. J. Morin, *Bell Syst. Tech. J.*, **35**, 535 (1956) and later publications.

action we have the equilibrium constant K'.

$$K' = \frac{a_{A^+ \cdot B^-}}{a_{A^+} \cdot a_{B^-}}$$

Since we are concerned with dilute solutions, Henry's law holds and therefore the activity coefficients will be constant. As a result we have the concentrations related to a constant Λ in the following manner.

$$\Lambda = \frac{\mathscr{P}}{(N_A - \mathscr{P})(N_B - \mathscr{P})}$$

Knowing the coulombic energy of interaction, we may, in fact, derive quantitatively the value of Λ. This treatment was originally performed by Fuoss and extended in scope by Reiss. We will approach the problem in a more thermodynamic fashion.

Let us consider a crystal containing N_{A^+} ions of type $A^+ + N_{B^-}$ ions of type B^- and let there be no pairs formed. This crystal will have a free energy G_i. Now let $\mathscr{P}$ pairs form; as a consequence, the number of A ions is now $(N_A - \mathscr{P})$ and the number of B ions is $(N_B - \mathscr{P})$. The crystal free energy will now be G. Each pair will be associated with an enthalpy of formations ΔH_h, and a vibrational entropy charge ΔS_v. In addition there will be a mixing entropy change $\Delta(\Delta S_m)$.

Originally there was an entropy of mixing:

$$\Delta S_{m_i} = k \ln \frac{N!}{N_{A^+}! \, N_{B^-}! \, (N - N_{A^+} - N_{B^-})!}$$

Using Stirling's approximation we find

$$\Delta S_{m_i} = -R[(1 - X_{A^+} - X_{B^-}) \ln (1 - X_{A^+} - X_{B^-}) \\ + X_{A^+} \ln X_{A^+} + X_{B^-} \ln X_{A^-}]$$

Let there now be formed $\mathscr{P}$ pairs. The entropy of mixing ΔS_m will consist of two terms; the first will be the entropy of mixing of the lattice minus the clusters or pairs. The numbers of A^+ ions and B^- ions are now $(N_{A^+} - \mathscr{P})$ and $(N_{B^-} - \mathscr{P})$ respectively, and the number of total lattice sites excluding those involved in the cluster will be $(N - 2\mathscr{P})$. This entropy term will therefore be given as

$$\Delta S_1 = \\ k \ln \frac{(N - 2\mathscr{P})!}{(N_{A^+} - \mathscr{P})!(N_{B^-} - \mathscr{P})! \, [(N - 2\mathscr{P}) - (N_{A^+} - \mathscr{P}) - (N_{B^-} - \mathscr{P})]!}$$

Using Stirling's approximation we have

$$\Delta S_1 = -R\left[\left(X_{A^+} - \frac{\mathscr{P}}{N}\right) \ln \left(\frac{N_{A^+} - \mathscr{P}}{N - 2\mathscr{P}}\right) + \left(X_{B^-} - \frac{\mathscr{P}}{N}\right) \ln \left(\frac{N_{B^-} - \mathscr{P}}{N - 2\mathscr{P}}\right)\right.$$
$$\left. + (1 - X_{A^+} - X_{B^-}) \ln \left(\frac{N - N_{A^+} - N_{B^-}}{N - 2\mathscr{P}}\right)\right]$$

In addition to ΔS_1 there is an entropy of mixing terms involving the clusters or pairs and the matrix. There are $\mathscr{P}$ clusters or $2\mathscr{P}$ sites occupied by clusters and there are, therefore, $(N - 2\mathscr{P})$ sites unoccupied by clusters. Thus there is an entropy of mixing associated with clusters and lattice given by

$$\Delta S_2 = \tfrac{1}{2}k \ln \frac{N!}{(2\mathscr{P})!\,(N - 2\mathscr{P})!}$$

The factor of $\tfrac{1}{2}$ is present because ΔS_2 is desired in terms of entropy per cluster and not per atom.

By use of Stirling's approximation we find

$$\Delta S_2 = -R\left[\frac{\mathscr{P}}{N} \ln \frac{2\mathscr{P}}{N} + \left(\frac{N - 2\mathscr{P}}{2N}\right) \ln \frac{N - 2\mathscr{P}}{N}\right]$$

The total entropy of the system will be

$$\Delta S_m = \Delta S_1 + \Delta S_2$$

As a result after formation of the clusters the free energy is given by

$$G = G_i + \mathscr{P}\,\Delta H_b - \mathscr{P}T\,\Delta S_{\text{vib}} - T(\Delta S_m - \Delta S_{m_i})$$

At equilibrium G will be a minimum and thus $\partial G/\partial\mathscr{P} = 0$. Differentiating and using the fact that, for most semiconductor systems, $N_A \ll N$, $N_B \ll N$, and thus $\mathscr{P} \ll N$, we have

$$\frac{\partial G}{\partial\mathscr{P}} = \Delta H_b - T\,\Delta S_{\text{vib}}$$
$$+ \frac{RT}{N}\left[\ln \frac{2\mathscr{P}}{N} - \ln \left(\frac{N_A - \mathscr{P}}{N}\right) - \ln \left(\frac{N_B - \mathscr{P}}{N}\right)\right] = 0$$

Upon rearrangement

$$\frac{\mathscr{P}}{(N_A - \mathscr{P})(N_B - \mathscr{P})} = \frac{1}{2N} \exp \left(\frac{\Delta S_{\text{vib}}}{k}\right) \exp \left(-\frac{\Delta H_b}{kT}\right)$$

and hence Λ is equal to

$$\Lambda = \frac{1}{2N} \exp \left(\frac{\Delta S_{\text{vib}}}{k}\right) \exp \left(-\frac{\Delta H_b}{kT}\right) \qquad (14.50)$$

The binding enthalpy ΔH_b of a pair is given by

$$\Delta H_b = \frac{\mathscr{L}_{A^+}\mathscr{L}_{B^-}e^2}{\kappa x_0}$$

where x_0 is the distance of closest approach between the ions of opposite charge in the lattice. Pairing only occurs when $\mathscr{L}_{A^+}$ and $\mathscr{L}_{B^-}$ have opposite charges and thus ΔH_b is negative. From equation 14.50 we see, therefore, that pairing is more intense at lower temperatures than at high temperatures.

The vibrational entropy charge upon pairing is probably rather small and thus we may approximate equation 14.50 by

$$\Lambda \cong \frac{1}{2N} \exp\left(-\frac{\mathscr{L}_{A^+}\mathscr{L}_{B^-}e^2}{\kappa k T x_0}\right) \qquad (14.51)$$

Reiss, Morin, and Fuller have calculated $\mathscr{P}$ as a function of $N_{A^+} + N_{B^-}$ (assumed equal for simplicity) and T for the case of pairing between an interstitial solute and a substitutional solute which have valences of 1 and -1 respectively. x_0 in this case is less than the value for two substitutional solutes and pairing will thus be more intense. These results are shown in Fig. 14.21.

From Fig. 14.21, we see that, at low temperatures, pairing between ions of unlike charge may be very intense, and approaches 100%. As a result the total solubility of a substance at a relatively low temperature may be markedly different from the intrinsic solubility if sufficient impurities of opposite size are present since the ion exists in the free or intrinsic state and in the associated or extrinsic state. Also the electron scattering factor as well as ion diffusion may be markedly affected by pairing.

Interaction between Atomic and Electronic Defects

Apart from the direct physical association of atomic defects described in previous sections, there is a more subtle but actually more important type of interaction. This type of interaction results from the law of mass action and not from physical association. As an example consider an intrinsic crystal at a given temperature. This crystal will contain a particular concentration of intrinsic vacancies characteristic of the temperature. A fraction of these vacancies will be charged negatively since it is known that vacancies act as electron acceptors; the concentration of acceptor sites filled may be determined from Fermi-Dirac statistics. The rest of the vacancies will be neutral. Accordingly we have the following equation for the formation of negative vacancies.

$$V^0 + e^- = V^-$$

Suppose now that a donor impurity is added to the intrinsic crystal.

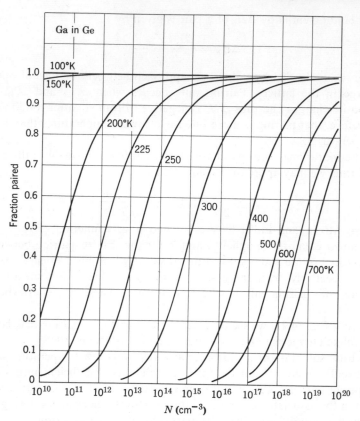

Fig. 14.21 Fraction of unlike impurities paired in germanium as a function of temperature and impurity content. $x_0 = 1.7 \times 10^{-8}$ cm; $\kappa = 16$; $e = 4.77 \times 10^{-10}$ e.s.u. From H. Reiss, C. S. Fuller, and F. J. Morin, *Bell Syst. Tech. J.*, **35**, 535 (1956).

Without considering any direct physical pairing between vacancy and impurity, the total vacancy concentration will be changed since the donor impurity will increase the concentration of electrons in the system. This will drive reaction 14.51 to the right, according to the law of mass action. The concentration of neutral intrinsic vacancies converted to charged vacancies will be replenished to their original concentration by diffusion of vacancies into the crystal from the crystal surface and from dislocations. The concentration of neutral vacancies may be thought of a constant at a given temperature with $[V^-]$ changing to an extent dependent upon the free electronic concentration of the crystal. It can be seen that the relative effect diminishes at high temperatures, because the free electron concentration of an intrinsic crystal increases with temperature, and thus the addition of a given number of electrons from a fixed number of donor impurities will be smaller at high temperatures than at low temperatures.

This problem has been quantitatively treated by Longini and Greene.[1] A crystal at a given temperature has a total number $[V]_t$ of vacancies. The Fermi level of the crystal is E_F and the vacancy acceptor is E_A. From Fermi-Dirac statistics, the number of acceptor levels containing one vacancy or $[V^-]$ is

$$[V^-] = \frac{[V]_t}{1 + \frac{1}{2} \exp (E_A - E_F)} \tag{14.52}$$

The concentration of unchanged vacancies is considered to be an intrinsic property of the crystal, as previously discussed. Hence, the concentration will be given only as a function of temperature.

$$[V^0] = A \exp [- \Delta H_V / kT] \tag{14.53}$$

Since

$$[V]_t = [V^0] + [V^-] \tag{14.54}$$

$[V^-]$ may be expressed in terms of $[V^0]$ by substitution of equation 14.54 into 14.52. Thus

$$[V^-] = 2[V^0] \exp [(E_F - E_A)/kT] \tag{14.55}$$

It is convenient to compare $[V^-]$ in a crystal containing donor or acceptor impurities having a Fermi level E_F with $[V^-]_i$ for an intrinsic crystal with Fermi level E_{F_i} at the same temperature. Thus we find

$$\frac{[V^-]}{[V^-]_i} = \exp \left[\frac{(E_F - E_{F_i})}{kT} \right] \tag{14.56}$$

From Fig. 14.17, we see that $(E_F - E_{F_i})$ is *positive* for the addition of *donor* impurities and *negative* for the addition of *acceptor* impurities. For example, in germanium the ratio $[V^-]/[V^-]_i$ is found to be about 8 at 300°C when 10^{18} donor impurities are added to the crystal, and is about 0.12 when the same concentration of acceptor impurities is present instead of the donors. From these considerations, it is clear that, aside from the effect of physical complexing, the total concentration of vacancies may be controlled through the law of mass action or by control of the Fermi level, to use the language of statistics.

Let us now consider the effect of dissolved impurities on the solubility of a solute. As an illustration, we shall use Li, which acts as a donor as

[1] R. L. Longini and R. F. Greene, *Phys. Rev.*, **102**, 992 (1956).

the solute of interest, and we shall consider the impurity to be a fully ionized acceptor, A^-. Following Reiss, we may write the reactions

$$Li = Li^+ + e^-$$
$$+$$
$$A = A^- + e^+$$
$$\|$$
$$e^-e^+ \tag{14.57}$$

There are three reactions which must be considered; the two horizontal reactions involving ionization of the impurities and a vertical reaction expressing the recombination of electrons and holes. Consider that an intrinsic sample is in contact with a reservoir containing a large amount of lithium at a constant activity. Lithium will dissolve in the crystal and ionize according to the first horizontal reaction, until equilibrium is reached for both the horizontal reaction and vertical reaction. The donor energy level associated with lithium is about 0.04 ev below the conduction band and is considerably higher than the Fermi level for temperatures above room temperature. If the donor concentration is not too high, as shown in Fig. 14.17, virtually none of the donor sites will be occupied and almost all the dissolved lithium will be ionized according to Fermi-Dirac statistics. Now let an acceptor be added to the crystal according to the second horizontal reaction, and thus $[e^+]$ is increased. The criterion for total ionization of the acceptor is that $(E_F - E_A) \gg 0$. This means that the acceptor levels are close to the valence band. These three equilibrium reactions are shown schematically in Fig. 14.22.

The increase in the concentration of holes from the acceptor will drive the vertical reaction in 14.57 down, tending to exhaust the concentration of electrons. Correspondingly, more lithium will dissolve in the crystal from the external source to maintain the electronic concentration, thereby increasing the amount of dissolved lithium. Conversely, if another donor instead of an acceptor is added to the crystal, the vertical reaction will be driven upward and dissolved lithium ions would have to recombine with electrons and move out of solution into the reservoir, thereby lowering the lithium solubility.

Let us now examine the situation quantitatively. Considering the donor solute of interest, the solubility step may be divided into two processes. Let D^+ and D represent the concentration of ionized donors and the total concentration of donors respectively.

(1)   Donor in external phase = *un-ionized donor in crystal*

(2)   *Un-ionized donor in crystal = ionized donor + electron*

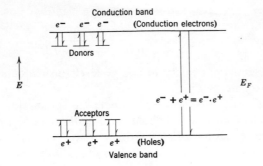

Fig. 14.22 Equilibrium between electrons in acceptor levels and valence band, electrons in donor levels and conduction band, and between electrons in valence band and conduction band.

The solute is considered to be present in dilute solution and thus the activity coefficient of solute in the crystal is a constant. From the law of mass action we obtain the following equilibrium constants for reactions (1) and (2):

$$K_1 = \frac{(D - D^+)}{a_{\text{ext}}} \tag{14.58}$$

$$K_2 = \frac{nD^+}{(D - D^+)} \tag{14.59}$$

where $(D - D^+)$ represents the concentration of unionized solute and a_{ext} represents the activity of solute in the external phase (if the solute is pure, $a_{\text{ext}} = 1$).

If the acceptor impurity is present and A^- and A refer to the concentration of ionized acceptors and the total concentration of acceptors we have an equilibrium for it similar to 14.59.

$$K_3 = \frac{pA^-}{(A - A^-)} \tag{14.60}$$

Also for the electron-hole equilibrium we know

$$K_4 = np \tag{14.61}$$

In addition, change neutrality must be maintained in the crystal, thus

$$D^+ + p = A^- + n \tag{14.62}$$

From Fermi-Dirac statistics, we have

$$(D - D^+) = \frac{D}{1 + \frac{1}{2} \exp\left[(E_D - E_F)/kT\right]} \tag{14.63}$$

and the number of electrons in the conductive band is

$$n = \sum \frac{Z_i}{1 + \exp\left[(E_i - E_F)/kT\right]} \qquad (14.64)$$

where Z_i represents the density of energy levels on the conduction band corresponding to energy E_i.

At this point it might be wise to examine the assumption that Henry's law and the law of mass action hold for equations 14.58 through 14.61. Let us examine equation 14.59 in this connection. According to the law of mass action and Henry's law, K_2 may vary with temperature, but at a given temperature it must be constant and thus be independent of composition.

To check this, let us substitute equations 14.63 and 14.64 into equation 14.59. When this is done, it is seen that K_2 depends in a complicated fashion upon E_F, E_i, E_D and Z_i. The last three quantities are not strongly dependent upon solute concentration but the first term E_F varies strongly with concentration as shown in Fig. 14.17. As a result, K_2 will be dependent upon solute concentration. *We must conclude, therefore, that the law of mass action coupled with Henry's law is not valid for reactions of the type represented by equation 14.59 if Fermi-Dirac statistics must be applied.*

Let us now examine the case for which classical statistics applies, namely where $(E_D - E_F) \gg 0$ and where $(E_i - E_F) \gg 0$ in equations 14.63 and 14.64. In this case we find

$$(D - D^+) = 2D \exp\left[(E_F - E_D)/kT\right] \qquad (14.65)$$

Furthermore, since $(E_D - E_F) \gg 0$, $(D - D^+) \sim 0$ and $D^+ \cong D$. Also

$$n = \exp\left(E_F/kT\right) \sum Z_i \exp\left(-E_i/kT\right) \qquad (14.66)$$

Upon substitution of equations 14.65 and 14.66, coupled with the conclusion that $D^+ \cong D$, into 14.59, we find

$$K_2 = \frac{\sum Z_i \exp\left(-E_i/kT\right)}{2 \exp\left(-E_D/kT\right)} \qquad (14.67)$$

From equation 14.67 we find that K_2 is now independent of solute concentration and therefore we find that the *law of mass action is valid for reactions of the type represented by equation* 14.59 *if classical statistics may be used.*

In order to simplify the quantitative treatment of the influence of one impurity upon the solubility of another, let us assume that classical statistics may be used.

Physically, this means that the temperature must be reasonably high, the donor level must be close to the conduction band, and the donor solubility may not be too large. From Fig. 14.17 it is seen that if these criteria are not fulfilled, $(E_D - E_F)$ will not be significantly greater than kT.

Adding equations (1) and (2) from above gives

$$\text{Donor (external source)} = donor\ (in\ crystal) + \text{electron}$$

or in the case of lithium

$$\text{Li}(a = a_{\text{ext}}) = \text{Li}^+ + e^-$$

At equilibrium $\Delta G = 0$ and therefore

$$\mu_{\text{Li(ext)}} = \mu_{\text{Li}^+} + \mu_{e^-} \tag{14.68}$$

The chemical potential of the lithium ion in the external solvent is given by

$$\mu_{\text{Li(ext)}} = \mu_{\text{Li}}{}^\circ + kT \ln a_{\text{ext}} \tag{14.69}$$

The chemical potential of a lithium ion in the solvent is

$$\mu_{\text{Li}^+} = \mu_{\text{Li}^+}^\circ + kT \ln \gamma_{\text{I,i}^+}^\circ + kT \ln D^+ \tag{14.70}$$

$\mu_{\text{Li}^+}^\circ$ is not necessarily identical with $\mu_{\text{Li}}{}^\circ$, and $\gamma_{\text{Li}^+}^\circ$ is the Henry's law activity coefficient. Combining the two constants gives

$$\mu_{\text{Li}^+} = \mu_{\text{Li}^+}^{\circ\prime} + kT \ln D^+ \tag{14.71}$$

As shown in an earlier section,

$$\mu_{e^-} = E_F \tag{14.72}$$

Combining equations 14.69, 14.71, and 14.72, according to equation 14.68, yields

$$a_{\text{ext}} = D^+ \exp\left(\frac{\mu_{\text{Li}}{}^\circ - \mu_{\text{Li}^+}^{\circ\prime}}{kT}\right) \exp\left(\frac{E_F}{kT}\right) \tag{14.73}$$

Since $D^+ \simeq D$ for the solute

$$a_{\text{ext}} = D \exp\left(\frac{\mu_{\text{Li}}{}^\circ - \mu_{\text{Li}^+}^{\circ\prime}}{kT}\right) \exp\left(\frac{E_F}{kT}\right)$$

At a given temperature $\mu_{\text{Li}}{}^\circ$ and $\mu_{\text{Li}^+}^{\circ\prime}$ are constant. Also a_{ext} is a constant ($a_{\text{ext}} = 1$, if Li is pure). Thus

$$D = K'(T) \exp\left(-E_F/kT\right)$$

The ratio of the donor solubility in a crystal doped with another substance to the solubility in the intrinsic crystal D_i is therefore

$$\frac{D}{D_i} = \exp\frac{E_{F_i} - E_F}{kT} \tag{14.74}$$

Thus, if a crystal is doped with an acceptor, $(E_{F_i} - E_F) > 0$, as shown on Fig. 14.17, and therefore $D/D_i > 1$. If the crystal is doped with another donor, $D/D_i < 1$, in agreement with the qualitative predictions made earlier.

A similar derivation for the solubility of an acceptor as influenced by doping agents may be made with the result

$$\frac{A}{A_i} = \exp \frac{-(E_{F_i} - E_F)}{kT} \tag{14.75}$$

Because of the exponential dependence of the solubility of the donor, D, on E_F, a small shift in the Fermi level will result in large changes in the

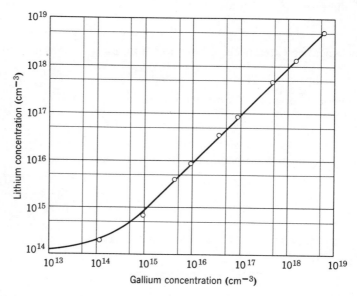

Fig. 14.23 Influence of the presence of an acceptor (gallium) on the solubility of a donor (lithium) at room temperature. From H. Reiss, C. S. Fuller, and F. J. Morin, *Bell Syst. Tech. J.*, **35**, 535 (1956).

measured solubility. To illustrate, consider the solubility of Li in germanium at room temperature with various amounts of the acceptor, gallium, present. The intrinsic solubility of lithium at room temperature is about $10^{14}/cm^3$. By addition of gallium, the solubility may be increased almost a million times! These data are shown in Fig. 14.23.

14.3 SUMMARY

In the presentation thus far, emphasis has been placed on the possible relationships among defects and on the quantitative assessment of these interactions. It is perhaps clear by now that the intrinsic concentration of a given defect at a particular temperature is an elusive quantity and can only be measured in exceedingly pure materials. In any impure material a wide variety of complexes may occur, thereby altering the total concentration of a particular defect. The situation is analogous to the occurrence of a given element in a wide variety of compounds. In this case the total concentration of an element would be the sum of the element in all the various compounds present.

The association of defects has far-reaching importance both from a fundamental and a technological standpoint. From a fundamental standpoint many important crystalline properties are related to defect complexes. As examples, the mechanical properties of a crystal are functions of impurity-dislocation interactions, impurity-stacking fault interactions, and impurity-crystal boundary interactions. The atomic diffusion coefficient is dependent upon the total concentration of vacancies as governed by vacancy-impurity interaction and vacancy-electronic defect interactions. Also the jumping frequency of a given atom is determined by its interaction with other impurities. The optical and electrical properties are related to the concentrations and types of defect complexes. More will be said about these topics in the next chapter.

From a technological point of view, it is important to understand these interactions since the properties of crystals dependent upon these defects may be controlled to some extent by control of the defects themselves.

chapter 15

Defects in Compounds

The term "compound" in the title of this chapter is used very generally. It is used in the sense that the crystal is composed of different types of atoms arranged in a definite fashion. The discussion applies to classic ionic crystals such as LiF as well as purely covalent crystals such as InSb. Since the compounds which will be discussed cover a wide range of crystal structures and involve a wide range of ion sizes and types of bonding, the types of defects which are prominent depend on the nature of the compound and unlike the case of elemental crystals discussed in Chapter 14, a wide variety of basic defect types must be considered.

In addition the concentrations of defects in compounds may be caused to vary over much wider limits than in the case of elemental crystals. For example in wustite (FeO) the concentration of vacancies in the iron sublattice may reach several per cent. As a result, it is extremely important that the defect structure of a compound undergoing experimental investigation be controlled, since many properties depend to a marked extent upon the defect structure. A given type of measurement made on a particular material in several laboratories may vary over wide limits because of the difference in defect structure of the material. On the other hand this sensitivity of defect structure offers a means of selective control of defect concentrations if used properly. The subject of defect control has gained considerable interest because of the technological interest in compound semiconductors.

15.1 POSSIBLE TYPES OF DEFECTS

In the last chapter, defects in elemental crystals were discussed. It was found convenient to consider two general classes of defects; those classed as primary defects and those classed as secondary defects. The primary defects, in turn, could be classed as atomic defects and electronic defects

272

(excess electrons in the conduction bond or holes in the valence bond). In the case of atomic defects, five types must be considered for a stoichiometric compound MX where M refers to the metallic component and X to the nonmetallic component.

A great many crystals do not exist as stoichiometric compounds but for sake of clarity in presentation it is advantageous to discuss stoichiometric crystals first as a special case. For this case, therefore, any disorder in the crystal must be such as to preserve the stoichiometry of the crystal. We know that disorder will exist since, as shown in Chapter 13, some disorder at a temperature greater than absolute zero is always stable. Consequently the disorder will always occur in pairs and the five basic types of atomic disorder which are possible are listed below. A stoichiometric crystal may contain one or more of these types.

(a) *Frenkel disorder on* M *sublattice*—equal numbers of vacancies on the M sublattice and M interstitial ions (shown in Fig. 15.1a).

(a) (b) (c) (d)

Fig. 15.1 Basic types of disorder in a stoichiometric crystal. (a) Frenkel disorder; (b) Schottky disorder; (c) interstitial disorder; (d) substitutional disorder.

(b) *Frenkel disorder on* X *sublattice*—equal numbers of vacancies in the X sublattice and X interstitial ions.

(c) *Schottky disorder*—equal number of vacant sites on M sublattice and X sublattice (shown in Fig. 15.1b).

(d) Equal concentrations of M and X interstitials (shown in Fig. 15.1c).

(e) *Substitutional disorder*—M ions occupy X sites and X ions occupy M sites (shown in Fig. 15.1d).

It is readily seen that the ratio of the concentration of M atoms to X atoms in the crystal is not changed by the occurrence of these types of disorder.

In Table 15.1 are summarized the basic types of disorder and some of the important types of defect complexes. It might be pointed out that all of the compounds discussed will be semiconductors or insulators and hence are characterized by an energy gap.

As Table 15.1 indicates, there is a great variety of defects which must

TABLE 15.1
Defect Classification

I. Primary Defects

   A. Atomic defects
     1. Frenkel disorder
     2. Schottky disorder
     3. Substitutional disorder

   B. Electronic defects
     1. Excess electrons in conduction band
     2. Electron holes in valence band

II. Secondary defects

   A. Impurity-vacancy pairs
   B. M vacancy-X vacancy pairs
   C. Trapped electron at defect contributing holes to valence band
   D. Defect acts as donor and contributes electrons to conduction band

___

be considered. The concentrations of these defects are not independent but are interrelated through the law of mass action. Fortunately, nature has somewhat simplified the problem, since in a given crystal a few defect types will predominate because of a wide range of values for the different enthalpies of formation. For a nonstoichiometric crystal the five basic types of defects discussed need not occur. In these cases the only important factor governing defect formation is the need for electroneutrality of the crystal. There is nothing sacred in nature, contrary to popular belief, about the need for stoichiometry! In fact many types of crystals are most stable when they are nonstoichiometric. An example is FeO which, in nature, is actually unstable when the concentration of iron ions is equal to the concentration of oxygen ions. The stable composition actually approximates more closely to $Fe_{0.95}O$. Indeed many other examples may be cited and these may be seen very readily upon examination of phase diagrams.

In order to accomplish this nonstoichiometry and also maintain charge balance in an ionic crystal, secondary defects such as shown in Table 15.1 must exist. An extremely large number of secondary defects may be proposed, and in fact a great variety of defect types have been invoked to explain optical properties of crystals. Some of these are shown in Fig. 15.2. If an ionic compound is considered, for example, and there is found to be an excess of M^+ ions over X^- ions, obviously the charges will not balance unless some other defect is added to the crystal. Let us suppose that the mechanism by which there are more M^+ ions in the crystal than

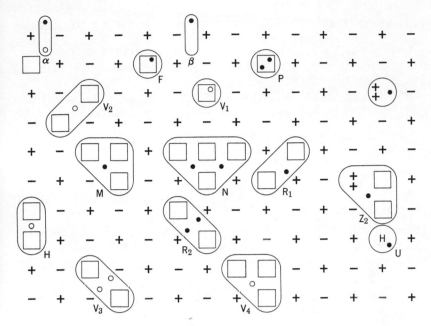

Fig. 15.2 Some defect complexes proposed to explain optical effects in alkali halides. ● electron; ○ hole; □ vacancy; ⧺ divalent impurity; – proton. From F. Seitz in *Imperfections in Nearly Perfect Crystals*, Wiley, New York, 1952.

X^- ions is due to the occurrence of anion vacancies. If the anion vacancies trap an electron from the valence band, the charges will balance. This is the defect complex listed as type IIC in Table 15.1. Similarly an excess of X^- ions in the crystal may occur if the cation vacancies contribute electrons to the conduction band (type IID in Table 15.1).

Experimental information suggests that the principal defect responsible for nonstoichiometry in many of the alkali halides (in particular, NaAl, KCl, KBr) is type IIC, whereas the important type in silver halides (AgCl, AgBr) and in CdO and ZnO is the existence of cation interstitials. The important type in many transition metal oxides and sulfides (FeO, NiO, CoO, FeS, CrS) as well as Cu_2O is type IID.

In view of the wide variety of defect types found in nature, it might be wise before proceeding to a discussion of the thermodynamics of defects to discuss the properties of defects in some detail and to investigate whether or not generalizations may be made as to factors responsible for the existence of a particular defect. We shall pick the simplest case for analysis, namely the situation for a classic ionic compound. This is the easiest to perform calculations on.

15.2 ENERGY OF DEFECT FORMATION IN IONIC COMPOUNDS

Since the important term governing the concentration of a particular defect is the enthalpy or energy of formation, this term will be examined in some detail.

It will be recalled from Section 6.4, from discussion of the Born-Haber cycle, that the lattice energy of the crystal, E_l, is given by the reaction

$$M^+(g, 1 \text{ atm}) + X^-(g, 1 \text{ atm}) = MX(s, 1 \text{ atm})$$

This lattice energy was found to be given by

$$E_l = -\frac{N_0 \mathscr{A} e^2}{x_0}\left(1 - \frac{1}{n}\right) \tag{15.1}$$

In this equation $\mathscr{A}$ is the Madelung constant, x_0 is the interatomic spacing, and n is the quantity occurring in the exponent of the Born repulsion term. Since there are N_0 atoms in the crystal, the binding energy per atom is

$$E = -\frac{\mathscr{A} e^2}{x_0}\left(1 - \frac{1}{n}\right) \tag{15.2}$$

The process of vacancy formation on the cation sublattice may be divided into three steps:

(1) $M^+(\text{interior of crystal}) = M^+(g)$, ϵ_1
(2) $M^+(g) = M^+(\text{surface})$, ϵ_2
(3)   Relaxation of atoms around vacancy, ϵ_3

The energy for process (1) is the negative of equation 15.2. Thus

$$\epsilon_1 = \frac{\mathscr{A} e^2}{x_0}\left(1 - \frac{1}{n}\right)$$

Upon completion of process (2), one-half of the energy expended in process (1) will be regained as discussed in Chapter 9. Thus

$$\epsilon_2 = -\frac{\mathscr{A} e^2}{2x_0}\left(1 - \frac{1}{n}\right)$$

The energy for vacancy formation, excluding relaxation of atoms around the vacancy, will be $(\epsilon_1 + \epsilon_2)$ or

$$(\epsilon_1 + \epsilon_2) = \frac{\mathscr{A} e^2}{2x_0}\left(1 - \frac{1}{n}\right)$$

Let us now examine what happens in the region of the crystal where the vacancy has been created. This is shown schematically in Fig. 15.3. In

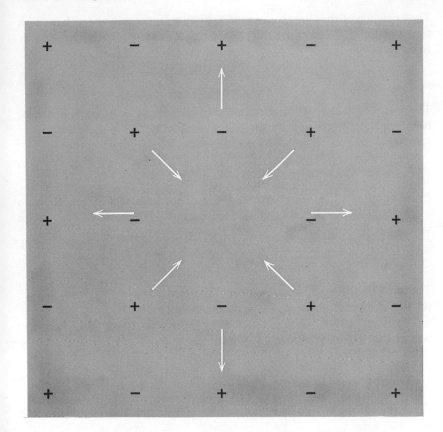

Fig. 15.3   Relaxation of atoms around vacancy in an ionic crystal.

most ionic crystals, the nearest neighbors to a cation will be anions. Removal of the positive ion will have the same effect on the neighbors as the substitution of a negative charge. The interatomic distances in the crystal are governed by the balance of positive and negative charges. Removal of the positive ion will allow the positive ions surrounding the vacancy to relax inward because of repulsion from neighbors surrounding the ions. Conversely the negative ions will move outward. This will result in polarization of the ions in the vicinity of the vacancy since the field about them is now assymmetric. The vacancy behaves as if it has negative charge. Jost has examined the problem using classical dielectric theory. The cation vacancy in the crystal is treated as a spherical cavity of charge $-e$ inside homogeneous material of dielectric constant κ. The radius of the spherical cavity will be the radius of the positive ion R_+.

The existence of the charge $-e$ in the cavity will result in the polarization of the material around the cavity. Jost calculates the polarization energy to be given by

$$P_+ = - \frac{e^2}{2R_+}\left(1 - \frac{1}{\kappa}\right) \tag{15.3}$$

The energy of vacancy formation will thus be reduced by P_+ upon polarization. The energy of vacancy formation is equal to $(\epsilon_{1+} + \epsilon_2 + P_+)$ or

$$\epsilon_{V^+} = \frac{\mathscr{A}e^2}{2(R_+ + R_-)}\left(1 - \frac{1}{n}\right) - \frac{e^2}{2R_+}\left(1 - \frac{1}{\kappa}\right) \tag{15.4}$$

In equation 15.4 the interatomic distance x_0 has been replaced by the sum of the radii $(R_+ + R_-)$. Similarly, the energy of formation of an anion vacancy is

$$\epsilon_{V^-} = \frac{\mathscr{A}e^2}{2(R_+ + R_-)}\left(1 - \frac{1}{n}\right) - \frac{e^2}{2R_-}\left(1 - \frac{1}{\kappa}\right) \tag{15.5}$$

The polarization term may be very important and, in fact, may reduce the defect formation energy by several electron volts.

The energy of formation of a Schottky defect (M vacancy + X vacancy) will be the sum of equations 15.4 and 15.5, or

$$\epsilon_{\text{Schottky}} = \frac{\mathscr{A}e^2}{(R_+ + R_-)}\left(1 - \frac{1}{n}\right) - \frac{e^2}{2}\left(1 - \frac{1}{\kappa}\right)\left(\frac{1}{R_+} + \frac{1}{R_-}\right) \tag{15.6}$$

The values of $(\epsilon_1 + \epsilon_2)$ and P_+ are shown in Table 15.2 for NaCl and KCl

TABLE 15.2
Energy of Formation of Schottky Defects

Substance	$(\epsilon_1 + \epsilon_2)$ (ev)	P_+ (ev)	P_- (ev)	ϵ_{V^+} (ev)	ϵ_{V^-} (ev)	$\epsilon_{\text{Schottky}}$ (ev)
NaCl	3.97	−3.32	−2.76	0.65	1.21	1.86
KCl	3.59	−2.71	−2.39	0.88	1.20	2.08

as calculated by Rittner, Hutner, and DuPre.[1] From these data it is seen that the energy of formation of a Schottky defect in NaCl is calculated to be 1.86 ev, considering polarization. Neglecting the polarization term, $\epsilon_{\text{Schottky}}$ would be 7.94 ev, which implies that the concentration of this type of defect would be unimportant in NaCl because of its large energy of formation, if polarization did not occur. It is also observed that ϵ_{V^+} is

[1] E. S. Rittner, R. A. Hutner, and F. K. DuPre, *J. Chem. Phys.*, **17**, 198 (1949).

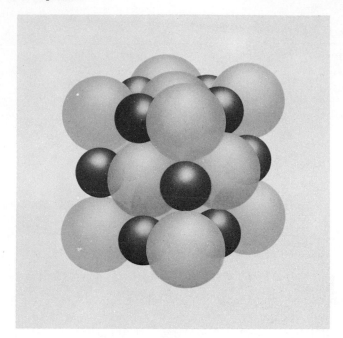

Fig. 15.4 Sodium chloride structure. From L. Azaroff, *Introduction to Solids*, McGraw-Hill, New York, 1960.

less than ϵ_{V^-}. The reason for this is that in a crystal with ionic bonding, the radii of anions are much larger than the radii of cations, as shown schematically in Fig. 15.4 and Table 15.3. As a result P_+ will be more negative than P_- in a given crystal, and hence ϵ_{V^-} will be larger than ϵ_{V^+}. As a result, we may say that cation vacancies will generally occur in preference to anion vacancies unless their sizes are similar (such as Ba^{2+} and O^{2-} in Table 15.3) or unless the dielectric constant is small.

In connection with interstitial ions, anion interstitials should be more difficult to form because of the large size of anions in most cases. As a result, Frenkel defects would not generally be expected to occur on the anion sublattice except in special cases as mentioned above.

With regard to the preference of a crystal for Schottky or Frenkel defects, it is more difficult to make quantitative calculations. Generally speaking, in more close packed structures, Schottky defects would be preferred since the energy to move the M^+ ion into the interstitial site would be larger than that for formation of an anion vacancy. Thus, in stoichiometric NaCl and KCl, Schottky defects are preferred over Frenkel defects. For more open structures and for compounds where R_+ is much less than R_-, the energy for formation of an interstitial M ion becomes less than

TABLE 15.3
Ionic Radii[a]

		Li^+	Be^{2+}		
		0.60	0.31		
O^{2-}	F^-	Na^+	Mg^{2+}	Al^{3+}	Si^{4+}
1.40	1.36	0.95	0.65	0.50	0.41
S^{2-}	Cl^-	X^+	Ca^{2+}	Sc^{3+}	Ti^{4+}
1.84	1.81	1.33	0.99	0.81	0.68
Se^{2-}	Br^-	Rb^+	Sr^{2+}	Y^{3+}	Zr^{4+}
1.98	1.95	1.48	1.13	0.93	0.80
Te^{2-}	I^-	Cs^+	Ba^{2+}	La^{3+}	Ce^{4+}
2.21	2.16	1.69	1.35	1.15	1.01

[a] From L. Pauling, *Nature of the Chemical Bond*, Third Edition, Cornell, Ithaca, 1960.

the anion vacancy and Frenkel defects on the cation sublattice will be the primary form of disorder.

In general, substitutional disorder is not important for crystals with predominantly ionic bonding, because of the mismatch in atomic size and charge. As the bonding becomes less ionic and hence the atomic sizes become more similar, substitutional disorder becomes more important. Thus, substitutional disorder would be important in intermetallic compounds, III–V compounds such as GaSb and InP, but not in halides, oxides, etc., where the electronegativity difference between components M and X are large and hence the size difference and valence difference will be large.

15.3 ELECTRONIC NATURE OF DEFECTS

The electronic considerations of defects in compounds are virtually identical with the considerations discussed in Chapter 14 concerning elemental semiconductors. Compounds are either insulators or semiconductors depending upon the magnitude of the energy gap, E_g, for the particular crystal. Thus the crystal will have a concentration of electrons in the conduction bond $[e^-]$ and a concentration of holes in the valence bond $[e^+]$ given by the law of mass action.

$$[e^-][e^+] = K$$

In addition, defects themselves may act as donors or acceptors with the extent of occupancy of a particular state given by the Fermi-Dirac function.

Consider first an interstitial atom M_i in compound MX. This is an electropositive element and thus will tend to give up an electron to the conduction band according to the reaction

$$M_i^0 = M_i^+ + e^- \qquad E_1 \qquad (15.7)$$

Similarly there may be a tendency to ionize further.

$$M_i^+ = M_i^{2+} + e^- \qquad E_2 \qquad (15.8)$$

Thus we see that a metallic interstitial atom tends to act as a donor in the compound. The extent to which either of the above reactors will occur

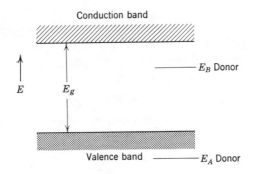

Fig. 15.5 Donor states for an interstitial atom M in MX. E_A corresponds to tight binding and E_B to loose binding.

depends on the energy of the valence electrons in atom M in an interstitial position relative to the edge of the conduction bond and valence bond. If the electron is tightly bound in the interstitial (position E_A in Fig. 15.5) the interstitial atom will be neutral since the value of $(E_A - E_F) \ll 0$ in the Fermi-Dirac equation for occupancy of state,

$$n_A = \frac{Z}{1 + \tfrac{1}{2}\exp\left(\dfrac{E_A - E_F}{kT}\right)}$$

The number of states Z will be equal to the number of interstitial atoms M_i, and n_A, the number of electrons in levels corresponding to E_A, will be equal to M_i^0. For a crystal close to being intrinsic, E_F will lie close to the center of the energy gap. In the case shown in Fig. 15.5, $(E_A - E_F) \ll 0$ and $M_i^0 \simeq M_i$. If the electron is much less tightly bound, corresponding, for example to E_B, $(E_B - E_F) \gg 0$ and thus $M_i^0 \simeq 0$ and almost all of the interstitial ions will be ionized. The energy E_1 for reaction 15.7 corresponds to the difference between the edge of the conductor bond and the donor level or $E_1 = (E_C - E_B)$. Assuming that the donor level corresponds to E_B and virtually complete ionization has occurred, consideration must be then given that reaction 15.8 might occur. This second electron will, however, be more tightly bound than the first and hence, the donor level will lie below E_B. Thus the tendency for this step to occur is smaller. The energy for reaction 15.8, E_2, is equal to $(E_C - E_D)$ where E_D corresponds to the energy of the second electron. The situation which exists for a given interstitial depends, of course, on the nature of the levels for the particular crystal. In one type of crystal virtually all interstitials will be neutral, in another, complete ionization, according to 15.7, will occur, whereas in still another case a fraction of the ions formed through 15.7 may be doubly ionized, etc.

In the case of interstitial X ions, X_i, the situation is reversed. Because of the electronegative nature of the neutral X atom, it will tend to capture electrons according to the reaction

$$X_i^0 + e^- = X_i^- \qquad E_1$$
$$X_i^- + e^- = X_i^{2-} \qquad E_2$$

These reactions may also be written in terms of electron holes e^+.

$$X_i^0 = X_i^- + e^+$$
$$X_i^- = X_i^{2-} + e^+$$

If the captured electron has a high energy, corresponding to E_B in Fig. 15.5, the number of occupied states will be small and hence most interstitial ions X_i will be neutral, X_i^0. On the other hand, if the energy of the captured electron is low, most of X_i will exist as X_i^- according to the Fermi-Dirac equation. If an electron is captured, the energy level for a second captured electron will be higher and so will not be as likely to occur as single ionization. The situation for a given compound depends on the relation of the particular levels to the energy gap and Fermi level. This particular defect is not too important, however, since because of the large size of negative ions, the probability of their occurrence in interstitial sites is small.

Consider now the case of cation vacancies and anion vacancies, designated as V_M and V_X respectively. It is found that cation vacancies tend to act as electron acceptors and anion vacancies tend to act as electron donors. When a cation vacancy is neutral it is known as a V_1 center and a neutral anion vacancy is known as an F center. For the ionization of cation and anion vacancies we have a set of reactions

$$V_M = V_M^- + e^+ \qquad E_1$$
$$V_M^- = V_M^{2-} + e^+ \qquad E_2$$
etc.

and

$$V_X = V_X^+ + e^- \qquad E_3$$
$$V_X^+ = V_X^{2+} + e^- \qquad E_4$$

The extent of these reactions is, of course, dependent on the position of the donor levels (anion vacancies) or acceptor levels (cation vacancies) relative to the Fermi level as just discussed for interstitials. The electronic behavior of cation vacancies in ionic crystals is exactly analogous to the behavior of vacancies in germanium and silicon.

The existence of substitutional disorder will also be associated with electronic effects. The structure of a compound is generally such that an electronegative X species is surrounded by the electropositive M species as nearest neighbors and vice versa. If a negative X ion is placed on an M site (denoted by X_M) it will be surrounded by negative charge and to reduce to electrostatic repulsive energy will tend to lose negative charge and hence act as a donor:

$$X_M^- = X_M^0 + e^- \qquad E_1$$
$$X_M^0 = X_M^{-1} + e^- \qquad E_2$$

The extent to which these reactions occur depends on the energy level of the electrons associated with the atom in the wrong site relative to the Fermi level in the same fashion as for the defects discussed previously. Conversely, using similar reasoning, an M ion on an X site will tend to act as an electron acceptor.

$$M_X^+ = M_X^0 + e^+ \qquad E_1$$
$$M_X^0 = M_X^- + e^+ \qquad E_2$$

In summary, it has been shown that interstitial X ions, X_i, anion vacancies, V_X, and anions on cation sites, X_M, all tend to act as electron donors in compounds. Conversely, interstitial cations, M_i, cation vacancies, V_M, and cations on anion sites, M_X, tend to act as electron acceptors. Since the individual defects cannot exist by themselves, the electronic nature of the various combinations must be considered. In the case of Schottky disorders (vacancies on M sublattice and X sublattice) the electronic effects will tend to cancel each other, since V_M behaves as an acceptor and V_X behaves as a donor. Complete cancellation will only be accomplished if the Fermi level is equidistant from the two centers. Generally, this will not be the case and hence there will be a net electronic effect. The same situation is true for Frenkel defects. In the case of a Frenkel defect on the M sublattice, the M_i interstitial acts as a donor and the vacancy V_M acts as an acceptor. Similarly for a Frenkel defect on the X sublattice the vacancy V_X acts as a donor and the interstitial X_i acts as an acceptor, again resulting in partial cancellation. In analogous fashion, substitutional disorder yields the same result, since the anions on cation sites X_M act as donors and the cations on anion sites act as acceptors.

It will be recalled from discussion presented in an earlier chapter that some crystalline disorder is always stable as a result of the second law of thermodynamics. It will be recalled further, that the extent of this disorder increases as the temperature increases. At some early stage in the manufacturing process of a crystal, an elevated temperature is generally necessary which is responsible for the introduction of disorder. As the temperature is lowered, the disorder will tend to diminish through ionic diffusion. Generally, however, the cooling rate is too fast to permit equilibrium to be achieved at low temperatures and thus a considerable amount of disorder may be "quenched" into the crystal at room temperature. Because of the electronic nature of these defects, it is often difficult to measure the equilibrium electronic structure of a crystal characteristic of room temperature. A crystal which has a very large energy gap, and hence is an insulator, may behave as an n-type or p-type semiconductor because of the existence of defects and the corresponding donor or acceptor levels, close to the conduction and valence bands respectively.

15.4 THERMODYNAMICS OF DEFECTS

The thermodynamics treatment of defects was originally developed by Schottky and Wagner in a long series of papers. The principles developed have since been elaborated by several workers. The particular approach used in the treatment presented here is that developed by Kroger and Vink.[1] Reading of much of the work by various investigators is confusing because no standard notation has been used. For example, a cation vacancy may be designated by V_M, □, or $M_□$. The symbols which will be used here are summarized in Table 15.4 for crystal MX. A ($^+$) superscript refers to a positive charge and a ($^-$) superscript refers to a negative charge. When a superscript is missing, the defect is considered to be neutral in charge.

It is convenient for the sake of clarity to divide the thermodynamic treatment of defects in ionic crystals into two parts: defects in stoichiometric compounds and nonstoichiometric compounds. The majority of equations developed in the section on stoichiometric compounds are

[1] A comprehensive treatment of this approach is given by F. A. Kroger and H. J. Vink in *Solid State Physics*, **3**, 307 (1956), F. Seitz and D. Turnbull, eds. For additional reading the reader is referred to C. Wagner, *Thermodynamics of Alloys*, Addison-Wesley, Cambridge, 1952, and K. Hauffe, *Reaktionen in und an Festen Stoffen*, Springer, Berlin, 1955.

TABLE 15.4
Summary of Defect Nomenclature

Defect	Symbol	Defect	Symbol
Cation	M	Cation on anion site	M_X
Anion	X	Anion on cation site	X_M
Interstitial cation	M_i	Anion vacancy-cation vacancy pair	$(V_M V_X)$
Interstitial anion	X_i	Electron in conduction bond	e^-
Cation vacancy	V_M	Electron hole in valence bond	e^+
Anion vacancy	V_X		

general equations and will be used in later sections. The law of mass action will be used throughout. This places one important restriction upon the approach, since it will be recalled from the last chapter that in order to apply the law of mass action to a reaction of the type

$$V = V^+ + e^- \qquad K = \frac{[V^+][e^-]}{[V]}$$

the electronic concentration n_i at energy E_i must follow classical statistics. This means that

$$(E_i - E_F) > 4kT$$

and implies that virtually complete ionization of the defect has occurred. More complicated cases will not be considered.

Stoichiometric Compounds

As mentioned earlier, this classification represents somewhat of an idealized case since most compounds are not truly stoichiometric. Some important compounds, however, can be considered to be nearly stoichiometric. That is to say the composition limits are extremely narrow and the compound would appear as a line on a phase diagram. Some examples of nearly stoichiometric compounds are the alkali halides, the silver halides, PbS, and the III–V compounds.

In considering the thermodynamics of a process we begin by writing the reaction for the process. Considering first Frenkel defects on the M sublattice, we shall have a crystal MX containing equal numbers of M atoms and X atoms. Upon formation of a Frenkel defect we remove a fraction δ of M atoms leaving δ vacancies, δV_M, and form an equal number of interstitials, δM_i. The composition of the crystal with regard to atoms on regular sites in the appropriate sublattice is $M_{(1-\delta)}X$. We may write the overall reaction as follows.

$$MX(s) = M_{(1-\delta)}X(s) + \delta V_M + \delta M_i \qquad (15.9)$$

At equilibrium, $\Delta G = 0$. Thus

$$\mu_{MX} = \mu_{M_{(1-\delta)}X} + \mu_{V_M} + \mu_{M_i} \tag{15.10}$$

There is a standard free energy $\Delta G°$ associated with reaction 15.9 and hence there is an equilibrium constant

$$K' = \frac{(a_{M_{(1-\delta)}X})(a_{V_M})(a_{M_i})}{a_{MX}} \tag{15.11}$$

If the restriction is placed that $\delta \ll 1$, the defects will obey Henry's law and hence

$$a_{V_M} = \gamma_{V_M}°(\delta V_M)$$
$$a_{M_i} = \gamma_{M_i}°(\delta M_i)$$

By definition, $a_{MX} = 1$ if crystalline MX is stable at the temperature of interest. Since the defect concentration δ is small, the activity of the solvent crystal follows Raoult's law and hence, since $\delta \ll 1$,

$$a_{M_{(1-\delta)}X} \cong a_{MX} \cong 1$$

Insertion of these relations into equation 15.11 yields a new constant

$$K'' = (\delta_{V_M})(\delta_{M_i})$$

where

$$K' = K''\gamma_{M_i}°\gamma_{V_M}°$$

Since δ_{M_i} and $\delta_{V_M} \ll 1$, it is not particularly convenient to use this nomenclature. It is more convenient to use concentration units in terms of number of defects per cubic centimeter of crystal or $[M_i]$ and $[V_M]$. These are related to δM_i and δV_M respectively by a constant equal to the number of M sites per cubic centimeter. Thus, there is a constant

$$K_1 = [V_M][M_i] \tag{15.12}$$

The constant K_1, for a crystal, according to thermodynamic theory, is not a function of composition but depends only on temperature. Thus K_1 is the same regardless of composition and is equally valid for nonstoichiometric and stoichiometric crystal. The implications of this are far reaching since, regardless of the types of defects present, the neutral vacancy concentration on the cation lattice is always related to the concentration of neutral interstitial M atoms by a constant through equation 15.12. The equilibrium constant K' in equation 15.11 is given by

$$K' = \exp(-\Delta G_1°/kT) = \exp(\Delta S_1°/k)\exp(-\Delta H_1°/kT) \tag{15.13}$$

where $\Delta H_1°$ and $\Delta S_1°$ are the enthalpy and entropy respectively, associated with reaction 15.9. From 15.9 it is seen that $\Delta H_1°$ represents the enthalpy of formation of a cation vacancy V_M plus the enthalpy of formation of a cation interstitial M_i, or

$$\Delta H_1{}^\circ = \Delta H_{V_M} + \Delta H_{M_i}$$

Since K_1 is related to K'', and thus to K', by a constant, we may write

$$K_1 = A_1 \exp\left(\Delta S_1{}^\circ/k\right) \exp\left(-\Delta H_1{}^\circ/kT\right) \qquad (15.14)$$

The primary term in equation 15.14 is $\Delta H_1{}^\circ$. If $\Delta H_1{}^\circ$ is very large, K_1 will be very small.

The formalism is now set up for a whole sequence of defect reactions. For Frenkel defects on the anion sublattice

$$MX = MX_{(1-\delta)} + \delta V_X + \delta X_i \qquad (15.15)$$

and

$$K_2 = [V_X][X_i] \qquad (15.16)$$

where

$$K_2 = A_2 \exp\left(\Delta S_2{}^\circ/k\right) \exp\left(-\Delta H_2{}^\circ/kT\right) \qquad (15.17)$$

For Schottky disorder

$$MX = M_{(1-\delta)}X_{(1-\delta)} + \delta V_M + \delta V_X \qquad (15.18)$$

$$K_3 = [V_M][V_X] \qquad (15.19)$$

$$K_3 = A_3 \exp\left(\Delta S_3{}^\circ/k\right) \exp\left(-\Delta H_3{}^\circ/kT\right) \qquad (15.20)$$

For substitution disorder

$$MX = M_{(1-\delta)}X_{(1-\delta)} + \delta X_M + \delta M_X \qquad (15.21)$$

$$K_4 = [X_M][M_X] \qquad (15.22)$$

$$K_4 = A_4 \exp\left(\Delta S_4{}^\circ/k\right) \exp\left(-\Delta H_4{}^\circ/kT\right) \qquad (15.23)$$

The term $\Delta H_2{}^\circ$ will consist of the sum of the enthalpy for formation of an anion vacancy and the enthalpy of formation of an anion interstitial. ΔH_3 will equal the sum of the enthalpies of formation of an anion vacancy and a cation vacancy.

Some of the various defects may also be ionized according to the equations discussed in the last section. For a cation vacancy we have the reaction

$$V_M = V_M{}^- + e^+ \qquad \Delta E_5 \qquad (15.24)$$

where ΔE_5 represents the energy of the vacancy acceptor level minus the energy of the top of the valence band. To be consistent with our use of the Gibb's free energy enthalpies should be used instead of energies. For a solid, however, the $\Delta(PV)$ term in the expression

$$\Delta H = \Delta E + \Delta(PV)$$

is small, and thus $\Delta H \cong \Delta E$.

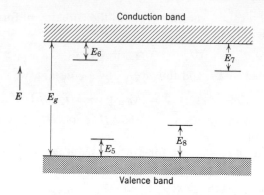

Fig. 15.6 Donor and acceptor levels associated with defects.

Furthermore, most reference texts cite energy levels and not enthalpy levels. The relation of ΔE_5 to the energy gap is shown on Fig. 15.6. There is a standard free energy for reaction 15.24 and hence an equilibrium constant. If the defect concentration is small, Henry's law will be followed by the vacancies and electron holes and thus

$$K_5 = \frac{[e^+][V_M^-]}{[V_M]} \tag{15.25}$$

where $[e^+]$ is the concentration of holes in the valence band. Also

$$K_5 = A_5 \exp\left(-\Delta E_5/kT\right) \tag{15.26}$$

if classical statistics is followed. It will be noted that a small value of ΔE_5 corresponds to a large value of K_5, which in turn indicates a high degree of ionization.

For anion vacancies

$$V_X = V_X^+ + e^- \qquad \Delta E_6 \tag{15.27}$$

The term e^- represents an electron in the conduction band. ΔE_6 thus represents the energy difference between the bottom of the conduction band and the donor level as shown in Fig. 15.6. Similarly, there is an equilibrium constant.

$$K_6 = \frac{[V_X^+][e^-]}{[V_X]} \tag{15.28}$$

$$K_6 = A_6 \exp\left(-\Delta E_6/kT\right) \tag{15.29}$$

For the ionization of a cation interstitial

$$M_i = M_i^+ + e^- \qquad \Delta E_7 \tag{15.30}$$

ΔE_7 is shown on Fig. 15.6.

$$K_7 = \frac{[M_i^+][e^-]}{[M_i]} \tag{15.31}$$

$$K_7 = A_7 \exp(-\Delta E_7/kT) \tag{15.32}$$

For the ionization of an anion interstitial

$$X_i = X_i^- + e^+ \qquad \Delta E_8 \tag{15.33}$$

$$K_8 = \frac{[X_i^-][e^+]}{[X_i]} \tag{15.34}$$

$$K_8 = A_8 \exp(-\Delta E_8/kT) \tag{15.35}$$

For the ionization of a cation on an anion site

$$M_X = M_X^- + e^+ \qquad \Delta E_9 \tag{15.36}$$

$$K_9 = \frac{[M_X^-][e^+]}{[M_X]} \tag{15.37}$$

$$K_9 = A_9 \exp(-\Delta E_9/kT) \tag{15.38}$$

For the ionization of an anion on a cation site

$$X_M = X_M^+ + e^- \qquad \Delta E_{10} \tag{15.39}$$

$$K_{10} = \frac{[X_M^+][e^-]}{[X_M]} \tag{15.40}$$

$$K_{10} = A_{10} \exp(-\Delta E_{10}/kT) \tag{15.41}$$

In addition to these ten equations there is a relation between the concentration of anion interstitials and cation interstitials. Thus there are eleven equations expressing the interrelation of defect concentrations. In principle, the equilibrium constants may be determined from ΔG° data. As unknowns in these eleven equations there are $[V_M]$, $[M_i]$, $[V_X]$, $[X_i]$, $[X_M]$, $[M_X]$, $[V_M^-]$, $[e^+]$, $[V_X^+]$, $[e^-]$, $[M_i^+]$, $[X_i^-]$, $[M_X^-]$, and $[X_M^+]$, giving a total of 14 unknowns. Three more equations may be readily obtained. One expresses the relation between the concentration of electrons in the conduction band and concentration of holes in the valence band as discussed in the last chapter.

$$K_{12} = [e^-][e^+]$$
$$K_{12} = A_{12} \exp(-\Delta E_g/kT) \tag{15.42}$$

In addition, the crystal must remain electrically neutral, so

$$[V_M^-] + [e^-] + [X_i^-] + [M_i^-] = [V_X^+] + [e^+] + [M_i^+] + [X_M^+] \tag{15.43}$$

The thirteen equations derived thus far are all applicable to a crystal regardless of stoichiometry. In this particular section a stoichiometric MX crystal is being considered, so there is an additional equation stating that

$$\sum [M] = \sum [X]$$

or

$$[M_i] + [M_i{}^+] + [M_X] + [M_X{}^-] - [V_M] - [V_M{}^-] = [X_i] + [X_i{}^-]$$
$$+ [X_M] + [X_M{}^+] - [V_X] - [V_X{}^+] \quad (15.44)$$

Thus, in principle, there are fourteen equations expressing the relationship between fourteen unknowns and the concentration of each type of defect may be found if the K values are known. As seen from the equations, the equilibrium constants are experimentally related to the enthalpies of formation of the defects. For a given crystal the enthalpies of formation of various defects are considerably different. As a result, generally only one type of atomic defect will predominate in a given crystal and consequently the fourteen unknowns reduce to a more manageable number of six as shown below.

As an example consider a crystal MX in which the only important type of atomic defect is of the Schottky type. Consider further that a certain fraction of the cation vacancies and anion vacancies are singly ionized. Thus the following reactions must be considered

$$MX = M_{(1-\delta)}X_{(1-\delta)} + \delta V_M + \delta V_X$$
$$K_3 = [V_M][V_X]$$
$$V_M = V_M{}^- + e^+$$
$$K_5 = \frac{[e^+][V_M{}^-]}{[V_M]}$$
$$V_X = V_X{}^+ + e^-$$
$$K_6 = \frac{[V_X{}^+][e^-]}{[V_X]}$$

Assuming that, in principle, the three equilibrium constants can be obtained from thermodynamic data, there are six unknowns, $[V_M]$, $[V_M{}^-]$, $[V_X]$, $[V_X{}^+]$, $[e^-]$, and $[e^+]$. The additional relations come from the condition of electroneutrality, the condition for stoichiometry, and the relation between $[e^+] + [e^-]$ which are respectively

$$[V_M{}^-] + [e^-] = [V_X{}^+] + [e^+]$$
$$[V_M] + [V_M{}^-] = [V_X] + [V_X{}^+]$$
$$K_{12} = [e^+][e^-]$$

Solving these six equations simultaneously yields the concentration of each of the imperfections.

For the case of singly ionized Frenkel defects on the M sublattice there are the following relations

$$MX = M_{(1-\delta)}X + \delta V_M + \delta M_i$$

$$K_1 = [V_M][M_i]$$

$$V_M = V_M^- + e^+.$$

$$K_5 = \frac{[V_M^-][e^+]}{V_M}$$

$$M_i = M_i^+ + e^-$$

$$K_7 = \frac{[M_i^+][e^-]}{[M_i]}$$

In addition the electroneutrality condition, stoichiometric condition, and the relation between $[e^+]$ and $[e^-]$ are respectively

$$[V_M^-] + [e^-] = [M_i^+] + [e^+]$$

$$[V_M] + [V_M^-] = [M_i] + [M_i^+]$$

$$K_{12} = [e^+][e^-]$$

Nonstoichiometric Compounds

An excellent example of nonstoichiometric compounds is the iron-oxygen binary system illustrated in Fig. 15.7. The compound Fe_2O_3 has very narrow composition limits but is not exactly stoichiometric (% oxygen > 60.0 at %). Fe_3O_4 has very narrow composition range at low temperatures which increase as the temperature is elevated. FeO (wustite) actually is not stable at 50 at % iron and 50 at % oxygen but contains an excess of oxygen. Considering FeO at 1200°C, it is seen that the oxygen content of FeO in equilibrium with pure iron is about 51.2 at %, but when FeO is in equilibrium with Fe_3O_4 the composition is 54.0 at % oxygen. Since the crystal structure of the FeO is invariant in the single phase field, the only way nonstoichiometry may be achieved is through the formation of defects. The activity of oxygen across the wustite field and hence composition can be varied through the reaction

$$\tfrac{1}{2}O_2(g) = O \text{ (in wustite)}$$

$$K = \frac{a_O}{p_{O_2}^{1/2}} \qquad (15.45)$$

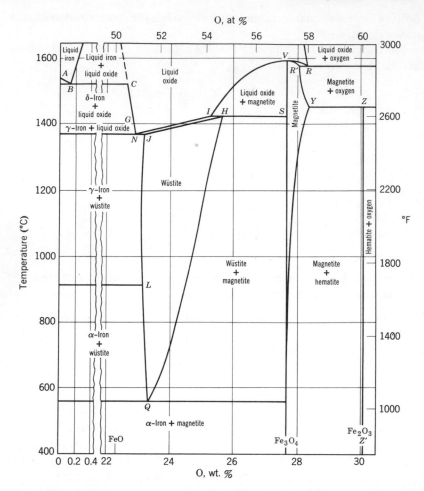

Fig. 15.7 Fe-O system illustrating nonstoichiometric nature of compounds. From L. S. Darken and R. W. Gurry, *J. Am. Chem. Soc.*, **68**, 798 (1946).

which shows that the activity of oxygen in wustite is proportional to the square root of the partial pressure of oxygen in the ambient. At the phase boundary where FeO is in equilibrium with iron, the equilibrium pressure of oxygen at 1200°C for equation 15.45 is found to be

$$p_{O_2} = 10^{-12} \text{ atm}$$

This pressure will be the minimum needed to oxidize iron. The oxygen pressure in equilibrium with oxygen in FeO at the other phase boundary is 10^{-9} atm. In the present case various compositions of FeO may be readily obtained at 1200°C by varying the oxygen pressure between the limits

$$10^{-12} \leq p_{O_2} \geq 10^{-9} \text{ atm}$$

This points up one important way of controlling the defect structure of a crystal; namely through variation of the pressure of one of its constituents in the gas phase. In most crystals of interest, component M exists in the monatomic state when in the vapor phase, whereas component X often exists in the diatomic state (O_2, Cl_2, I_2, F_2, S_2, Br_2, etc.).

First, let us consider the reaction concerning formation of a perfect MX crystal at a temperature where M is stable as a solid and X as X_2 in the vapor.

$$M(s) + \tfrac{1}{2}X_2(g) = MX(s) \qquad \Delta G°$$

If MX is pure, $a_{MX} = 1$, and

$$K_{15}' = \frac{1}{a_{M(in\ MX)}p_{X_2}^{1/2}} \tag{15.46}$$

M, in the compound, is in equilibrium with $p_M{}^e$ in the vapor. By definition

$$a_{M(in\ MX)} = \frac{p_M}{p_M{}^e} \tag{15.47}$$

At a given temperature $p_M{}^e$ is a constant, and substituting 15.47 into 15.46 and combining $p_M{}^e$ with the equilibrium constant yields

$$K_{15} = p_M \cdot p_{X_2}^{1/2} \tag{15.48}$$

If $p_M > p_M{}^e$, the crystal MX will tend to be nonstoichiometric with an excess of M present in the crystal (or deficit of X). From equation 15.48, this condition is the same as the condition that $p_{X_2} < p_{X_2}{}^e$. Conversely, when $p_M < p_M{}^e$, there will tend to be a deficit of component M in the crystal (or excess of X). Equation 15.48 indicates that a given state may be achieved either through variation of p_M or p_{X_2} since the product $p_M \cdot p_{X_2}$ must be a constant if MX is stable.

An excess of M may be incorporated in the crystal lattice in one of two ways.

(a) Placement of an M atom on a normal site M_M with formation of an anion vacancy V_X.
(b) Placement of an M atom in an interstitial site from the gas phase.

$$M(g) = M_M + V_X \qquad \text{(reaction } a) \qquad (15.49)$$
$$M(g) = M_i \qquad \qquad \text{(reaction } b) \qquad (15.50)$$

For the former reaction

$$K_{16}' = \frac{[M_M][V_X]}{p_M} \tag{15.51}$$

The quality $[M_M]$ is approximately constant, since δ is considered to be small. Incorporating this constant with K_{15}' gives a constant

$$K_{16} = \frac{[V_X]}{p_M} \tag{15.52}$$

If the latter type of defect is important, there is the relation

$$K_{17} = \frac{[M_i]}{p_M} \tag{15.53}$$

In analogous fashion an excess of X in the lattice may be formed by

(a) placement of an X atom on a normal site X_X with formation of a cation vacancy;

(b) placement of an X atom in an interstitial site from the gas phase.

$$\tfrac{1}{2}X_2(g) = X_X + V_M \tag{15.54}$$
$$\tfrac{1}{2}X_2(g) = X_i \tag{15.55}$$

The constants associated with reactions 15.54 and 15.55 are respectively

$$K_{18} = \frac{[V_M]}{p_{X_2}^{\frac{1}{2}}} \tag{15.56}$$

and

$$K_{19} = \frac{[X_i]}{p_{X_2}^{\frac{1}{2}}} \tag{15.57}$$

Thus we see that the concentration of defects in a crystal is simply related to the partial pressure of the components in the gas phase.

At this point, the formalism necessary for the complete treatment of defects in crystals has been developed with particular reference to equilibration with the components in the gas phase. Let us now apply it to some simple cases.

Consider for example, the case of FeO. Jette and Foote[1] have prepared FeO equilibrated at various partial pressures of oxygen and subsequently determined the lattice parameter by x-ray analysis as well as the specific gravity. The results of their work are listed in Table 15.5. From the table it is seen that as the iron content of the crystal increases toward stoichiometric FeO, an expansion of the unit cell occurs along with a

[1] E. R. Jette and F. Foote, *J. Chem. Phys.*, **1**, 29 (1933).

TABLE 15.5

Lattice Parameter and Density of FeO[a]

Composition	Lattice parameters (a)	Density (gm/cm^3)
$Fe_{0.91}O$	4.282	5.613
$Fe_{0.92}O$	4.285	5.624
$Fe_{0.93}O$	4.292	5.658
$Fe_{0.945}O$	4.301	5.728

[a] From E. R. Jette and F. Foote, *J. Chem. Phys.*, **1**, 29 (1933).

corresponding increase in density. A deviation from stoichiometry of the type found for Fe_xO (an excess of oxygen) may occur in the two ways discussed previously: (a) formation of cation vacancies, or (b) formation of oxygen interstitials. If the latter factor were responsible for non-stoichiometry, the density and the lattice parameter should decrease as the Fe/O rate increases toward one. On the other hand the reverse situation should occur if cation vacancies are responsible. Table 15.5 shows that the density and lattice parameter increase as the Fe/O ratio approaches one, indicating that the defect responsible for nonstoichiometry in FeO is type (a). This type of defect structure in which there is an excess of oxygen through formation of cation vacancies is given by an equation of the type given in 15.54.

$$\tfrac{1}{2}O_2(g) = O_O \text{ (in FeO)} + V_{Fe} \tag{15.58}$$

Equation 15.58 is not complete, however, since cation vacancies may act as acceptors. Thus, to equation 15.58 must be added

$$V_{Fe} = V_{Fe}^- + e^+$$
$$V_{Fe}^- = V_{Fe}^{2-} + e^+$$

giving

$$\tfrac{1}{2}O_2(g) = O_O + V_{Fe}^{2-} + 2e^+ \tag{15.59}$$

if cation vacancies are assumed to be doubly ionized. From this equation it is seen that for each additional oxygen present over the ratio Fe/O = 1, two holes may be formed in the valence band. This type of disorder is Type IID listed in Table 15.1. As pointed out earlier, a large number of compounds show this type of disorder. Some other examples are NiO, Cu_2O, FeS, CoO, CrS. These materials should all be p-type semiconductors if this ionization occurs, since the atomic disorder is associated with excess holes in the valence band. Confirmation of the presence of this type of disorder may be obtained from an investigation of the electrical conductivity and Hall coefficient as a function of equilibration pressure of

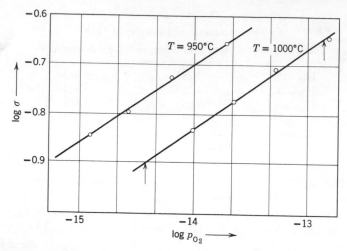

Fig. 15.8 Dependence of electrical conductivity of FeO upon oxygen pressure. From K. Hauffe and H. Pfeiffer, *Z. Metallk.*, **44**, 27 (1953).

oxygen. The conductivity of FeO as a function of oxygen pressure is shown in Fig. 15.8. Electrical measurements show that FeO is indeed a *p*-type semiconductor and from the slope of the curves in Fig. 15.8, it is found that the conductivity σ is related to the oxygen pressure according to the relation

$$\sigma \sim p_{O_2}^{1/6}$$

Let us now see if this relation may be explained by equation 15.59. According to this equation we have an equilibrium constant (if vacancies holes follow Henry's law).

$$K = \frac{[e^+]^2[V_{Fe}^{2-}]}{p_{O_2}^{1/2}} \tag{15.60}$$

Since two electron holes are formed for every cation vacancy and the intrinsic hole concentration is considered to be small, we see from equation 15.59 that

$$2[e^+] = [V_{Fe}^{2-}]$$

Substitution into equation 15.60 yields for the hole concentration as a function of oxygen pressure

$$[e^+] = 2^{1/3}Kp_{O_2}^{1/6}$$

Since the energy gap is large, virtually all conduction results from holes formed according to 15.59, and thus we find that

$$\sigma \sim p_{O_2}^{1/6}$$

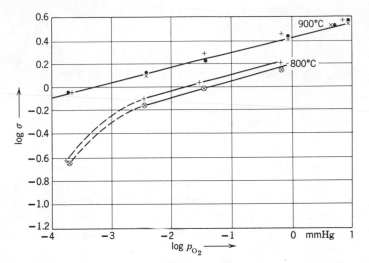

Fig. 15.9 Dependence of electrical conductivity of Cu_2O upon oxygen pressure. From J. Gundermann, K. Hauffe, and C. Wagner, *Z. physik. Chem.*, **B37**, 148 (1937).

in agreement with experiment. Thus we see that cation vacancies appear to be doubly ionized.

Let us now consider the case for Cu_2O. In Fig. 15.9 is shown the conductivity of Cu_2O as a function of oxygen pressure. It is found from this figure that the conductivity at high temperatures is given by

$$\sigma \sim p_{O_2}^{1/2}$$

and that Cu_2O is a p-type semiconductor at high temperatures. Thus the conductivity should be proportional to the concentration of electron holes in the valence band, since the energy gap is large, and hence the conduction band is virtually unoccupied. The concentration of electron holes is related to the composition of Cu_2O and hence is related to the oxygen pressure. Consider a sequence of reactions similar to those derived for FeO. For Cu_2O the situation is somewhat different since, for every oxygen put in the lattice, two cation vacancies must be created instead of one as for FeO. If we consider the cation vacancies to be singly ionized we have an equation analogous to 15.59.

$$\tfrac{1}{2}O_2(g) = O_O + 2V_{Cu}^- + 2e^+ \qquad (15.61)$$

and

$$K = \frac{[V_{Cu}^-]^2[e^+]^2}{p_{O_2}^{1/2}} \qquad (15.62)$$

According to equation 15.61, electron holes and cation vacancies are created in equal concentrations. Hence

$$[V_{Cu}{}^-] = [e^+]$$

Substituting this relation into 15.62 and solving for e^+ gives

$$[e^+] = Kp_{O_2}^{1/8}$$

Since $\sigma \sim [e^+]$ we see that theoretically

$$\sigma \sim p_{O_2}^{1/8}$$

This theoretical prediction of the dependence of conductivity upon oxygen is in reasonable agreement with the experimental observations. It should be noted at this point that the conductivity changes caused by variation of oxygen pressure are not particularly small. At 900°, σ is about 0.8 (ohm cm)$^{-1}$ when $p_{O_2} = 10^{-4}$ mm Hg pressure. If p_{O_2} is changed to 1 mm Hg pressure, σ increases to 2.6 (ohm cm)$^{-1}$.

The crystals just discussed are good examples of the influence of defect formation upon electrical properties. If the compounds contained no defects, the crystals would be insulators, but the presence of nonstoichiometry converts them to p-type semiconductors with quite large conductivities.

The examples discussed above are somewhat unusual in that the defect concentration is quite large and large differences in lattice parameter and density therefore result. In many cases the defect structure must be inferred from a combination of indirect experiments, such as, conductivity measurements in conjunction with atomic diffusion measurements. The mechanism of electrical conductivity of a compound may be through: (a) the motion of electrons in the conduction band, (b) the motion of electron holes in the valence band, (c) the diffusion of cations, or (d) diffusion of anions. The first two mechanisms are classified as *electronic conductivity* and the last two as *ionic conductivity*. Electrons or electron holes generally diffuse rapidly through the crystal if present in the conduction and valence bands respectively, and give rise to a high conductivity. Cations and anions will be attracted to the cathode and anode respectively upon application of an electric field, but the diffusion of these species is generally slow, since ionic diffusion depends upon the existence of atomic defects in the crystal. If cation interstitials are the major defects in a crystal catior diffusion will be relatively fast since, to facilitate diffusion, the interstitial ion is surrounded by empty interstitial sites in which to move. On the other hand, if the major type of defect present is the cation or anion vacancy (or both) diffusion will be much slower since, for example, in order for a cation to move toward the cathode, a cation vacancy must move into a nearest neighbor position. The possible types of conductivity are shown schematically in Fig. 15.10. The fraction of current carried a given defect is represented by a quantity called a transference number. The transference numbers of the various current carriers in solids are determined in a fashion similar to the techniques used by chemists for aqueous solutions. If the current is solely of the electronic type, there will be no change in composition of the compound near the anode or the cathode, and the electransference number $t_e \sim 1$. If the

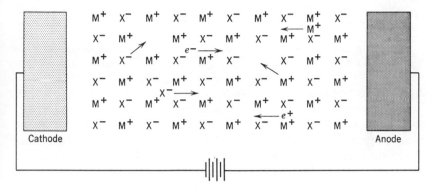

Fig. 15.10 Illustration of possible mechanisms of electrical conductivity.

current is not carried by electrons, $t_e \sim 0$, and composition changes will then occur near the anode and cathode due to the migration of ions toward the electrodes. If cations carry most of the current, $t_+ \sim 1$, the concentration of component M near the cathode will be higher than the average composition. On the other hand, if most of the current is carried by the anions, the composition of X near the anode will be higher than average. The current, no matter how small, must be carried by something, so

$$t_+ + t_- + t_e = 1$$

The crystal will be an insulator if $t_e \sim 0$ and will be a semiconductor if $t_e > 0$. The predominance of electrons in the conduction band and holes in the valence band may be determined through Hall coefficient measurements. The type of atomic defects present may only be found through detailed examination of self-diffusion and the effect of external influences such as p_M, p_{X_2} or impurities upon conductivity or ionic diffusion or both.

A list of the transference numbers of some compounds is given in Table 15.6, from which it is seen that $t_e = 0$ for NaCl. Hence one may conclude that NaCl is an insulator and no appreciable concentration of defects is electrically charged. Further, it is seen that at low temperatures virtually

TABLE 15.6

Transference Numbers of Some Compounds[a]

Compound	$T(°C)$	t_+	t_-	t_e	Compound	$T(°C)$	t_+	t_-	t_e
NaF	550	1.00	0.00		Ag_2S	180	0.01	0.00	0.99
NaCl	400	1.00	0.00	0.00	BaF_2	500	0.00	1.00	0.00
	500	0.98	0.02	0.00	$BaCl_2$	500	0.00	1.00	0.00
	600	0.95	0.05	0.00	PbI_2	270	0.45	0.55	0.00
NaBr	600	0.96	0.04	0.00	$CuCl_2$	18	0.00	0.00	1.00
KCl	600	0.88	0.12	0.00		110	0.03	0.00	0.97
AgBr	200	1.00	0.00	0.00		300	0.98	0.00	0.02
AgCl	200	1.00	0.00	0.00	Cu_2O	1000	0.00	0.00	1.00

[a] From F. S. Stone in *Solid State Chemistry*, W. E. Garner, ed., Academic Press, New York, 1955.

all of the current is carried by cations. From this one concludes that there is either the presence of Frenkel disorders with interstitial sodium ions and sodium vacancies, or the presence of Schottky defects with only cations being mobile at low temperatures. Other evidence to be presented later points to Schottky disorder. It is seen from Table 15.6 that the mobility of anions increases relative to cations at high temperatures, since the ratio t_-/t_+ increases. Table 15.6 also shows that AgBr is an insulator with $t_+ = 1$. In this case other evidence obtained points toward Frenkel disorder as the important type. The crystal Ag_2S is observed from Table 15.6 to be a semiconductor with a small contribution to conductivity resulting from Ag^+ ions. BaF_2 and $BaCl_2$ are insulators with all of the current being carried by the anions. Cu_2O is a *p*-type semiconductor as discussed earlier.

Up to this point the only method of defect control which has been discussed is equilibration of the crystal with a partial pressure of one of its components. Another important method is through the introduction of impurities having a different electrical charge. Consider for example the mixing together of $CdCl_2$ and NaCl. A Cd^+ ion has an atomic size of such magnitude that it may be easily substituted for a sodium ion in NaCl. NaCl, even with $CdCl_2$ dissolved in it, is found to be an insulator. Let us consider as a hypothesis that Shottky defects are the only important atomic defects. Theoretical calculations support this hypothesis as discussed earlier. The condition for electroneutrality therefore for an insulator is

$$[Na^+] + 2[Cd^{2+}] = [Cl^-]$$

For a gram atom of crystal there are $\frac{1}{2}N_0$ cation sites and $\frac{1}{2}N_0$ anion sites in NaCl. If Cd^{2+} ions were simply substituted for Na^+ ions on cation sites, there would be an excess of positive charge equal to $[Cd^{2+}]$. The only way to satisfy the electroneutrality condition is for Na^+ vacancy to form for each Cd^{2+} ion dissolved. This may be expressed by the equation

$$CdCl_2 = Cd_{Na}^+ + V_{Na} + 2NaCl + e^-$$

If Schottky defects are present, we have an equilibrium constant given by

$$K = [V_{Na}][V_{Cl}] = A \exp[-\Delta H^\circ/kT] \qquad (15.63)$$

It will be recalled that ΔH° represents the enthalpy of formation of a cation vacancy V_{Na} plus an anion vacancy V_{Cl}. This term is, of course, positive and hence K increases with temperature. In a pure crystal $[V_{Na}] = [V_{Cl}]$

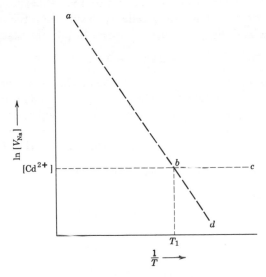

Fig. 15.11 Cation vacancy concentration as a function of temperature for NaCl.

to maintain charge neutrality and hence from equation 15.63 we have for a pure crystal

$$[V_{Na}] = \sqrt{A} \exp[-\Delta H^\circ/2kT] \qquad (15.64)$$

In Fig. 15.11, $\ln[V_{Na}]$ is plotted versus the reciprocal of temperature for the pure crystal and is shown by line *abd*. Suppose now, cadmium is introduced into the crystal at some concentration $[Cd^{2+}]$. In order to satisfy neutrality the vacancy concentration $[V_{Na}]$ must be introduced in a concentration equal to $[Cd^{2+}]$. At high temperatures there is little disturbance since there will be a large value of $[V_{Na}]$ through equation 15.64. At low temperatures, however, the concentration of vacancies given by equation 15.64, will be too low and hence extrinsic vacancies will dominate. The condition where $[V_{Na}] = [Cd^{2+}]$ is shown on Fig. 15.11 by line bc. The vacancy concentration of the crystal will therefore be intrinsic and follow equation 15.64 and line abd when $T > T_1$. The vacancy concentration will be extrinsic at $T < T_1$, and will be equal to $[Cd^{2+}]$ or line bc. Some evidence for the existence of Schottky defects and the intrinsic and extrinsic concentration of vacancies may be obtained from measurements of the self-diffusion of sodium in NaCl doped with cadmium. The self-diffusion constant D is given by

$$D = g \nu p_s \cdot p_E \tag{15.65}$$

where g is a geometric constant, ν is a vibrational frequency, p_s is the probability that the ion of interest is next to a suitable site, and p_E is the probability that the ion has enough energy to surmount the energy barrier between its site and the adjacent site. From Boltzmann statistics

$$p_E = a \exp(-\Delta E/kT) \tag{15.66}$$

where a is a constant and ΔE represents the height of the energy diffusion barrier. For a Schottky defect, and hence a vacancy mechanism of diffusion, p_s is equal to the probability that a given sodium ion is next to a cation vacancy.

This is equal to $b[V_{Na}]$ where b is a constant and thus p_s is given by

$$p_s = b_2[V_{Na}] = b\sqrt{A} \exp(-\Delta H^\circ/2kT) \tag{15.67}$$

when $T > T_1$, and

$$p_s = [V_{Na}] = [Cd^{2+}] \tag{15.68}$$

when $T < T_1$. Thus

$$D = \nu abg\sqrt{A} \exp\left(-\frac{\Delta H^\circ/2 + \Delta E}{kT}\right) \tag{15.69}$$

when $T > T_1$, or

$$\ln D = \ln(\nu abg\sqrt{A}) - \left(\frac{\Delta H^\circ/2 + \Delta E}{kT}\right) \tag{15.70}$$

at high temperatures.

At low temperatures on the other hand

$$D = ga[Cd^{2+}]\nu \exp\left(-\frac{\Delta E}{kT}\right)$$

or

$$\ln D = \ln(ga[Cd^{2+}]\nu) - \frac{\Delta E}{kT} \tag{15.71}$$

In Fig. 15.12 is shown $\ln D$ versus the reciprocal of temperature for the diffusion of sodium in NaCl containing impurities. At high temperatures we see that the slope is larger than at low temperatures, as it should be

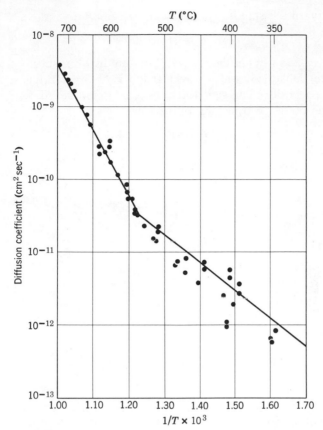

Fig. 15.12 Self-diffusion coefficient of sodium in crystals of NaCl doped with $CdCl_2$. From D. E. Mapother, H. N. Crooks, and R. J. Maurer, *J. Chem. Phys.*, **18**, 1231 (1950).

according to equations 15.70 and 15.71. From these data, ΔH° and ΔE may be determined experimentally from the two portions of the curve. It is found that ΔH°, the enthalpy of formation of a Schottky defect, is equal to 2.06 ev, in fairly good agreement with the value of 1.86 ev calculated theoretically, as discussed earlier.

Another interesting case concerning the influence of impurities on the defect structure of a crystal is NiO. NiO has the same defect structure of FeO and Cu_2O, namely cation vacancies and electron holes in the valence band through the equation

$$\tfrac{1}{2}O_2(g) = O_O + V_{Ni}^{2-} + 2e^+$$

$$K = \frac{[V_{Ni}^{2-}][e^+]^2}{p_{O_2}^{1/2}}$$

If the oxygen pressure is held constant

$$K = [V_{Ni}{}^{2-}][e^+]^2 \tag{15.72}$$

Now let us add Li_2O to the crystal. Lithium dissolves substitutionally on the nickel sublattice as a monovalent ion Li^+. Since Li^+ is substituting for Ni^{2+}, a positive charge is lost for each Li^+ ion added. According to the condition of electroneutrality therefore

$$[e^+] = [Li_{Ni}{}^-] + 2[V_{Ni}{}^{2-}] \tag{15.73}$$

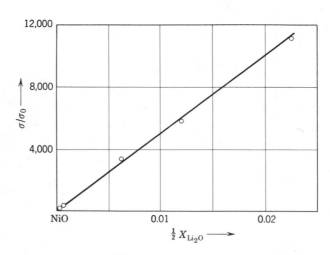

Fig. 15.13 The electrical conductivity of NiO as a function of the dissolved lithium oxide content of the crystal. From E. J. W. Verwey, P. W. Hoayman, and F. C. Romeyn, *Chem. Weekblad*, **44**, 705 (1948).

Substitution of the relation for $[V_{Ni}]$ obtained from equation 15.73 into 15.72 yields

$$[e^+]^3 - [e^+]^2[Li_{Ni}{}^-] = 2K \tag{15.74}$$

Since the electrical conductivity is proportional to $[e^+]$, the influence of $[Li_{Ni}{}^-]$ upon conductivity may be obtained from solution of equation 15.74. The situation becomes simpler from an analytical standpoint if $[Li_{Ni}{}^-] \gg [V_{Ni}]$. If this is the case we find, from 15.73, that

$$[e^+] \cong [Li_{Ni}{}^-]$$

and thus

$$\sigma \sim [Li_{Ni}{}^-]$$

In Fig. 15.13, the ratio of the conductivity σ for a lithium-doped crystal to the intrinsic conductivity σ_0 is plotted versus $[Li_{Ni}{}^-]$ (or X_{Li_2O}), confirming the relation above. It will be noted from Fig. 15.13 that the conductivity of NiO is increased 10,000-fold upon addition of only 2 at % lithium to the crystal.

Instead of adding Li_2O to the crystal, suppose that an oxide containing a metallic ion such as Cr_2O_3 is dissolved. The condition for neutrality is now

$$[e^+] + [Cr_{Ni}^+] = 2[V_{Ni}^{2-}] \qquad (15.75)$$

Substitution of $[V_{Ni}^{2-}]$ from equation 15.75 into 15.72 yields

$$[e^+]^3 + [e^+]^2[Cr_{Ni}^+] = 2K' \qquad (15.76)$$

From equation 15.76, it is seen that as $[Cr_{Ni}^+]$ is increased, $[e^+]$ is decreased, thus decreasing the conductivity. From equation 15.72 it is seen that if

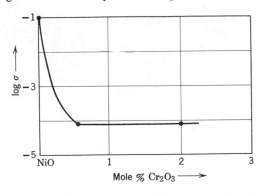

Fig. 15.14 The electrical conductivity of NiO as a function of the dissolved chromium content of the crystal. From K. Hauffe and J. Block, *Z. physik. Chem.*, **198**, 232 (1951).

$[e^+]$ is decreased, $[V_{Ni}^{2-}]$ is increased, resulting in an increase in diffusion constant for Ni. In Fig. 15.14 is plotted the conductivity of NiO doped with Cr_2O_3.

Besides changing the electrical conductivity of a compound, impurity additions may have a profound influence on other properties, for example, the oxidation rate of metal. The growth of an oxide film depends upon the diffusion of cations from metal to the air-oxide interface and the diffusion of oxygen from the atmosphere to the metal-oxide interface. The diffusion rate is related to the defect concentration, which in turn may be strongly altered by the addition of appropriate impurities to the metal.

15.5 SOME CASE STUDIES OF DEFECT CRYSTALS

The fundamental principles relating to the thermodynamics of defects have been presented and applied somewhat concisely to several cases. In order to gain more appreciation for the manner in the defect structure of a substance is elucidated, it might be profitable to consider some actual cases of how defect structure is determined. The particular cases to be discussed are chosen so as to illustrate a variety of defect types.

Zinc Oxide

ZnO crystallizes with the wurtzite structure shown in Fig. 15.15. The wurtzite structure has a rather open character as is evident from the figure.

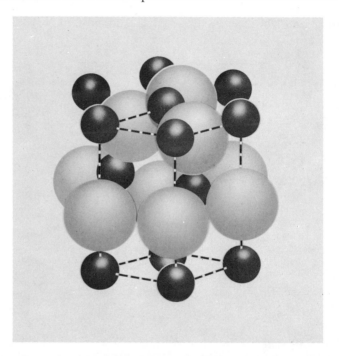

Fig. 15.15 Crystal structure of ZnO (wurtzite structure). From L. Azaroff, *Introduction to Solids*, McGraw-Hill, New York, 1960.

As a result one might expect that the zinc ions in the crystal could readily exist in the interstitial sites as well as the normal lattice sites. Because of the large size of the oxygen ions, one would not expect the existence of oxygen in interstitial sites to be energetically feasible. The calculations presented previously with regard to the energy of formation of Schottky defects indicated that the energy was sufficiently low, so that this could well be the predominant type of defect in most crystals, unless some particular characteristic of the compound allowed some other defect to be energetically more favorable. The structure of ZnO fits this particular situation. Experimental information must be obtained, however, to decide what defect type is predominant. In Fig. 15.16 is shown the conductivity of ZnO as a function of oxygen pressure. Temperature studies of the conductivity and Hall measurements indicate that ZnO is an n-type semiconductor, and from Fig. 15.16 it is observed that the conductivity and hence concentration of electrons in the conduction band decrease as the partial pressure is increased. From Fig. 15.16 we find that

$$\sigma \sim [e^-] \sim p_{O_2}^{-\frac{1}{4}}$$

In addition, chemical analysis of ZnO crystals indicate that ZnO is nonstoichiometric with [Zn]/[O] > 1, indicating an excess of zinc.

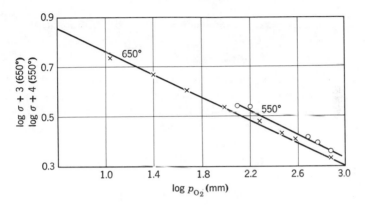

Fig. 15.16 Conductivity of ZnO as a function of oxygen pressure. From H. H. Baumbach and C. Wagner, *Z. physik. Chem.*, **B22**, 199 (1933).

Thomas[1] has immersed ZnO crystals in Zn vapor and found that the conductivity increased compared with crystals before treatment. Clearly, therefore, the concentration of electrons in the conduction is associated with an excess of Zn. Hall measurements of Hutson[2] indicate that the donor level lies 0.05 ev below the conduction band and therefore the donors are completely ionized at room temperature as well as at higher temperatures. The band gap of ZnO has been determined to be 3.3 ev from optical studies. This situation is shown in Fig. 15.17. Excluding the unlikely possibility of substitutional disorder, there are two possible mechanisms for explaining the behavior

(a) Formation of anion vacancies with complete ionization of anion vacancy donors according to the following reaction

$$ZnO = ZnO_{(1-\delta)} + \delta V_O^- + \delta(\tfrac{1}{2}O_2(g)) + \delta e^-$$

[1] D. G. Thomas, *J. Phys. Chem. Solids*, **3**, 229 (1957).
[2] Reported in same paper.

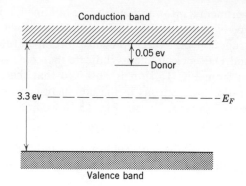

Fig. 15.17 Energy associated with electronic defects in ZnO.

or

$$O^{2-} = \tfrac{1}{2}O_2(g) + V_O^- + e^- \tag{15.77}$$

Physically, this reaction corresponds to the removal of a doubly charged anion from the crystal and the removal of two electrons from the anion, which are left at the vacancy giving the vacancy a double negative charge. An anion vacancy tends to act as a donor, as mentioned previously, and so is able to contribute an electron to the conduction band. A second ionization step could also proceed with a donor level somewhat lower in the energy gap.

(b) Formation of ionized cation interstitials according to the following reaction

$$Zn(g) = Zn_i^+ + e^- \tag{15.78}$$

Physically, this corresponds to transferring a neutral zinc atom from the vapor phase to an interstitial position. As discussed earlier, interstitial cations tend to act as donors and, in this case, since the donor lies so close to the conduction band, the interstitials would be completely ionized. There could be a second ionization step according to

$$Zn_i^+ = Zn_i^{2+} + e^-$$

The equilibrium constants for processes (a) and (b) are

$$K_a = p_{O_2}^{1/2} \cdot [V_0^-][e^-] \tag{15.79}$$

$$K_b = \frac{[Zn_i^+][e^-]}{p_{Zn}} \tag{15.80}$$

The quantities p_{Zn} and p_{O_2} are not independent of each other, since for the reaction for the formation of ZnO,

$$Zn(s) + \tfrac{1}{2}O_2(g) = ZnO(s)$$

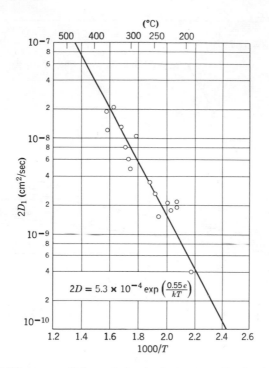

Fig. 15.18 Self-diffusion coefficient of zinc in ZnO. From D. G. Thomas, *J. Phys. Chem. Solids*, **3**, 233 (1957).

there is an equilibrium constant

$$K = p_{Zn} \cdot p_{O_2}^{\frac{1}{2}} \tag{15.81}$$

Substitution of equation 15.81 into 15.80 yields

$$KK_b = [Zn_i^+][e^-]p_{O_2}^{\frac{1}{2}} \tag{15.82}$$

Comparison of equations 15.79 and 15.82 with the data in Fig. 15.16 shows qualitative agreement, since, according to either of these equations, if p_{O_2} is decreased, $[e^-]$ is increased, and therefore so is the conductivity σ.

Further evidence concerning the nature of the defect structure comes from self-diffusion studies of Zn in ZnO. These data are shown in Fig. 15.18. From these data it is found that the diffusion coefficient is given by

$$D = 5.3 \times 10^{-4} \exp(-0.55/kT)$$

Thus, the activation energy for the diffusion of zinc in ZnO is 0.55 ev or 12,700 cal/gm-atom. This value is too low for diffusion by a vacancy mechanism. Also D itself is large. The only way to explain this fast

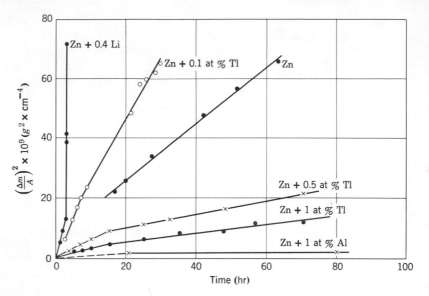

Fig. 15.19 Weight gain during oxidation of zinc at one atmosphere oxygen pressure at 390°C as a function of impurity addition. From C. Gensch and K. Hauffe, *Z. physik. Chem.*, **196**, 427 (1950).

diffusion is to postulate the existence of interstitial Zn, thereby giving support to alternative (b) above. According to reaction 15.78, interstitial zinc ions are produced in concentration equal to the electron concentration $[e^-]$. Thus

$$[Zn_i^+] = [e^-]$$

Substitution of this relation into 15.82 gives

$$\sigma \sim [e^-] \sim p_{O_2}^{-\frac{1}{4}}$$

which is in agreement with the results of Baumbach and Wagner presented in Fig. 15.16.

In addition to these studies the rate of oxidation of zinc containing various doping additions has been investigated by Gensch and Hauffe.[1] Their results are shown in Fig. 15.19. It is observed from Fig. 15.19 that small amounts of alloying additions have a profound effect on the oxidation characteristics of zinc. For example, addition of 1 at % aluminum or thallium reduces the oxidation rate of zinc by a factor of 100 whereas addition of 0.4 at % lithium increases the oxidation rate by a factor of 100. The explanation for this behavior lies in the influence of these

[1] C. Gensch and K. Hauffe, *Z. Phys. Chem.*, **196**, 427 (1950); **195**, 386 (1950).

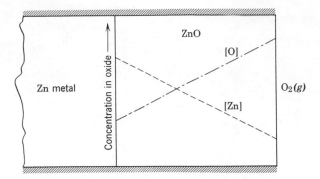

Fig. 15.20 Concentration gradients of zinc and oxygen in ZnO layer during oxidation.

impurities on the defect structure. After a thin oxide layer has built up on the zinc, further oxidation depends on transport of oxygen through the ZnO layer of the metal for reaction to form ZnO, or transport of metal through oxide to gas-oxide interface for reaction. Concentration gradients will exist in the oxide as shown in Fig. 15.20. As previously discussed, the principal defects in ZnO appear to be fast diffusing Zn_i^+ interstitials, so the primary transport will be due to metallic zinc dissolving in ZnO as Zn_i^+ and e^- and diffusion to a gas-oxide interface for reaction. Let us consider first the effect of Al_2O_3 additions to ZnO upon oxidation kinetics. As would be expected from chemical valence considerations, Al tends to dissolve as $Al^{3+} + 3e^-$. Thus one would expect, upon substitution of an Al atom for a Zn atom on a substitutional site in ZnO, the addition of one net electron to the conduction band according to the reaction

$$\tfrac{1}{2}Al_2O_3 = Al_{Zn}^+ + e^- + ZnO + \tfrac{1}{4}O_2(g) \tag{15.83}$$

This is also confirmed from conductivity measurements as shown in Fig. 15.21, since addition of aluminum is found to increase the n-type conductivity.

From equation 15.78 we have

$$Zn(g) = Zn_i^+ + e^-$$

with the equilibrium constant

$$K_b = \frac{[Zn_i^+][e^-]}{p_{Zn}}$$

If ZnO is in contact with essentially pure zinc, p_{Zn} will be constant and hence

$$K_b' = [Zn_i^+][e^-] \tag{15.84}$$

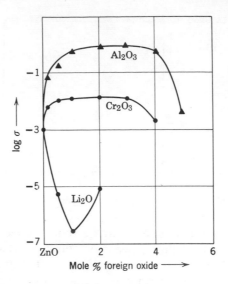

Fig. 15.21 Conductivity of ZnO as a function of impurity content. From K. Hauffe and A. L. Vierk, *Z. physik. Chem.*, **196**, 160 (1950).

It is now clear what the addition of Al does. From equation 15.83, substitution of aluminum on zinc sites increases the concentration of electrons in the conduction band. From 15.84, however, the product $[Zn_i^+][e^-]$ is constant, so if $[e^-]$ is increased because of the presence of aluminum donors, $[Zn_i^+]$ must decrease. If $[Zn_i^+]$ decreases, the flux of Zn ions through the oxide to the gas-oxide interface is reduced and hence the system would be more resistant to oxidation in agreement with observation. Thallium has an effect similar to aluminum but it is not so pronounced, presumably because thallium is not ionized to the extent of aluminum in ZnO.

In the case of additions of lithium, the electrical measurements shown in Fig. 15.21 indicate that lithium dissolved in ZnO acts as an acceptor according to the reaction

$$\tfrac{1}{2}Li_2O + \tfrac{1}{4}O_2 = Li_{Zn}^- + ZnO + e^+$$

Thus substitution of lithium on zinc sites in ZnO tends to increase the hole concentration in the valence band. Since there is the following relation between holes and electrons

$$K = [e^-][e^+]$$

an increase in $[e^+]$ will result in a decrease in $[e^-]$. From equation 15.84, a decrease in $[e^-]$ will result in an increase in $[Zn_i^+]$ and hence there will be a greater flux of Zn to the gas-oxide boundary.

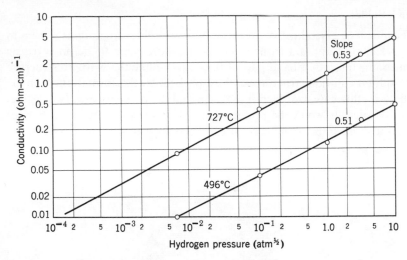

Fig. 15.22 Conductivity of ZnO as a function of hydrogen pressure. From D. G. Thomas and J. J. Lander, *J. Chem. Phys.*, **25**, 1136 (1956).

An interesting investigation of the nature of dissolved hydrogen in ZnO has been made by Thomas and Lander.[1] These investigators found that the conductivity of ZnO increased upon introduction of hydrogen. Since $\sigma \sim [e^-]$ for an n-type semiconductor, it appears that the following reaction must occur.

$$\tfrac{1}{2}H_2(g) = H_i^+ + e^-$$

$$K = \frac{[H_i^+][e^-]}{p_{H_2}^{\frac{1}{2}}}$$

Since an H_i^+ ion is formed for each electron created, $[H_i^+] = [e^-]$, and thus

$$[e^-] = K p_{H_2}^{\frac{1}{4}}$$

Therefore the conductivity should be expressed by the relation

$$\sigma \sim p_{H_2}^{\frac{1}{4}}$$

or

$$\log \sigma \sim \tfrac{1}{4} \log p_{H_2} \sim \tfrac{1}{2} \log p_{H_2}^{\frac{1}{2}}$$

In Fig. 15.22 is plotted $\log \sigma$ versus $\log p_{H_2}^{\frac{1}{2}}$. The slope of the line is found to be 0.51 and 0.53 at 496°C and 727°C respectively, in excellent agreement with the value of 0.50 predicted theoretically.

[1] D. G. Thomas and J. J. Lander, *J. Chem. Phys.*, **25**, 1136 (1956).

Lead Sulfide

Lead sulfide crystallizes with the sodium chloride structure as shown in Fig. 15.23 and appears from electrical measurements to be an intrinsic semiconductor with a band gap of 0.40 ev. Unlike the wurtzite structure the sodium chloride structure is close packed, so the formation of interstitials in this case would not be expected to be energetically feasible. Schottky defects would be preferred in this case as for the alkali halides which also have this structure. Bloem[1] has investigated the conductivity

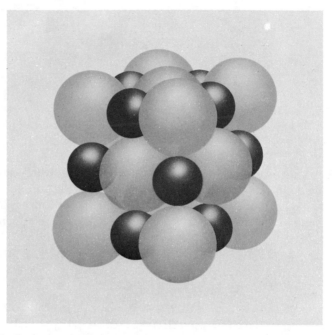

Fig. 15.23 Structure of PbS (sodium chloride structure). From L. Azaroff, *Introduction to Solids*, McGraw-Hill, New York, 1960.

and Hall effect of pure and doped PbS single crystals as a function of the partial pressure of sulfur. The results of this investigation are shown in Fig. 15.24. These data were obtained at room temperature after annealing at the temperature indicated on the curves and rapidly cooling to freeze the high temperature defect structures. The curves show that the electron concentration (and conductivity) decrease initially as the pressure of S_2 is increased until an abrupt change of slope occurs, whereupon a further increase in pressure results in increased conductivity. The Hall measurements indicate that the conductivity is due to excess electrons in the

[1] J. Bloem, *Philips Res. Repts.*, **11**, 273 (1956).

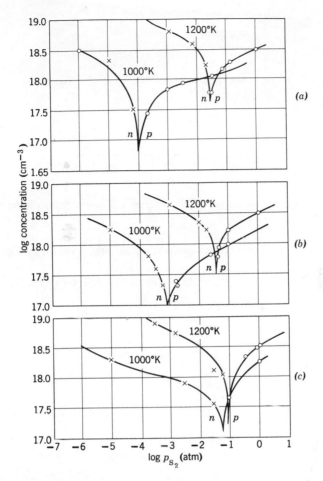

Fig. 15.24 Concentration of electrons or holes in PbS as a function of pressure of sulfur. (*a*) Doped with 10^{18} Ag/cm^3; (*b*) pure; (*c*) doped with 10^{18} Bi/cm^3. From J. Bloem, *Philips Res. Repts.*, **11**, 273 (1956).

conduction band (*n*-type) over holes in the valence band at low sulfur pressures up to the discontinuity in slope. At pressures greater than that where the discontinuity in slope appears the conduction is due to excess of holes in the valence band over electrons in the conduction band (*p*-type). From Fig. 15.24, it is noted that the pressure of sulfur at the point where $[e^+] = [e^-]$ (where abrupt change of slope occurs) is lower at lower temperatures. Also the effect of addition of silver is to lower the critical pressure compared with pure PbS and the effect of bismuth is to increase

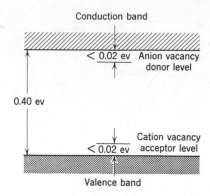

Fig. 15.25 Position of anion vacancy donor level and cation vacancy acceptor level in PbS.

it. This implies that silver acts as an acceptor and bismuth acts as a donor in PbS.

Assuming that the atomic defects are of the Schottky type we have

$$PbS = Pb_{(1-\delta)}S_{(1-\delta)} + \delta V_{Pb} + \delta V_S \qquad (15.85)$$

$$K_1 = [V_{Pb}][V_S] \qquad (15.86)$$

The cation vacancies also may act as acceptors:

$$V_{Pb} = V_{Pb}^- + e^+ \qquad (15.87)$$

$$K_2 = \frac{[V_{Pb}^-][e^+]}{[V_{Pb}]} \qquad (15.88)$$

and the anion vacancies may act as acceptors:

$$V_S = V_S^+ + e^- \qquad (15.89)$$

$$K_3 = \frac{[V_S^+][e^-]}{[V_S]} \qquad (15.90)$$

Hall effect data indicate that the acceptor and donor levels are close to the valence and conduction bands respectively as shown in Fig. 15.25. Because of the small ionization energies of reactions 15.87 and 15.89, K_2 and K_3 are large and hence virtually complete ionization occurs. For formation of the crystal there is the reaction

$$Pb + \tfrac{1}{2}S_2 = PbS(s)$$

$$K_4 = p_{Pb} \cdot p_{S_2}^{1/2} \qquad (15.91)$$

According to the law of mass action, raising the sulfur pressure will tend to cause sulfur to move into the cation vacancies. At equilibrium between sulfur in the vapor and sulfur in the crystal

$$a_{S(in\ gas)} = a_{S(in\ crystal)}$$

Since the activity of S in the crystal varies monatonically with mole fraction, an increase in p_{S_2} will result in an increase in [S] in the crystal. Conversely the concentration of Pb in the crystal is monatonically related to p_{Pb}. The condition for electroneutrality in addition is

$$[V_S{}^+] + [e^+] = [V_{Pb}{}^-] + [e^-] \tag{15.92}$$

For a stoichiometric crystal these quantities all have the same value but if p_{S_2} is increased above that which maintains the crystal as stoichiometric, $[V_S{}^+]$ will be decreased. From reaction 15.87, $[V_{Pb}{}^-] = [e^+]$, and from 15.89, $[V_S{}^+] = [e^-]$. Therefore if electroneutrality is to be maintained, a cation vacancy and electron hole must be formed for each anion vacancy filled and electron removed. A similar situation holds between the concentration of Pb in the crystal and p_{Pb}. These relations may be expressed by the following equations

$$\tfrac{1}{2}S_2(g) = S_S + V_{Pb}{}^- + e^+ \tag{15.93}$$

$$K_5 = \frac{[V_{Pb}{}^-][e^+]}{p_{S_2}^{1/2}} \tag{15.94}$$

and

$$Pb(g) = Pb_{Pb} + V_S{}^+ + e^- \tag{15.95}$$

$$K_6 = \frac{[V_S{}^+][e^-]}{p_{Pb}} \tag{15.96}$$

There is also the relation between electrons and holes.

$$K_7 = [e^-][e^+] \tag{15.97}$$

Substitution of equations 15.88, 15.90, and 15.97 into 15.86 yields

$$K' = \frac{K_1 K_2 K_3}{K_7} = [V_{Pb}{}^-][V_S{}^+] \tag{15.98}$$

The results shown in Fig. 15.24 are now readily understood from these relations. Equation 15.91 specifies that the product $p_{Pb} \cdot p_{S_2}^{1/2}$ is constant. At low pressure of sulfur, p_{Pb} will therefore be high. From equation 15.96, therefore, a high value of p_{Pb} corresponds to a high value of $[V_S{}^+]$ and $[e^-]$. As a result, a high n-type conductivity will result, corresponding to the left side of Fig. 15.24. As p_{S_2} increases, p_{Pb} decreases, according to 15.91, and hence $[e^-]$ decreases and the conductivity decreases, as is apparent from Fig. 15.24. This trend continues until the concentration of electrons is reduced to the intrinsic concentration $[e^-]_i$ expressed by equation 15.95.

$$[e^-]_i = [e^+]_i = \sqrt{K_7}$$

This corresponds to the position on Fig. 15.24, where a discontinuity in slope occurs. Up to this point $[e^-] > [e^+]$ and the conductivity has been n-type. At the discontinuity in slope $[e^-] = [e^+]$. At higher pressures of sulfur, $[e^-]$ is decreased further and now $[e^-] < [e^+]$. As a result, the conductivity changes to p-type and from equation 15.97, $[e^+]$ increases as $[e^-]$ is decreased, corresponding to an increase in p_{S_2} and the conductivity now begins to increase. Also, since K_7 increases with temperature, the value of $[e^-]_i = [e^+]_i$ increases as the temperature increases and hence the discontinuity will correspond to larger values of p_{S_2} at higher temperatures.

From Fig. 15.24, values of some of the equilibrium constants may be obtained. From Fig. 15.24b, it is seen that at the intrinsic point $[e^-]_i = [e^+]_i \cong 10^{17}$ at $1000°K$. Thus $K_7 \cong 10^{34}$. At $1200°K$, $[e^-]_i = [e^+]_i \cong 10^{17.5}$ and $K_7 \cong 10^{35}$. Also at the intrinsic point, since $[e^-]_i = [e^+]_i$, $[V_{Pb}] = [e^+]_i$, and $[V_S^+] = [e^-]_i$ from 15.93 and 15.95 respectively. Thus

$$[V_{Pb}^-] = [V_S^+] = [e^+]_i = [e^-]_i = 10^{17}$$

at $1000°K$. Therefore

$$K' \cong 10^{34}$$

at $1000°K$ (actually more detailed analysis shows that residual impurities influence the intrinsic point and $[e^-]_i = [e^+]_i \cong 10^{18}$ at $1000°K$). The temperature dependence of K' is given by, according to these data,

$$K' \cong 10^{43.4} \exp{(-1.75/kT)}$$

where 1.75 ev represent the work to form anion and cation vacancies. The constant $10^{43.4}$ may be readily compared with the value to be expected by theory. From earlier considerations we found that an equilibrium constant K for a reaction is given by

$$K = \exp{(\Delta S°/k)} \exp{(-\Delta H°/kT)}$$

where $\Delta S°$ represents the *vibrational* entropy change for the reaction and $\Delta H°$ represents the enthalpy for the reaction. For solid state reactions such as the one of interest,

$$PbS = Pb_{(1-\delta)}S_{(1-\delta)} + \delta V_{Pb}^- + \delta V_S^+$$

$\Delta S°$ is often small and hence let us assume $\Delta S° \cong 0$. Thus

$$K = \exp{(-\Delta H°/kT)} = [X_{V_{Pb}^-}][X_{V_S^+}]$$

for our reaction where the concentrations of cation and anion vacancies are expressed as atom fractions. K' in 15.98, however, is expressed in terms of $[V_{Pb}^-]$ and $[V_S^+]$, the number of sites vacant per cubic centimeter. The relation between $X_{V_{Pb}^-}$ and $[V_{Pb}^-]$ is

$$X_{V_{Pb}^-} = \frac{[V_{Pb}^-]}{N_{Pb}}$$

and similarly

$$X_{V_S^+} = \frac{[V_S^+]}{N_S}$$

where N_{Pb} and N_S are the number of lead and sulfur sites per cubic centimeter. These are found from density measurements to be

$$N_{Pb} = N_S \cong 2 \times 10^{22}$$

Thus

$$X_{V_{Pb}^-} \cdot X_{V_S^+} = \frac{[V_{Pb}][V_S^+]}{N_{Pb}^2} \cong \exp\left(\frac{-\Delta H^\circ}{kT}\right)$$

or

$$K' = [V_{Pb}^-][V_S^+] = 10^{44.6} \exp\left(-\Delta H^\circ/kT\right)$$

Comparison of the calculated value of $10^{44.6}$ with the experimental value $10^{43.4}$ shows quite good agreement with the approximation that $\Delta S^\circ \cong 0$.

Barium Oxide

The defect structure of BaO is not so well elucidated as the previous cases considered but is discussed here for the sake of completeness, since the experimental evidence indicates that the defect structure is somewhat unusual. BaO crystals have been obtained which are transparent and colorless. Optical measurements indicate that the energy gap is at least 3.8 ev hence the intrinsic conductivity is low. Pell[1] has found from Hall measurements that the conduction is n-type. The experimental value of conductivity is low but not as low as expected for a material with an energy gap of 3.8 ev. It is deduced therefore that the conductivity results from the presence of defects of some type. Some evidence about the defect comes from optical measurements. If a colorless crystal is put in contact with liquid barium at an elevated temperature, the crystal turns red. Further, if the crystals are heated at 1000°C in barium vapor, the crystal becomes blue. The absorption constant of monochromatic light has been measured as a function of wavelength and is shown in Fig. 15.26. The wavelength is converted to energy units and the absorption constant is

---

[1] E. M. Pell, *Phys. Rev.*, **87**, 457 (1957).

also plotted versus energy of the photons. It is to be noted that a maximum in absorption is observed for light for about 0.6 μ in wavelength or 2.0 ev in energy. This peak is not there for transparent crystals and so indicates that it is this particular absorption which gives rise to the blue color. This evidence, coupled with the conductivity experiments of Pell showing the

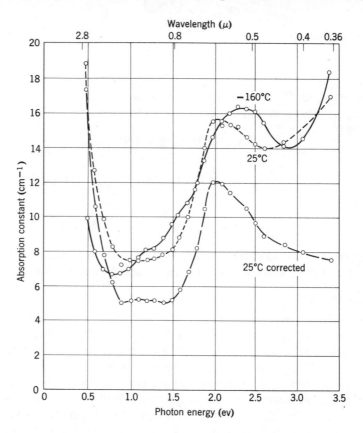

Fig. 15.26 Absorption constant as a function of wavelength (or photon energy) for BaO. From W. C. Dash, *Phys. Rev.*, **92**, 68 (1953).

conductivity to be *n*-type, indicates that there is a donor center lying 2.0 ev below the conduction band as shown in Fig. 15.27. The blue color of the crystal results from the exchange of electrons between the donor levels and the conduction band. Upon the passage of white light through the crystal, electrons at the donor levels absorb energy from the 2.0 ev photons and are excited to the conduction band. The color and hence the defect responsible may be removed upon heating the crystal under reduced

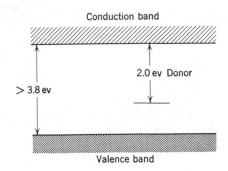

Conduction band

2.0 ev Donor

> 3.8 ev

Valence band

Fig. 15.27 Donor level in BaO determined optically.

pressure at an elevated temperature. The high temperature heating causes a return of BaO to the stoichiometric composition. Crystals immersed in the barium vapor which show the blue color have the composition $Ba_{1.03}O$ according to chemical analysis. According to our prior discussion the excess barium resulting in the formation of very slightly ionized donors could be accommodated one of two ways.

(a) Interstitial barium

$$Ba(g) = Ba_i$$

(b) anion vacancies

$$Ba(g) = Ba_{Ba} \text{ (in BaO)} + V_O$$

with interstitial barium or oxygen vacancies being the weakly ionized donor defect with the donor level 2.0 ev below the edge of the conduction band. Actually the evidence, upon which rests a decision as to which mechanism is responsible, is quite weak; the effective diffusion constant pertaining to the rate of color advance to the crystal has been studied and is found to be very different from the diffusion constant of barium in BaO. It is consequently tentatively concluded that anion vacancies are the principal defect. For more detail on BaO, the reader is referred to a paper by Thomas.[1]

[1] D. G. Thomas in *Semiconductors*, N. B. Hannay, ed., Reinhold, New York, 1959.

List of Major Symbols

C_P heat capacity at constant pressure
C_V heat capacity at constant volume
E energy
F Helmholtz free energy
G Gibbs free energy
H enthalpy
K equilibrium constant
M atomic weight, cation
N number
N_0 Avogadro number
P pressure
Q heat
R gas constant
S entropy
T temperature
V volume, vacancy
W work
X anion
X_i mole fraction of component i
Z coordinator number
Z_i number of states of energy E_i occupied

a_i activity of component i
e unit of electronic change
f fraction
g gas
h Planck's constant
k Boltzmann constant
l liquid
n number of moles
p partial pressure, probability
s solid

t transference number
x distance

$\mathscr{A}$ Madelung constant
$\mathscr{B}$ mobility
$\mathscr{E}$ electric potential
$\mathscr{F}$ Faraday constant
$\mathscr{S}$ long range order parameter
$\mathscr{W}$ number of ways of arranging particles
$\mathscr{Z}$ partition function, valence

Δ difference
Ω interaction parameter

α volume thermal expansion coefficient
β compressibility
γ_i activity coefficient of component i
ϵ energy per particle
θ Debye temperature
κ dielectric constant
μ chemical potential
ν frequency
ρ density
σ interfacial tension, stress

$\boldsymbol{\sigma}$ short range order parameter

a   lattice parameter

G_i° standard state
$G_i^{\bullet}$ property of pure phase
$\bar{G}_i$ partial molal quantity
G_i^{xs} excess quantity

General Physical Constants

Quantity	Value
1 calorie, cal	4.185×10^7 erg
1 joule, J	10^7 erg
Gas constant, R	1.986 cal/°K
Boltzmann's constant, k	1.380×10^{-16} erg/°K
1 electron volt/atom, ev	2.303×10^4 cal/mole
Avogadro's number, N_0	6.023×10^{23}
1 atmosphere, atm	760 mm Hg
Density of mercury	13.6 gm/cm³
Gravitational acceleration, g	980 cm/sec²
Faraday, $\mathscr{F}$	96,489 absolute coulombs
Planck's constant, h	6.626×10^{-27} erg sec
1 liter-atmosphere, 1 atm	24.21 cal
Ideal gas volume at 1 atm and 0°C	22.41 liters/mole

appendix 3

Problems

CHAPTER 2

2.1 Gray tin and white tin have densities of 5.75 and 7.28 gm/cm³, respectively. Calculate the work done by our system upon the surroundings when white tin transforms to gray tin at 13°C and 1 atm pressure. Express answer in calories per mole.

2.2 Calculate $\Delta H°$ for the following reaction at 800°K as accurately as possible.

$$3AgCl(l) + B(s) = BCl_3(l) + Ag(s)$$

2.3 The melting point of CaTiSiO₅ is 1400°C and the heat of fusion is 29.6 kcal/mole. Calculate the heat of fusion at 800°C.

2.4 Consider a well-insulated calorimeter. A heating element is situated in the calorimeter which has a resistance of 100.0 ohms. Upon passage of 1.00 amp of current for 75 minutes, a temperature change of +0.47°C occurs. A 5-gram sample of crystal A in the α state which undergoes an allotropic phase transformation is placed in the calorimeter. Upon reaching the phase transformation temperature, α transforms to the high temperature β form and a sudden temperature drop of 0.16°C occurs. Calculate the heat of transformation. Assume the molecular weight of A to be 106.

2.5 Could a polycrystalline array of a particular phase be represented by an equation of state? Explain your answer in detail.

2.6 Given a liquid phase which has a surface tension of 500 dynes/cm, calculate the work done by the system if a mole of liquid is converted from the form of spheres 0.1 mm in diameter to a thin film 1 μ thick.

2.7 Suppose that the material in Problem 2.6 has a density of 10 gm/cm³, a molecular weight of 102, and a heat capacity C_P of 7 cal/mole degree and that the process is performed adiabatically. Calculate the temperature change of the system.

CHAPTER 3

3.1 Calculate the entropies of fusion for K_2SO_4, Ag, Ge, and MgO at their melting points.

3.2 Calculate the entropy change associated with the reaction of Problem 2.3.

3.3 From the statement $(\Delta S_{syst} + \Delta S_{surr}) > 0$, coupled with $dS = DQ/T$ for a reversible process, derive equation 3.13.

3.4 Derive equation 3.35. What is the relation between the volume thermal expansion coefficient and linear expansion coefficient?

3.5 One gram of liquid UO_2 at 2900°C is mixed with 5 gm of UO_2 at 3400°C. (a) Find the temperature after mixing. (b) Find the entropy change of system and surroundings. (c) Is the process spontaneous? Assume that $C_P = 24.0$ cal/mole degree and is independent of temperature.

3.6 Calculate the entropy change for system and surroundings of the following reaction:

$$UO_2(s, 2500°K) = UO_2(l, 2500°K)$$

3.7 Suppose that, in the *Illustration* dealing with the thermoelastic effect, the stress applied to the system exceeded the yield point of the crystal. Explain whether or not equation 3.35 is applicable.

3.8 In the same *Illustration*, calculate the entropy change of system and surroundings. Is the total in agreement with the second law of thermodynamics?

3.9 Prove that, for a chemical reaction such as

$$A + B = C + D$$

equation 3.59 follows from equation 3.58.

3.10 By use of an emf technique the free energy of a reaction ΔG is directly obtained. Suppose that values of ΔG are obtained for a particular reaction at several temperatures. By curve fitting it is found that the following equation fits the data over the temperature range studied:

$$\Delta G = -400{,}810 - 3.98T \log T + 87.64T \text{ cal/mole}$$

Calculate ΔS and ΔH for the reaction at 400°K. Will the reaction proceed spontaneously?

3.11 Calculate ΔG for the gray tin to white tin transformation at (a) 13°C, (b) 20°C, (c) 5°C. Assume for the purpose of calculations that the heat capacities of the two phases are equal. Do the values agree with the criterion of spontaneity discussed in the chapter?

3.12 Derive that

$$dG = V\left(\frac{\partial P}{\partial V}\right)_T dV + \left[V\left(\frac{\partial P}{\partial T}\right)_V - S\right] dT$$

CHAPTER 4

4.1 Given two dice with faces labeled 1 through 6, calculate the probability that (a) 5 will appear on both dice after a throw, (b) the sum will be 9 after a throw, (c) both dice will have the same number.

4.2 What is the probability that two kings will be drawn in succession from a 52-card deck?

4.3 What is the probability that a 5 will appear at least once in n throws of a die?

4.4 Consider a box of volume V divided in two by a partition. On one side of the partition are N gas molecules, and there is a vacuum on the other side. When the partition is removed, the gas molecules will distribute themselves randomly. Calculate the entropy difference between the two states, using the Boltzmann relation.

4.5 Derive equation 4.3.

4.6 In the example concerning the number of ways of arranging 2 balls in 4 boxes, why were the values of $_8C_2$, $_6C_2$, $_4C_2$, $_2C_2$ multiplied together to give $\mathscr{W}$ and not added together?

4.7 Calculate the probability that, upon filling six boxes at random with 6 objects, one box will contain 3, two will contain 0, and three boxes will contain 1 each.

4.8 It will be recalled that the second law states, for a spontaneous process, $(\Delta S_{syst} + \Delta S_{surr}) > 0$. What is ΔS_{surr} for the mixing process? What will be the sign of $(\Delta S_{syst} + \Delta S_{surr})$?

4.9 Consider a crystal containing N sites. Let us fill only N_a sites with atoms, leaving $(N - N_a)$ vacant. Calculate the mixing entropy change for this process.

CHAPTER 5

5.1 It has been shown that the thermal expansion coefficient of a substance is zero at $T = 0$; prove that the coefficient of tension defined as $(1/P)(\partial P/\partial T)_V = 0$ at $T = 0°K$.

5.2 Suppose that a random solid solution of B in A is cooled rapidly to low temperatures. What is $S_0°$ for this material?

5.3 Interpret why α goes to zero at $T = 0$ but the compressibility β does not.

5.4 Using heat capacity data, prove that $\Delta S_0° = 0$ for the reaction

$$Sn(gray) = Sn(white).$$

Graphical integration will aid in the solution.

5.5 Suppose that one is able to quench, say, liquid lead to absolute zero. What would $S_0°$ be in this case?

5.6 Calculate $\Delta S°$ for the following reaction at $1300°K$.

$$MnSiO_3(s) + 2Al(l) = Al_2O_3(s) + Mn(s) + Si(s)$$

CHAPTER 6

6.1   Given the compound A_5B_7, which melts at 1000°K, calculate ΔS_f. Consider the arrangement of atoms in the liquid solution to be completely random.

6.2   Why would you expect Trouton's rule to apply with better accuracy than Richards' rule?

6.3   A compound AB forms which has a value of $\Delta H_f°$ equal to -5000 cal/mole. A and B are both face-centered cubic in the elemental state with values of 3.52 and 4.04 A, respectively. The crystal structure of AB is the NaCl structure. Compute the molar volume of AB.

6.4   Evaluate the constant C in equation 6.12 for the NaCl and CaCl structures.

6.5   Using the Born-Haber cycle, calculate $\Delta H_f°$ for RbI.

CHAPTER 7

7.1   Estimate the pressure needed to convert graphite to diamond at 1500°C. What assumptions did you make?

7.2   Calculate the heat of sublimation of BeO(s) at 300°K and 1000°K from vapor pressure data. Estimate the value at 0°K.

7.3   At the melting point, would ΔH_s become discontinuous? What is the relation between ΔH_v and ΔH_s of liquid and solid respectively?

7.4   Consider a vacuum furnace containing a crucible of magnesium. What is the value of the best vacuum attainable at 1000°C in the system?

7.5   Suppose that a vapor phase over a solid follows the equation of state; $PV = RT + AP$. Calculate the fugacity.

7.6   Suppose that the magnesium of Problem 7.4 is under a hydrostatic pressure of 1000 atm. Calculate the change in vapor pressure.

7.7   Would it be possible for $\Delta G°$ to equal zero? Explain.

7.8   Calculate $\Delta G°$ for the reduction of $SiO_2(s)$ by Al(l) at 1200°K. Would pure Al reduce SiO_2?

7.9   Calculate the equilibrium oxygen pressure between Al_2O_3 and Al(l) at 1000°K. Could the best laboratory vacuum currently available prevent the oxidation of Al?

7.10 Suppose CaO is placed in a vacuum in which the partial pressure of oxygen is 10^{-5} mm Hg. Will CaO be reduced?

7.11 Calculate the equilibrium constant for the reaction

$$O_2(g, 1 \text{ atm}) = O_2(g, 0.1 \text{ atm})$$

7.12 Suppose the vapor pressure of a specific concentration of Zn dissolved in Cu is 3×10^{-3} mm Hg at 600°C. Calculate the activity of Zn in the alloy. Calculate the free energy change of Zn upon solution.

7.13 Calculate the error in oxygen pressure for Problem 7.9.

7.14 Using Fig. 7.4, calculate ΔG° for the following reaction at $1000°K$.

$$\tfrac{3}{2}Si(s) + Al_2O_3(s) = 2Al(l) + \tfrac{3}{2}SiO_2$$

Will the reaction proceed to the right or the left if the elements are in their standard states? At what temperature, if any, will the reactants and products be in equilibrium?

7.15 Suppose that in Problem 7.14 Si is not at $1000°K$ but at $800°K$; can the free energy of reaction be calculated? Explain.

7.16 What would be the value of ΔG° for the following reactions at $298°K$?
   (a) $O_2(1 \text{ atm}) = O_2(5 \text{ atm})$
   (b) $Al = Al(\text{dissolved in Cu}, X_{Al} = 0.01)$
   (c) $Al(s) + \tfrac{3}{2}O_2(\tfrac{1}{2} \text{ atm}) = Al_2O_3(s)$

7.17 Calculate the standard entropy of formation of $GeO(g)$ at $1000°K$.

CHAPTER 8

8.1 In a Ti-H solution $\Delta \bar{H}_H$ and $\Delta \bar{G}_H$ are given in the following table as a function of X_H at $636°C$ (ΔH values in calories per gram-atom).

X_H	0.1	0.2	0.3	0.4	0.5
$\Delta \bar{H}_H$	$-29,500$	$-29,700$	$-29,700$	$-29,700$	$-29,700$
$\Delta \bar{G}_H$	$-11,970$	$-9,660$	$-7,320$	$-4,940$	$+500$

(a) Find $\Delta \bar{G}_H$ at $X_H = 0.4$. (b) Find ΔG_m at $X_H = 0.4$. (c) Find $\Delta \bar{S}_H$ at $X_H = 0.4$. (d) Find $\Delta G_m{}^{xs}$, $\Delta \bar{G}_H{}^{xs}$, and $\Delta \bar{S}_H{}^{xs}$ at $X_H = 0.4$.

8.2 In Problem 8.1: (a) Find γ_H at $X_H = 0.2$. (b) Calculate a_H at $X_H = 0.2$. (c) Find the equilibrium H_2 pressure for an alloy of Ti containing 20 at % H (monatomic).

8.3 Solid Au-Cu alloys are regular in their thermodynamic behavior. ΔH_m at $500°C$ is listed as a function of composition in the following table.

X_{Cu}	0.1	0.2	0.3	0.4	0.5	0.6	0.7	0.8	0.9
ΔH_m	-355	-655	-910	-1120	-1230	-1240	-1130	-860	-460

(a) Find $\Delta \bar{H}_{Cu}$ and $\Delta \bar{H}_{Au}$ at $X_{Cu} = 0.3$. (b) Find ΔG_m at $X_{Cu} = 0.3$. (c) Calculate the partial pressure of Cu for an alloy containing 30 at % Cu, 70 at % Au. (d) Calculate the oxygen pressure in equilibrium with Cu in the alloy in (c) and Cu_2O.

8.4 In the preceding problem suppose that the Cu_2O scale in contact with NiO and a solution forms so that the activity of Cu_2O is 0.4. Calculate the equilibrium oxygen pressure for this case.

8.5 Derive expressions for $(\bar{H}_B - H_B{}^\circ)$ and $(\bar{V}_B - V_B{}^\circ)$ for the solute in a dilute solution.

CHAPTER 9

9.1 In a face-centered cubic lattice containing 40 at % A and 60 at % B in the form of a random solution, calculate the number of A–A pairs, B–B pairs, and A–B pairs in a gram-atom of solution.

9.2 ΔH_t for formation of ordered AB from a disordered solution of 50 at % A and 50 at % B on the body-centered cubic lattice is -500 cal/gm-atom at 500°K. A and B exist as body-centered cubic crystals in the pure state and have enthalpies of sublimation of 40,000 cal/gm-atom and 60,000 cal/gm-atom respectively. Calculate H_{AB}. Calculate ΔS_t and ΔG_t.

9.3 Element A in the pure state has a vapor pressure of 1.0 mm Hg at 500°K. Calculate the vapor pressure in the disordered alloy of Problem 9.2.

9.4 An alloy of composition 40% A and 60% B shows substantial short range order. P_{AB} is found from x-ray measurements to be 1.05 times the value for a random solution. Calculate P_{AA} and P_{BB} in a gram-atom of alloy.

9.5 From the heat of sublimation of A in Problem 9.2, estimate the enthalpy of formation of the diatomic molecule A_2 in the gas phase from monatomic molecules.

CHAPTER 10

10.1 At a given temperature, component B dissolves 0.7 at % A and component A dissolves 1.2 at % B. Calculate the activity coefficients of B in A and A in B. No intermediate phases exist in the binary system.

10.2 The temperature in Problem 10.1 is 500°K. At 700°K, component B still dissolves only 0.7 at % A but A dissolves 2.4 at % B. (a) Calculate the relative partial molal enthalpy of B in A and also of A in B. (b) Calculate the excess relative partial molar entropies of B in A and also of A in B. (c) Atomistically, what phenomenon is $\Delta \bar{S}_B{}^{xs}$ identified with?

10.3 An important reaction involved in the operation of vacuum tubes is the following

$$y\text{BaO}(s) + x\text{M}(X_M, s) = \text{M}_x\text{O}_y(\text{solid or gas}) + y\text{Ba}(g)$$

where M is an oxide-forming solute dissolved in the base nickel cathode. Calculate P_{Ba} in equilibrium at 900°C if M is C at 0.01% and M_xO_y is $\text{CO}_2(g)$. C is soluble to the extent of 0.1% in M.

10.4 The interfacial free energy σ between two solid phases can be divided into two parts, a chemical contribution, σ_c, and a geometric contribution resulting from the presence of dislocations in the boundary, σ_g. Phase β is normally body centered whereas α is normally face-centered cubic. $\sigma_{\alpha-\beta} = 600$ ergs/cm² with $\sigma_c = 150$ ergs/cm² and $\sigma_g = 450$ ergs/cm². When β particles are very small (~ 150 A in diameter) it is energetically favorable for the β phase to be face-centered cubic so as to be coherent with α. In this case $\sigma_g = 0$ and $\sigma_c = 150$ ergs/cm². The free energy of transformation of β from B.C.C. to the F.C.C. structure in α is equal to 150 cal/cm^3. Calculate the solubilities of B in the matrix in equilibrium with F.C.C. β and F.C.C. α. The solubility of B.C.C. β in F.C.C. α is 0.1 at %.

10.5 The phase diagram for the A–B system shows retrograde solubility in the α solution portion of the diagram. Both α and liquid behave as regular solutions with $\Delta \bar{H}_B$ equal to 800 cal/gm-atom in the liquid. The heat of fusion of B is 1500 cal/gm-atom, and the melting point of A and B are 1000°K and 1200°K respectively. (a) Calculate the minimum possible value of $\Delta \bar{H}_B{}^\alpha$ in α. (b) Calculate the temperature where the solubility of B in α is a maximum.

CHAPTER 11

11.1 Components A and B form a regular solution in the solid state for which ΔH_m is $5000 X_A X_B$ cal/gm-atom. At a temperature of 1000°K, calculate the composition of α' and α'' in equilibrium and the composition of the inflection points.

11.2 For the problem above calculate the temperature for immiscibility for a solution in which $X_B = 0.3$.

11.3 Draw schematically free energy versus composition diagrams for the Ag-Pt peritectic diagram at $T = 1300$°C, 1100°C, and 900°C.

11.4 Components A and B have melting temperatures of 1000°K and 900°K respectively. Regular solutions form with ΔH_m equal to $(5000/T) X_A X_B$ and $(50,000/T) X_A X_B$ cal/gm-atom in the liquid and solid states respectively. The enthalpies of fusion are 1500 cal/mole and 1300 cal/mole for A and B respectively. (a) Will a minimum occur in the solidus and liquidus? (b) If so, calculate the temperature of the minimum.

11.5 The distribution constant which is equal to $X_A{}^s / X_B{}^l$ is of considerable importance in the zone-refining operation. Consider that the liquid solution forms a regular solution and that the value of $X_A{}^s \ll X_B{}^l$ near the melting point of component A. Near the melting point of A the value of $k \rightarrow k°$, a constant. Determine the dependence of $k°$ on $\Delta \bar{H}_m{}^s$ and $\Delta \bar{H}_B{}^s$. What thermodynamic properties should the solute have in order to make the zone-refining operation easy?

11.6 Draw a phase diagram for which $\Delta H_m{}^s < \Delta H_m{}^l < 0$ but where $\Delta H_m{}^s$ is less than that shown in Fig. 11.22b but more than that shown in Fig. 11.22c.

CHAPTER 12

12.1 Suppose that a droplet of a liquid substance forms a spherical cap on a copper surface with a height of 1 mm and a contact diameter of 5 mm. (a) Calculate the surface tension of the liquid-copper interface and the liquid-atmosphere interface. (b) Calculate the total force which would be needed to remove the drop from the copper. In an experiment to measure this force, what acceleration is necessary for the drop to be removed from the copper?

12.2 Is a solid completely wetted by its own liquid at the melting point? Explain reasoning.

12.3 From quasichemical theory, calculate the ratio of the enthalpy of vacancy formation at the (111) surface of a face-centered cubic crystal to the enthalpy in the interior.

12.4 For a low angle crystal boundary, would $\Gamma_\beta{}^s$ be positive for impurity segregation? Consider both impurity atoms larger and smaller than the matrix. Explain your answer.

12.5 Calculate the surface enthalpy of tungsten for a (110) plane and a (100) plane.

12.6 Equation 12.34 indicates that ΔH^s and ΔG^s are functions of the plane exposed at the surface, whereas equation 12.45 does not lead to this prediction explicitly. Explain why equation 12.45 does not predict this dependence. What would have to be done in order for the effect of surface orientation to be taken into account?

12.7 Which plane would you expect to oxidize more easily for nickel if it formed the surface, the (111), (100), or (110) plane?

12.8 Suppose that a second phase particle has a hexagonal close-packed structure and the matrix has a face-centered cubic structure. What would you expect the particle shape to be? Why?

12.9 Calculate the interfacial energy of a Zn-Cu interface where the interface is parallel to the (0001) plane of Zn and the (111) plane of Cu. Compare with the grain boundary energies.

12.10 Estimate the grain boundary energy for nickel and platinum.

12.11 Suppose that the normal to a high angle grain boundary in a copper wire of 0.1-mm diameter is inclined to the wire axis at an angle of 20°. Upon annealing, what would you expect to happen to the grain boundary? Calculate the driving free energy for the process.

12.12 In the problem above the grain boundary in the initial state is simple 4° tilt boundary. Will the process predicted under the conditions of Problem 12.11 occur? Explain.

CHAPTER 13

13.1 For a compound AB, calculate ΔS_c if n A atoms exist on B sites and n B atoms on A sites.

13.2 Find the activity coefficient of a vacancy in a crystal in terms of equation 13.3.

13.3 The atoms in the crystal discussed in Section 13.3 have a chemical potential μ°. What is the chemical potential of a vacancy if the vacancies are in equilibrium? Why?

13.4 What is the chemical potential of an interstitial atom if interstitials are in equilibrium with the crystal?

CHAPTER 14

14.1 Consider a body-centered cubic crystal from which an atom is removed. Estimate the vibrational entropy change ΔS_V associated with vacancy formation. *Hint:* Use Boltzmann's relations between entropy and randomness; how is ΔS_V associated with a randomness? Calculate ΔH_V for vacancy formation for gold, using quasichemical theory. Compare answer with experimental result. If answers are not the same, examine them in view of neglected factors.

14.2 Suppose that the vacancy and interstitial concentration are related and not independent. Derive an equation, using the law of mass action, relating these concentrations.

14.3 Assume that a crystal has a dislocation density of $10^6/cm^2$; estimate the number of solute atoms which may be condensed at the dislocation per cubic centimeter of crystal.

14.4 Intrinsic crystal A has a vacancy content given by $X_V = 10 \exp \times (-30,000/RT)$. Suppose that crystal A contains 1.0% element B and element B and vacancy have a binding enthalpy of 4000 cal/gm-atom of complexes. Calculate the total vacancy concentration in crystal A at 1000°K.

14.5 Consider the intrinsic semiconductor germanium with an energy gap of 0.75 ev with a very small amount of impurity. This impurity acts as an acceptor with $(E_c - E_A) = 0.29$ ev. Calculate the fraction of impurity atoms which are negatively charged in the crystal at 300°K. Suppose that a donor impurity is now added to the crystal in rather high concentration. Will the fraction of acceptors ionized be increased or decreased? Explain. Assume for the first part of the problem that $E_F = (E_c + E_V)/2$.

14.6 In Problem 14.5, assume that the solubility of acceptor is $10^{15}/cm^3$ at 500°K. Calculate the solubility if $10^{18}/cm^3$ completely ionized donors are added to the crystal. Neglect pairing.

14.7 In the diamond lattice, would vacancies or divacancies diffuse more rapidly? Explain.

14.8 The vacancy concentration in an intrinsic crystal is given by

$$X_V = 10 \exp \left(-\frac{30,000}{RT} \right)$$

In a crystal containing an impurity

$$X_V = 75 \exp \left(-\frac{26,000}{RT} \right)$$

Calculate the binding enthalpy between vacancies and impurities.

14.9 Suppose that the solubility of carbon in a polycrystalline sample of an element is reported to be $10^{-5}\%$ at 1000°K. Estimate the concentration of carbon which might be in crystal boundaries and at dislocations. How would you design the experiment so as to obtain values of carbon solubility characteristic of the bulk crystal? Explain in some detail.

14.10 Suppose that the solubility of a solute is measured in a single crystal as a function of temperature with the result shown in Fig. A3.1. Discuss the factors which might give rise to the curvature. What experiments would you design to test these factors?

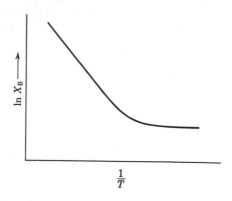

Fig. A3.1 Solubility of B in a single crystal as a function of temperature.

14.11 The yield point of a crystal disappears upon heating at 700°C. Calculate the binding enthalpy between dislocation and impurities, if the solute concentration in the bulk is 0.01 %.

14.12 In a study of the precipitation of lithium from silicon containing dissolved oxygen, Pell has found that the lithium does not precipitate to its equilibrium value but rather that the final lithium content $[Li^+] = 0.02[O]$ at room temperature. Calculate the enthalpy of binding between dissolved Li^+ and dissolved O.

CHAPTER 15

15.1 Suppose that crystal AB has an energy gap of 2.0 ev and that the electrons and holes have mobilities of 1000 and 300 cm/sec/dyne respectively. The conductivity at 300°K is 10^{-6} ohm^{-1} cm^{-1}. Find the conductivity at 500°K. Suppose that 10^{12} donors/cm^3 are dissolved in AB and that the donor level is 0.1 ev below the conduction band. Calculate the conductivity at 300°K, at 500°K.

15.2 Using calculated values of the enthalpy of formation of Shottky defects, estimate the concentration of $[V_{Na}]$ and $[V_{Cl}]$ at 300°K and at 600°K in NaCl.

15.3 For NaCl estimate the binding energy between a cation vacancy and anion vacancy. Will divacancies exist preferably at high temperatures or low temperatures? Estimate the critical temperature for divacancy formation.

15.4 Suppose that an NaCl crystal contains 10^{17} Schottky defects. At what temperature will there be a discontinuity in the slope of the conductivity versus temperature curve? What will be the value of the slope at high temperatures and low temperatures respectively?

15.5 Crystal AB is a p-type semiconductor with

$$\sigma \sim p_{B_2}^{-\frac{1}{8}}$$

What is the defect structure of the material?

15.6 Crystal AB has a free energy of formation $\Delta G°$ of $-50,000$ cal expressed by the reaction

$$A(s) + \tfrac{1}{2}B_2(g) = AB(s)$$

Component A has a partial pressure of 10^{-3} atm Hg at this temperature. In the stoichiometric crystal, A has an activity relative to pure A of 0.2. If AB is placed in a gas containing 1.8×10^{-4} atm of A pressure, the compound changes to $A_{(1-\delta)}B$ where $\delta = 0.05$. Calculate the activity and activity coefficient of A at this composition. Calculate the activity of B in AB and $A_{(1-\delta)}B$.

15.7 It has been found that the conductivity of Nb_2O_5 increases as p_{O2} is decreased. Is this suggestive of n-type or p-type behavior? Explain your answer.

15.8 Suppose that PbS contained Frenkel defects on the Pb sublattice with both interstitials and vacancies completely ionized. How would the conductivity vary with p_{Pb}? Compare with Fig. 15.24.

15.9 Evaluate K in equation 15.91 at $300°K$.

15.10 In one type of compound MX, where M and X exist as doubly charged ions, addition of Li_2X increases the electrical conductivity whereas, in another type of compound with the same valence, Li_2X additions decrease the conductivity. Compare the defect structure of the two materials.

15.11 Calculate the entropy of mixing associated with the formation of equal concentrations of cation vacancies and anion vacancies, $[V_{Na}]$ and $[V_{Cl}]$ respectively in NaCl.

15.12 In crystal MX, the enthalpy associated with the following reactions are

$$M(s) = M_i \qquad\qquad \Delta H = 1.0 \text{ ev}$$

$$M(\text{in } MX) = M(\text{surface}) \qquad \Delta H = 2.0 \text{ ev}$$

$$M_i = M_i^+ + e^- \qquad\qquad \Delta H = 0.04 \text{ ev}$$

$$V_M = V_M^- + e^+ \qquad\qquad \Delta H = 0.07 \text{ ev}$$

In MX the number of ions per cubic centimeter is 4×10^{22}, and for an intrinsic crystal

$$[e^-]_i = [e^+]_i = 10^{19} \exp(-0.70/kT)$$

Calculate approximately $[e^-]$, $[e^+]$, $[V_M]$, $[V_M^-]$, $[M_i]$, and $[M_i^+]$.

15.13 Suppose that MX in the problem above is equilibrated with X_2 in the gas phase. p_{X_2} for the stoichiometric crystal MX is 1 mm Hg. For the reaction

$$M(s) + \tfrac{1}{2}X_2(g) = MX, \qquad \Delta G° = 10,000$$

and p_M^e is 0.05 mm Hg. (a) Calculate $[e^-]$, $[e^+]$, $[V_M]$, $[V_M^-]$, $[M_i]$ + $[M_i^+]$ if p_{X_2} is changed to 2 mm Hg. (b) Compare conductivities for stoichiometric MX of Problem 15.12 and MX equilibrated according to this problem, if the mobilities of electrons and holes are 1000 and 300 cm/sec/dyne respectively. (c) Would the defects act as color centers? Why?

15.14 Suppose that you are given the task of elucidating the defect structure of a sulfide M_2S. M_2S has a melting point of 1200°K, and $\Delta G°$ for the reaction

$$2M(s) + \tfrac{1}{2}S_2(g) = M_2S(s)$$

is given by

$$\Delta G° = -6000 + 2T$$

The vapor pressure of M is given by

$$\log p = -\frac{2500}{T}$$

Describe completely the manner in which you would proceed to study the defect structure.

Index